SMITHSONIAN SCIENTIFIC SERIES

Editor-in-chief

CHARLES GREELEY ABBOT, D.Sc.

*Secretary of the
Smithsonian Institution*

Published by

SMITHSONIAN INSTITUTION SERIES, Inc.
NEW YORK

THE SUN AND
THE WELFARE OF MAN

By
CHARLES GREELEY ABBOT, D.Sc.
Secretary of the
Smithsonian Institution

59790
VOLUME TWO
OF THE
SMITHSONIAN SCIENTIFIC SERIES
1929

CONTENTS

ILLUSTRATIONS

LIST OF PLATES

LIST OF TEXT FIGURES

THE SUN AND
THE WELFARE OF MAN

THE SUN AND THE WELFARE OF MAN

CHAPTER I

WHY STUDY THE SUN?

> *"And Joseph said unto Pharaoh, The dream of Pharaoh is one: God hath shewed Pharaoh what he is about to do."*
>
> *"Behold, there come seven years of great plenty throughout all the land of Egypt:*
>
> *"And there shall arise after them seven years of famine; and all the plenty shall be forgotten in the land of Egypt; and the famine shall consume the land."*

THE sun was God in Egypt. Could the sun do these things?

On a mountain top in Chile, the Smithsonian Institution maintains a queer observatory. It has no telescope! "Impossible," you say, "an observatory without a telescope." Rather than "on a mountain," it would have been more accurate to have said "in a mountain." The delicate observing instruments are contained in a dark tunnel, over 30 feet deep, running horizontally southward from near the summit of the northern face of the peak. The observatory does no work at night, for its studies are confined to a single star, our own star, the sun. This orb is so bright that it needs no telescope to concentrate its rays.

Like Joshua of old, the observers make the sun's rays stand still. There is an instrument called the coelostat which reflects a steady horizontal beam of sun rays directly into the tunnel where the measuring instruments are set. By means of a prism, the light is broken up into its inherent colors like the rainbow. With an electrical thermometer, so sensitive that it records easily a millionth of a degree of temperature, are measured the heats of all the colors, and, besides that, the heats of invisible rays beyond the farthest violet and the deepest red of the spectrum.

Hardly ever does rain fall near the observatory. It lies in one of the most barren regions of the earth. Neither tree nor shrub, beast nor bird, snake nor insect, not even the hardiest of desert plants is found there. The observers must go twelve miles to the railway at Calama for water and all supplies. Not far away, the Andes lift giant peaks nearly 20,000 feet above the sea, but the snow which covers them never reaches the strange observatory on Mount Montezuma.

The weather is monotonous. Every day the sun glares down through cloudless sky upon the barren land. Every morning a dead calm prevails, or at most only the slightest of breezes breathes from the east. Almost precisely at 10 o'clock the wind reverses. Within a quarter of an hour it blows strongly from the west, and all the remainder of the day tries its best to dislodge the gravel from which all the fine dust has long ago been blown away.

For three years at a shift, the observers sacrifice themselves to dwelling in this wilderness, and for what? For the purpose of measuring that solar energy which supports every form of life and activity upon our earth, and especially of noting its changes. For if our supply of heat from the sun alters, weather and crops must be affected. If the sun's output of energy should permanently diminish or increase by considerable amounts, the whole future of civilization would be destroyed.

As the inquiry is a very difficult one, and the accuracy

[2]

required is of a high order, the Smithsonian Institution maintains not only this field station in Chile, but another in California for the purposes of such measurements. Even these being insufficient to obtain first-rate solar measurements each day in the year, the National Geographic Society, recognizing the world-wide application of the results, in the year 1925 made a grant to establish a cooperating observatory on a lonely mountain in South West Africa, among the Hottentots. This expedition, which began observing in November, 1926, is called "The National Geographic Society Solar Radiation Expedition in Cooperation with the Smithsonian Institution."

Thinking men agree that these studies are very important, measuring as they do the sun's life-influence. Indeed, from the mildness of Bermuda to the bleakness of Spitzbergen, from the teeming life of Brazilian forests to the deserted wind-swept wastes of the Southern Pole, conditions change at the bidding of the sun's rays. Since all of the life and warmth of our planet depends on them, few subjects are better worth our attention. It was this view which led Professor Langley to found the Astrophysical Observatory, when he left Allegheny Observatory to become Secretary of the Smithsonian Institution. The main study was to be the sun's rays, their energy, their variability, their relations to our atmosphere and to life.

"Uncle Joe" Cannon, who represented the State of Illinois in Congress for over forty years, was one day listening to a hearing before the House Committee on Appropriations. The small annual subsidy for the Astrophysical Observatory was being defended, but the unfamiliar words led a member of the Committee to remark, "The Chairman will have his troubles to explain this on the floor of the House." "No!" said Cannon, "I don't care very much about the stars that are so far away that it takes light a thousand years to come from them, and if they were abolished tonight our great-grandchildren would never know the difference. But

[3]

everything hangs upon the sun, sir, and it ought to be investigated. I think this appropriation is all right."

It was the great future usefulness of this work which Langley dwelt upon when he induced Congress to undertake its support. He spoke of the story of Joseph who, according to the words of the Book of Genesis, foretold that seven years of plenty would be followed by seven years of famine. Langley believed that changes in the sun are the cause of the vicissitudes in terrestrial climates, and he hoped that the Astrophysical Observatory might justify its support by discovering such solar changes, their causes, their periodicities, and effects they led to on the earth. In this way, as he hoped, the scientific man of the twentieth century might come to be able to emulate the ancient prophet, and foretell climatic events in a way to be of great value to mankind.

We have not quite reached this point, but the prospect now seems bright. The Astrophysical Observatory has indeed discovered that the sun is a variable star, and for many years has observed its variations. Never having received sufficient financial support from the Government to enable it to make these observations with enough completeness for the purpose, it has lately been possible to supplement the work, owing to the support of a wise, far-seeing friend, Mr. John A. Roebling. Not only by money and counsel has he aided in broadening the scope of the solar observations, but he has supported intensive study by Mr. H. H. Clayton and colleagues on the highly complex problem of the relations of solar variations to weather. Still more recently, as we have said, the National Geographic Society has taken part. The results of the combined attack are just beginning to appear.

The variations of the sun are small in percentage and apparently irregular in sequence and amount. We begin, however, to find certain interesting regularities therein. The changes produce effects on atmospheric temperatures and pressures, and on precipitation. Whether they and

PLATE 1

Smithsonian solar station at Montezuma, Chile. An observatory without a telescope where the sun's heat is measured daily

PLATE 2

Living quarters at the Smithsonian observatory in Chile, 9,000 feet above sea-level. No birds, beasts, insects, or vegetation are found here

PLATE 3

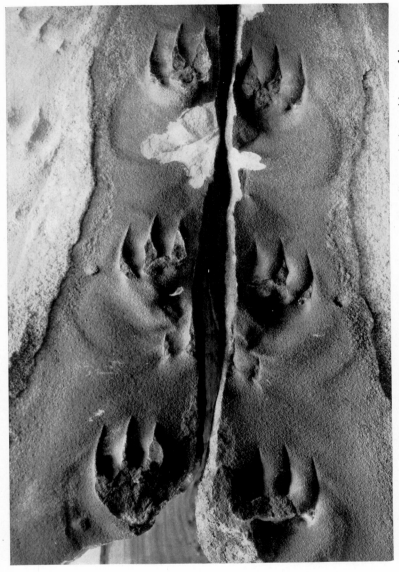

Fossil footprints give a record of creatures that lived ages ago. Equally convincing evidence of the presence of the chemical elements in stars stupendously distant in time and space is brought by the spectral rays

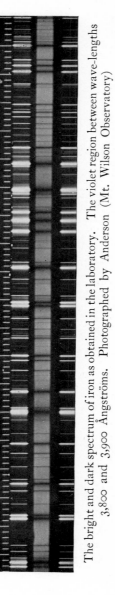

The bright and dark spectrum of iron as obtained in the laboratory. The violet region between wave-lengths 3,800 and 3,900 Ångströms. Photographed by Anderson (Mt. Wilson Observatory)

their effects shall become predictable for seasons or years in advance, we cannot as yet foretell. Having progressed thus far, we may entertain a lively hope that further progress is about to follow. But the work must go on for years before a long enough background will be laid to justify hope of seasonal forecasting.

The sun is a star. Though appearing to us to be almost a hundred thousand million times as bright as the stars of the first magnitude, this illusion is merely an effect of distance. If removed so as to be only as far away as the average distance of a dozen of the nearest stars, the sun would be little more than distinctly visible to the naked eye, and nearly a thousand stars would seem to be brighter.

In short, the sun is but average in brightness, average in diameter, average in mass, average in color, and it seems as if it had obeyed implicitly the advice of Robinson Crusoe's father and chosen the middle station as the happiest of all lots.

If, then, the sun is just an average star, what is its constitution and its physical state? Its diameter is over 800,000 miles; its mass, over 300,000 times as great as our earth; its density about one-fourth that of the earth, or 1.4 times that of water. Gravitation at the sun's surface is nearly thirtyfold that on the earth, so that a man, if he could exist there, would weigh over two tons by the spring balance. But a man could not exist there. The temperature of the surface of the sun is over 6,000° C. (nearly 11,000° F.), and therefore nearly twice as hot as the electric arc. Deep down, the temperatures must be expressed in millions, not thousands, of degrees.

At these exalted temperatures, all chemical substances separate into their atomic constituents. Pure hydrogen would not burn in the presence of pure oxygen. Absolutely no compound molecules exist in the sun except in the cooler regions which we call sun-spots. Even the atoms, those complex systems of positive and negative electrons, as modern physics proves them to be, are partly dissociated into their simple electronic constituents, in the fierce solar heat. This breaking up of atoms is not complete. The individual atoms lose one or more negative electrons but probably retain their central nuclei unaltered, and so we have, under solar conditions, a great variety of broken atomic structures which, as they react, vibrate to produce light in ways different indeed from their well-known rays in our laboratories, but still characteristic of the special chemical elements which gave them rise.

It is by the properties of light that we know almost all that is known of the sun and stars. Traveling 186,000 miles a second, light requires 8 minutes to journey from the sun, 4 years from the nearest star, perhaps 100,000 years from the farthest stars in our galaxy, but no less than about 1,000,000 years from the more distant celestial objects like the great nebula of the constellation Andromeda. Not even there does distance cease. The faintest nebulæ now photographed are being seen, it is believed, by light which they emitted several hundred million years ago, in early geological ages. The most revealing thing about light is found in the spectrum. It is not its beautiful variety of colors, but the dark lines which lie across the colors. If we form the spectrum of the sun, these lines lie sparsely in the red and yellow, more abundantly in the green, and are almost innumerable in the violet and beyond. I say beyond the violet, for a photograph shows many rays which the eye cannot see, and discovers a region extending far beyond, which we call the ultra-violet.

From these dark spectral lines, we read the composition of the sun and stars. For it is found that every chemical element, when highly heated, gives rise to special lines, bright, not dark, to be sure, but as closely matching the dark lines of the spectra of sun and stars as does a photograph its negative. Nay, more! By suitable arrange-

[6]

ments, even our laboratory sources may give dark lines on a bright ground, too, just like the sun and stars. Ages ago, there walked upon the earth races of animals now extinct. Their footprints are occasionally found in fossil preservation. As these fossils teach us the characteristic forms of the feet of creatures whose lives are separated from ours by an otherwise impassable gulf of time, so the dark lines of the spectrum give us the proof of the existence in the sun and stars of our own familiar elements, iron, hydrogen, and the rest, though there may stretch between us and these celestial bodies an otherwise impassable gulf, both of time and space.

At a temperature so high that compounds are impossible, molecules nonexistent, and even atoms partly dissociated, there are no solids nor liquids in the sun. The solar substance is not even gaseous in our ordinary sense. For in a gas on earth, the molecules are the smallest subdivisions. They are freely darting in all directions, and excepting in those gases which are greatly condensed by pressure, they seldom collide, because they are so small. But molecules are immense objects compared to the partly dissociated atoms which compose the interior of the sun. Hence, there the condition is, as we may say, supergaseous. Atomic collisions are very rare in the sun because of the infinitesimal sizes of the darting missiles. By "rare" we mean only that, compared to its own tiny diameter, a solar particle travels an immense distance before colliding with another. Though so infinitesimally small the subatomic particles, yet so mighty is the sun, and so enormous is their velocity at those tremendous temperatures, that they cannot dart in any direction without striking each other, and the collisions occur within intervals almost too brief to imagine.

So the sun, notwithstanding that it is compressed by its enormous gravitation to a state more dense than water, is, because of the extreme minuteness of its particles compared to those of ordinary gases, still in the state we speak of as the "perfect gas." The simplest laws of thermodynamics apply there with full rigor. Here is the ideal ground for the mathematical physicist, and right well have such men as Eddington tilled it. Hence, we know with great probability much more definitely the state of the sun's interior than we do that of the interior of our earth.

In this fervidness of temperatures, the loss of heat by radiation is perfectly unthinkable. The energy of the sun's rays given out every year amounts to as much as the burning of 400,000,000,000,000,000,000,000,000 tons of coal, and would be sufficient to melt 40,000,000,000,000,-000,000,000,000 tons of ice. Our earth intercepts only about 1/2,000,000,000 of all this, but the solar energy that our earth receives would be about 200,000,000,000,-000 horsepower if all could be turned into mechanical work.

In the pages that follow, we shall trace the methods of observing which have discovered some of these solar facts. Curious instruments will be described. Remarkable properties of our atmosphere will be discussed. We shall find that the energy of solar radiation fluctuates, but that, owing to the complex conditions of our earth, we can by no means predict from first principles whether a hotter sun would cause (for instance) a hotter or a cooler New York. We shall trace the investigations which are resolving such questions. We shall follow the astronomer to distant lands and lofty mountains, observe with him in the luxuriance of the tropics and in the desolation of the rainless desert. Our attention will remark the far-spread effects of the greatest volcanic eruptions of the earth, and the influences of the tremendously greater activities displayed upon the sun. The beauties of the sunset, the awe-inspiring influences of the total eclipse, and the loveliness of the azure sky, with its charming flocks of snow-white fleecy clouds shall all yield something to instruct us of the qualities of our star—the sun.

WHY STUDY THE SUN ?

Utility as well as curious and scientific interest will claim a place. The wonderful and manifold relations of plant growth to radiation will allure us. From this subject we shall pass most naturally through a consideration of fossil plant products, stored for us in coal and oil, to the possibilities of obtaining heat and power from solar rays without the intervention of plant chemistry.

CHAPTER II

FROM SHORE TO DESERT MOUNTAINS, MEASURING SUN RAYS

THIS is a story about the rays that support all life on earth. It begins with the studies of Dr. Samuel Pierpont Langley, third Secretary of the Smithsonian Institution and a man of vision. He was not a follower of beaten paths, but a pioneer of great enterprises. In the minds of most people it is his work on flying machines and on the principles of them that counts. But before all that, he was an astronomer in the first rank, along with Newcomb, Rowland, Young, and E. C. Pickering. His subject was the sun. Though his visual observations of the detailed structure of the solar surface and its spectrum are very notable, and though his charming book "The New Astronomy" was justly famous, yet his astronomical fame depends mainly on his pioneering studies of the rays of the sun and moon, and of the properties of our atmosphere which hinder these rays from reaching us. Here is Langley's problem expressed in his own words:

"If the observation of the amount of heat the sun sends the earth is among the most important and difficult in astronomical physics, it may also be termed the fundamental problem of meteorology, nearly all of whose phenomena would become predictable, if we knew both the original quantity and kind of this heat; how it affects the constituents of the atmosphere on its passage earthward; how much of it reaches the soil; how, through the aid of the atmosphere, it maintains the surface temperature of this planet; and how in diminished quantity and altered kind it is returned to outer space."

Realizing that the eye and photographic plate are both limited in their perception, he invented the bolometer about the year 1878. It is a wondrously delicate electrical thermometer, capable of measuring to a millionth of a degree, and of estimating the energy of all solar rays in their just proportions.

Formerly scientists used to distinguish between three kinds of rays which they called "actinic," "visible," and "heat" rays. This was because chemical receivers like the ordinary photographic plate and the foliage of plants are most sensitive to blue, violet, and ultra-violet rays; the eye, again, sees only within the seven colors of Newton, from the violet to the red; while beyond the visible red lie other rays, neither visible nor photographically active, but which at sea-level give as much heat as all the other rays combined in the solar spectrum. As much as anyone, Langley is entitled to the credit of abolishing the old distinction between "actinic," "visible," and "heat" rays, and showing that all of these rays are of a common nature, merely differing in respect to wave-length. Modern progress, indeed, has pushed their gamut to tremendously greater extent.

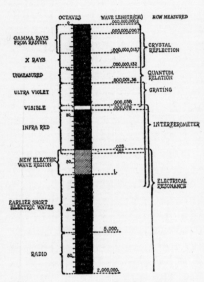

FIG. 1. The spectrum gamut from beyond X-rays through the ultra-violet, visible, and infra-red to the radio-rays. (After Nichols and Hull)

Röntgen's X-rays are but excessively short-wave ultra-violet rays; and Hertzian rays, which carry radio-telephony, are but excessively long-wave infra-red rays.

Being director of the then small observatory at Allegheny, Langley was a pioneer in introducing a novelty—accurate astronomical time-service for the public benefit. He obtained part of the funds for the support of his favorite solar studies by furnishing exact time to the Pennsylvania Railroad. He formed close friendships with that wealthy man of affairs, the late William Thaw of Pittsburgh, on the one hand, and with the then struggling steel worker and amateur optician, John A. Brashear, on the other. To these two men, and to his two assistants, James E. Keeler, afterward director of Lick Observatory, and Frank W. Very, he owed much of the success of his enterprises.

Langley's prime interest lay in studying the sun as the support of our lives. The value of the "solar constant," which represents the intensity of solar heat as it would be found if we could go outside our atmosphere at the earth's mean solar distance, as on the moon, for instance, had been, as many supposed, settled. In the year 1838, Pouillet determined it as 1.7633 "calories per square centimeter per minute." Forbes, Violle, Radau, and others, however, had pointed out flaws in the determination of Pouillet. Radau, in particular, had shown in the clearest possible manner that no mere measurements of the total intensity of the sun's complex beam, such as Pouillet's, could ever satisfy the requirements of the problem of finding the true intensity of the solar radiation as it is outside of our atmosphere. Spectrum energy measurements on the heat of each of the colors had to be made, but up to Langley's time no one had made them. It was to do this that he invented the bolometer.

For a year or two, Langley worked upon his problem at Allegheny, but he became satisfied that the pure air of mountain peaks rather than the smoke of Pittsburgh

PLATE 5

B—William Thaw, philanthropist of Pittsburgh, who assisted Professor Langley in his solar investigations and John A. Brashear in his optical work

A—Prof. C. A. Young, of Princeton, enthusiast for solar observation, who wrote lucidly on the subject

must be sought, if he would succeed. Aided by the U. S. Signal Service, financed by William Thaw, and carried in a special car across the continent by the interest of the Pennsylvania Railroad, he conducted, in the year 1881, his famous expedition to Mount Whitney, the highest peak of the California Sierras. Here, with the incomparable skill of Keeler at command, and with the driving power of Langley forcing a way through all obstacles, their bolometer revealed new invisible regions of the solar spectrum far beyond the red. In Plate 7 the reader may find Langley's own description of the discoverer's elation on penetrating this new spectral region. They measured the transparency of the atmosphere for a great range of wave-lengths, and, in combination with the actinometer of Violle, these novel bolometric observations furnished a new value of the solar constant of radiation, which held the field for over 20 years, displacing Pouillet's.

Unfortunately, Langley committed an error of logic in the reduction of these observations. Observing first at Lone Pine in the Owens Valley, he measured there the transparency of the atmosphere. Employing it, and taking into account the difference in barometric pressure, he computed what intensity of solar radiation ought to be found on Mount Whitney. Arrived at the high station, the actual observations gave values decidedly higher than he had thus computed. Upon this fact Langley reasoned as follows: If our computations fall below our observations for a station within the atmosphere, to which we can ascend, much more will they fall below what we should observe if we could go outside the atmosphere altogether.

But he overlooked the fact that his measures of atmospheric transmission determined at Lone Pine, though truly representative of the combined effect of all of the air strata from Lone Pine to the limit of the atmosphere, did not fairly suit the part which lay between Lone Pine and Mount Whitney, because this layer is far less transparent than the average of all the layers. In short, the formula of Bouguer and Lambert which he had used, although quite sound for reducing the results to the limit of the atmosphere, is entirely inapplicable to compute the intensity of the solar beam at any station intermediate between the observer and outside space.

Owing to this unfortunate misinterpretation, Langley published 3.0 calories per square centimeter per minute as the most probable value of the solar constant of radiation. A value near 2.1 calories would have represented his observations more correctly. The measurements made on the Mount Whitney expedition, owing to the difficulties of the problem and the pioneering character of the attack upon it, were not of a high order of accuracy. But the true method of approach was here, for the first time in the history of the subject, experimentally applied. No one else had done spectrum work on the energy of solar radiation. No one else had shown how to standardize the spectrum measurements against the pyrheliometer or actinometer. No one else had carried a complex outfit to a cloudless mountain station. These were the three indispensable requirements of the problem.

It was over 20 years before a new attempt was made to measure the intensity of solar radiation by Langley's method. There was certainly great need for attention to this problem. The "solar constant" measures the sun's energy, on which all terrestrial concerns depend. Yet up to the beginning of this present century this all-important quantity was unknown. People often ask if the sun's heat is changing. Some think the world has grown warmer since their childhood. They say we no longer have such winters as we had then. The main reason people hold this impression is because one remembers the first ten years better than any other ten years of his life. If there came a great snow-storm, or a very cold snap during that time, it made an indelible impression. That

one exceptional winter when childhood's vivid impressions were forming fixed forever for him the standard of a winter. Other hard winters later on in life were soon forgotten.

Long-continued meterological records of temperature and snowfall do not support this impression that climate is growing milder. Northern United States, indeed, is a trifle warmer, and southern United States a trifle colder than a century ago. If we go back to ancient times we find that in Syria and Egypt people raised the same crops before Christ that they do now in those regions. Unfortunately for exact knowledge, neither Tutankhamen nor Solomon nor even Sir Isaac Newton made exact measurements of the solar constant of radiation or, indeed, of climatic conditions. We have not the exact ancient measurements necessary to show whether the sun's heat is diminishing. Even as late as the year 1901, the solar constant was uncertain—between the limits of Pouillet's value, 1.76 calories, and Ångström's value, 4.0 calories. These and several other determinations are given without preference in Hann's standard work on meteorology published in 1901.

The work was taken up at the Astrophysical Observatory of the Smithsonian Institution in Washington in the year 1902. Though the place was unsuitable, the instrumental means had been greatly perfected in the interim since the Mount Whitney expedition. The actinometer of Crova, standardized against a modified form of Pouillet's pyrheliometer, was used in 1902 to measure the total intensity of the solar beam. K. J. Ångström, however, had invented, nearly a decade earlier, his ingenious and excellent electrical compensation pyrheliometer, but it was not available to us at the Astrophysical Observatory, and fortunately so, as later events proved.

Great improvements had been made in the bolometer. Langley has often told of the struggle to observe in the

Mount Whitney days, where, owing to accidental causes wholly unrelated to the solar measurements, the recording spot of light was sweeping across the reading scale at the rate of over a meter a minute. All this was past. The bolometer in 1902 was as steady as anyone could desire, and even easier to use accurately than the ordinary mercury thermometer. Its indications were automatically recorded on a photographic plate instead of being read upon a divided scale as in Langley's Mount Whitney measurements. Within 15 minutes, we could make a better energy curve of the solar spectrum than Langley and Keeler, with all their skill, could have determined in three days in the year 1881.

By what now seems a fortunate chance, the few solar-constant determinations made in the years 1902 and 1903 at Washington seemed to indicate a great and sudden change in the intensity of the sun's radiation. After all of the experience we now have, one hardly knows whether it was a real solar variation which we stumbled upon, or an accidental error of local atmospheric origin which assumed the aspect of a true solar change. Whichever it was, the results indicated that suddenly, about March 26, 1903, a fall of 10 per cent in the solar constant occurred.

At that time we assumed, as it was most natural to do, that if the sun's radiation fell off, the earth's temperature must everywhere fall off too. Hence, the obvious thing to do was to see if there had been a general fall of temperature in the world which could be attributed to the supposed change in the sun. Figure 2 shows what we found. Apparently our impression of a 10 per cent decrease of solar radiation was strongly supported by a nearly simultaneous diminution of the temperature of the whole North Temperate Zone. Secretary Langley accepted our results as apparently verified, and published an account of the experiments, from which I quote as follows:

"A series of determinations of the solar radiation out-

PLATE 7

sheltered from moisture, that its clearness and its ir~~~~~
compared favorably even in the visible spectrum, w~~ those
of the most perfect prism of glass, with the additional advantage
that it was permeable to the extreme infra-red rays in question.
This prism rested on a large azimuth circle turned by clockwork of the extremest precision, which caused the spectrum to
move slowly along, and in one minute of time, for example,
to move exactly one minute of arc of its length, before the
strip of the bolometer brought them successively in contact
with one invisible line and another. The bolometer was connected by a cable with the galvanometer, whose swing to the
right or the left was photographically registered on a plate
which the same clockwork caused to move synchronously and
uniformly up or down, by exactly one centimeter of space for
the corresponding minute. By this means the energy curve
of an invisible region, which directly is wholly inaccessible to
photography, is photographed upon the plate.

Let it be noted that whatever the relation of the spectrum
and the plate is (and different ones might be adopted) it was
absolutely synchronous,—synchrons at least to such a degree

S. P. Langley—New Spectrum. 411

that an error in the position of one of these invisible lines
could be determined with the precision of the astronomical
measurement of visible things, with that which is a relative
probable error of less than a second of arc: a statement which
might appear to the astronomer a hardy one but which the
writer repeated deliberately.

The spectator would perhaps gather a clearer idea of this
action if they imagine the map before them hung up at right
angles to its actual position, so that a rise in the energy curve
given would be seen to correspond to a deflection to the right,
and a fall to one to the left; for in this way the deflections
were written down on moving photographic plate from which
this print had been made. The writer was speaking, however,
of the refinements of the most modern practice; but there was
something in this retrospect of this instrument's early use
which brought up a personal reminiscence which he asked the
Academy to indulge him in alluding to.

This was that of one day in 1881, nearly twenty years ago,
when being near the summit of Mt. Whitney in the Sierra
Nevada, alone and at an altitude of 12,000 feet, he there with
this newly invented instrument was working in this invisible
spectrum. His previous experience had been that of most
scientific men, that very few discoveries come with a surprise; and
that they are usually the summation of the quiet work of years.

In this case, almost the only one in his experience, he had
the sensations of one who makes a discovery. He went down
the spectrum, noting the evidence of invisible heat die out on the
scale of the instrument, until he came to the apparent end even
of the invisible, beyond which the most prolonged researches
of investigators up to that time had shown nothing. There he
watched the indications grow fainter and fainter until they
too ceased at the point where the French investigators had
found the very end of the end. By some happy thought he
pushed the indications of this delicate instrument into the
region still beyond. In the still air of this lofty region, the
sunbeams passed unimpeded by the mists of the lower earth,
and the curve of heat, which had fallen to nothing, began to
rise again. There was something there. For he found, suddenly and unexpectedly, a new spectrum of great extent,
wholly unknown to science and whose presence was revealed
by the new instrument, the bolometer.

On the map it will be observed that while the work of the
photograph (much more detailed than that of the bolometer
where it can be used at all) had been stated to extend, as far as
regular mapping is concerned, to about 1"·: everything beyond
that is due to the bolometer, except that early French investi-

What Secretary Langley was accustomed to do to page proof. See
also near the bottom his description of the making of a pioneer discovery

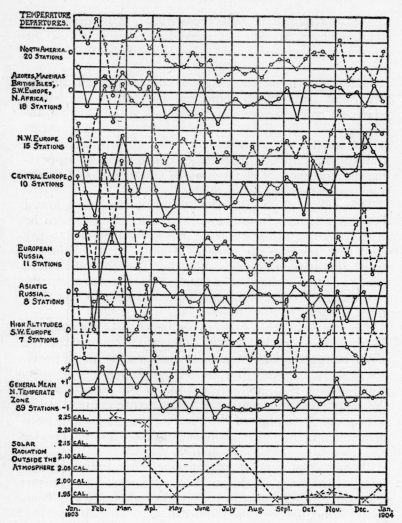

FIG. 2. The variable Washington solar observations of 1903, which led
Langley to suspect the sun to be a variable star governing the earth's
temperature changes

side the atmosphere (solar constant), extending from October, 1902, to March, 1904, has been made at the Smithsonian Astrophysical Observatory under the writer's direction.

"Care has been exercised to determine all known sources of error which could seriously affect the values relatively to each other, and principally the varying absorption of the Earth's atmosphere. Though uncertainty must ever remain as to the absorption of this atmosphere, different kinds of evidence agree in supporting the accuracy of the estimates made of it and of the conclusions deduced from them.

"The effects due to this absorption having been allowed for, the inference from these observations appears to be that the solar radiation itself fell off by about 10 per cent, beginning at the close of March, 1903. I do not assert this without qualification, but if such a change in solar radiation did actually occur, a decrease of temperature on the Earth, which might be indefinitely less than 7.5° C., ought to have followed it.

"On comparing the observed temperatures of 89 stations, distributed over the North Temperate Zone, with the mean temperatures of the same stations for many previous years, it is found that an average decrease of temperature of over 2° C. actually did follow the possible fall of the solar radiation, while the temperature continued low during the remainder of the year. Stations remote from the retarding influence of the oceans show a much greater variation than that of the general mean.

"While it is difficult to conceive what influence, not solar, could have produced this rapid and simultaneous reduction of temperatures over the whole North Temperate Zone, and continued operative for so long a period, the evidence of solar variation cannot be said to be conclusive. Nevertheless, such a conclusion seems not an unreasonable inference from the data now at hand, and a continuation of these bolographic studies of solar radiation is of increasing interest, in view of their possible aid in forecasting terrestrial climatic changes, conceivably due to solar ones.

"All the preceding observations, while under my general direction, have been conducted in detail by Mr. Abbot, to whom my thanks are especially due."

Was this a true solar change and a real meteorological effect of it? Many subsequent years of solar measurements, coupled with earnest study of the effects of solar changes on terrestrial temperatures, incline one to question the conclusion. We can not altogether say it was an error, but we are more than doubtful of its soundness. Whether true or false, it was the incentive to the long train of observing which has carried our expeditions to four continents, from sea-level to far above the clouds; and at length, after nearly a quarter of a century, it has not only demonstrated the reality of solar changes, but has discovered their unquestionable and important influences upon the earth's temperatures, pressures, and rainfalls. If it was all due to an accident, surely it was an accident of the same fortunate sort as those related in the "Arabian Nights" that led Ali Baba, after wood, to the treasure chamber of the forty thieves, and Morgiana, after oil, to the pannier of the concealed robber.

As I have said, it was also a fortunate circumstance which had prevented us from employing the excellent electrical compensation pyrheliometer of Ångström. Fortunate, because at that time there were still several sources of error in Ångström's pyrheliometer—sources since discovered and removed; fortunate because it led us to develop the type of the silver-disk pyrheliometer, which for constancy of scale over a long period of years has left little to be desired; and, finally, fortunate because it led us to invent and perfect the water-flow pyrheliometer, now the primary standard instrument of the world. Had we begun our measurements with so good an instrument as Ångström's, it is highly improbable that we should have developed these valuable pyrheliometers.

The Swedish family of Ångström in physics, like the American family of Adams in diplomacy, has been distinguished through several generations. The name of Anders Jonas Ångström (1814–1874) is immortalized in the unit of length of waves of light, called the Ångström, which is one ten-millionth of a meter. Visible light ranges from 4,000 to 7,000 Ångströms in its gamut from violet to deep red. Professor of physics at Upsala, A. J. Ångström was famous for his studies of the solar spectrum. His great spectrum map, published in 1868, was the standard of spectroscopy for almost a quarter-century, until displaced by Rowland's solar-spectrum map of even greater detail and accuracy. His gifted son, Knut Johan Ångström (1857–1910) was also a distinguished professor of physics at Upsala. Like Langley, he was greatly interested in problems of measurement in solar radiation, and like Langley made a famous and valuable expedition to a high mountain—Teneriffe in the Azores Islands. His radiation-measuring instruments are very ingenious, and remain to this day highly accepted by investigators the world over. Carrying on the Ångström tradition to the next generation is Anders Knut Ångström, his son, charming in personality and brilliant in theory and experiment. Though still a young man, he is already distinguished for his work in meteorology and radiation. We shall see more of him in a later chapter.

From 1902 to 1907, we made many solar-constant measurements at the Smithsonian Institution in Washington. But Doctor Langley recollected the wonderfully clear sky of the California mountains, and knew that nothing satisfactory could be done within the bounds of a smoky and dusty sea-level city. He proposed solar-radiation investigations as a principal object of attack for the Carnegie Institution, then being founded. These

PLATE 8

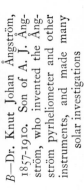

A—The first of a renowned Swedish family of solar investigators, Dr. Anders Jonas Ångström, 1814-1874. The unit of wave-length is named for him. He made the first great solar-spectrum map

B—Dr. Knut Johan Ångström, 1857-1910. Son of A. J. Ångström, who invented the Ångström pyrheliometer and other instruments, and made many solar investigations

C—Dr. Anders Knut Ångström, son of K. J. Ångström, an eminent meteorologist who has studied extensively the earth's dependence on radiation

PLATE 9

Dome of the five-foot telescope and two tower telescopes of the Mount Wilson Observatory.   Photograph
by F. Ellerman

proposals of Langley's led Dr. George E. Hale, at the very inception of the Mount Wilson Observatory, to invite Langley to send observers to the summit of Mount Wilson to carry on these researches.

The foundation of the Carnegie Institution with its several great departments for scientific investigation and publication was an epoch-making event in American culture. No one was more instrumental in planting and forming this grand idea in the mind of the great steel magnate than the late Dr. C. D. Walcott, then Director of the U. S. Geological Survey, and later Secretary of the Smithsonian Institution. While he was breakfasting with the Carnegies one day, mention was made of the Smithsonian Institution and its world-wide service. "Who was this man Smith?" said Carnegie. Doctor Walcott readily explained that James Smithson was an eminent English chemist, a graduate of Oxford and member of the Royal Society of Great Britain. He pointed out the extraordinary results of the alien Smithson's moderate bequest, and the opportunity still open for richly endowing science, developing the exceptional young genius, and making at the same time a perpetual, exalted, personal memorial and an incomparable contribution to civilization. Somehow the romance of the idea fired Andrew Carnegie, and the Carnegie Institution with $10,000,000 initial endowment was the startling outcome.

Secretary Langley of the Smithsonian Institution was for the moment almost beside himself, for he thought he read in this tremendous competing endowment the comparative extinction of the fame of the older scientific establishment under his care. At their first meeting he exclaimed to Walcott, "You have ruined the Smithsonian Institution!" Yet it did not prove so. For notwithstanding that Carnegie afterwards increased the endowment to $27,000,000, the Carnegie Institution, under the brilliant leadership of Dr. J. C. Merriam, now laments the inadequacy of its income to carry on the obvious scientific work in its domain. Meanwhile, Doctor Walcott, succeeding Langley, ably administered the Smithsonian Institution, which without in the least infringing on the Carnegie Institution's scientific fields, plainly sees in its own types of work demands for the expenditure of the income from at least an equal sum in researches of the highest interest and usefulness.

In the year 1905, the invitation of Hale was accepted. Messrs. C. G. Abbot and L. R. Ingersoll observed for the solar-constant on Mount Wilson from May until November under such constantly fine conditions as made Washington observing seem indeed futile. But the apparent variations of solar radiation continued to present themselves. Decreases of accidental error, depending on clearer sky conditions, did not bring constancy of results. We were encouraged to go on in the pursuit of solar variability.

Although Doctor Langley was cordially favorable to the expedition to Mount Wilson, there was a difference of view between us. I had become fully convinced that his solar-constant result from the Mount Whitney observations involved the error of logic already explained. We had discussed the matter several times, and it seemed to me that in his secret mind he admitted the error. I had even urged him to publish a note about it so that he might put himself right with posterity. His reply was, in substance: "Mr. Abbot, I published the Mount Whitney Report when I was at the height of my powers and working constantly in that field. If I was wrong, I cannot make a correction, now that I have long been out of touch with that work. As a witty Frenchman has said, 'What has posterity done for us, that we should care so much for the opinion of posterity!'"

As I was about to start for Mount Wilson, Doctor Langley and I had a final conference which, in fact, proved to be the last one we were ever to have. At the conclusion, he said: "I wish to emphasize that the expedition is primarily to test the variability of the sun. It is not primarily to measure the absolute value of the solar constant of radiation." Then, with a twinkle in his eye, he added, "In fact, Mr. Abbot, I may say that I regard that value of the solar constant as best which nearest approaches 3 calories!"

Doctor Langley had a fine sense of humor. The older members of the staff of the Smithsonian Institution love to rehearse together their recollections of him and his quaint sayings. One summer, while he was abroad, a small new laboratory was erected for some proposed work at the Astrophysical Observatory. Soon after Doctor Langley's return, he came over to the Observatory one day to discuss with me the work done during his absence. As he turned to go, his eye fell on the outer door of the little frame building, which had been painted green. Stopping an instant, he turned to me and said, " Your new door reminds me of a little saying we used to have when I was a boy—'Neat, not gaudy, as the Devil said when he painted his tail pea-green.' " With that, Doctor Langley, never waiting to hear my explosion, rushed away, as he always did after a joke, for with all his humor he had a very enlarged sense of the dignity which should hedge the Secretary of the Smithsonian Institution.

He was a wonderfully painstaking and interesting writer. His book "The New Astronomy" contains many gems. There came from his pen a long series of painstaking popular articles on scientific subjects. He could never be satisfied with his composition. It was not safe from alteration until actually bound up. A proof leaving his hands might well be called "printer's despair." Plate 7 is a facsimile of proof from an article he prepared in the year 1901, entitled "The New Spectrum."

While we speak of him, I must add one more incident to show something of the kindliness of the man, and the strong loyalty of his support to those he trusted. To appreciate this story, the reader must recall that in the

year 1900 I was little more than a boy, without any
standing in the world, while M. Deslandres, of whom we
shall speak, was a famous astronomer. At the total solar
eclipse of 1900, Dr. C. E. Mendenhall and I had measured
with the bolometer the heat received from the rays of the
solar corona, that delicate halo that always surrounds
the sun but can never be seen except during total solar
eclipses, when the moon shades the atmosphere for a brief
instant and thus dims the sky light. I had published an
interpretation of these observations, which ran counter to
the results and views of M. Deslandres. Doctor Langley
brought the weight of his reputation to my defense in a
brief note published in the *Astrophysical Journal*. It
closed as follows:

"I may add that the bolometer, however trustworthy
an instrument, demands an installment in a chamber of
uniform temperature, with much accessory apparatus for
its best effect, and that this was provided for it on the
present occasion. What is still more important, it, like
any other apparatus of the kind, should be in the hands
of one long familiar with it, to give reliable information
at a time so brief and trying as that of totality. While
I have familiarity myself in its use, yet considering that
Mr. Abbot was in more continuous recent practice, I
assigned the observation to him, and I have all the confidence in its results that I should have, had I made it
myself."

There was only time, after the return to Washington
late in the year 1905, to acquaint Doctor Langley of the
hopeful character of the results, before he passed away in
the winter of 1906. His dream of finding the solar
causes of the good years and the lean ones, like his dream
of teaching men to fly, he lived to see supported, but not
fully established, by the researches he initiated.

The funeral of Langley, while simple, was marked by
an impressiveness worthy of the passing of so great a
man. Borne by his friends and subordinates of the

Smithsonian, the remains of the pioneering astronomer and physicist entered All Soul's Church at Washington preceded by the great, gaunt, prophetlike form of that celebrated national figure, Dr. Edward Everett Hale, who strode on before in his priestly robe, saying with a strong voice: " 'I am the resurrection and the life: he that believeth in me, though he were dead, yet shall he live: and whosoever liveth and believeth in me shall never die.' "

In the year 1906, the expedition to Mount Wilson was renewed with the same observers. Not only were a great many solar-constant measurements made, but the comparative coolness of sun-spots, the reflecting power of clouds, the standardization of pyrheliometers, the quality of the blue of the sky, and other subjects, received careful observation. The association with such men as Hale, Adams, Gale, and others, who were making history in the rapidly developing Mount Wilson Solar Observatory, was highly inspiring.

Those were indeed great days upon Mount Wilson! It was before the completion of the great reflecting telescopes for stellar work. Everybody studied the sun, or some phenomena in the laboratory which were closely related to it. When the sun set, then observing was ended; and in the evenings, with the finest of good companionship, we crowded about the roaring fireplace in the library of the "Old Monastery." It was in the good old times when people still played straight whist and duplicate. Many a close game of duplicate was contested there, with 16 packs of cards required to prevent Adams from remembering on the second round all of the details of the fall of the cards in the first. Stories were read and told. The tale of Talmadge's sermon from the text "The Lord sent the hornet," and the strange revenge of the Turkish countryman who did business in Constantinople never failed of applause.

This latter story may be found at length in Robert Curzon's "Visits to Monasteries in the Levant." From many times of repetition, I quote it substantially as follows:

There was once a Turk who did business in Constantinople. He was a good, simple fellow, as many Turkish country people are, but he had occasion to deal with a sharp merchant who had a shop for all sorts of things in the bazaar. Our friend was sure to find that he had been cheated, either in the weight, or the quality, or something else. He became sore and touchy about it under the laughter of his friends, as they sat smoking together in the shade of the mosque, talking over the piastres and paras they had spent in the bazaar.

At last in his desperation he consulted an old Hadji, a grave long-bearded personage who had made two journeys to Mecca, both of which, from the judicious selection of the merchandise he had carried with him, had been no less profitable to his temporal concerns than the throwing of three stones at the Devil and seven at the Devil's sons had been to his eternal welfare.

"O Hadji!" said the poor bewildered Turk, "Tell me, of your goodness, of some means whereby I may be revenged on this Chifoot for the way he is continually cheating a true believer like myself. I might beat him, certainly, I might make him eat stick, but then I should get myself into trouble with the Cadi, and the end would be worse than the beginning."

The Hadji, who was a man of few words, giving out slowly a long whiff of smoke from his pipe, said: "My son, go to the merchant's shop. Seek out there some insignificant old thing, holding in your hand a purse of gold at the same moment. Pay him down instantly upon his counting-board whatever he may ask. Walk away rapidly, and with a cheerful countenance. Do this, and you will be revenged."

The Turk did not at all understand the advice which had been given him by the Hadji. He thought at first the Hadji might be joking. But he reflected that the Hadji was no joker, and, indeed, had never made a joke in his life. So he went to the merchant's shop, and saw there a mean box, worth perhaps twenty piastres. The merchant asked him two hundred. His great difficulty was to pay this money with a cheerful countenance, for he saw that he was being cheated again. However, he did so, and walked out trying to look as if he had done something clever.

That afternoon he met the Hadji, and the Hadji said to him: "Well, my son, have you done as I said? Have you taken my advice?"

"Yes," said the poor Turk. "See this box. What is it worth? Ten piastres! But that son of abomination is counting my two hundred piastres at this moment! May his soul be grilled, and made into two hundred skewers of kabobs! Alas, O Father! Do not laugh at my beard! Tell me, how am I to be revenged?"

"Yavash! Gently, my son," said the Hadji. "To-morrow, Inshallah, we shall see." He said no more, for he had talked much for him in the past two days. So he smoked his pipe, and said no more.

The next day, as our friend walked with a rueful face through the bazaar, he saw that the merchant's shop was shut up. A crowd of bystanders having collected, he asked one of them why the shop was shut.

"Oh, aga," said he. "Be it known to your nobility that yesterday a certain man who had had many dealings with this merchant, and to whom he was, as it were, an estate, a khashnádar, a treasure, from the profit the merchant had of him; this man having bought a certain box, worth nothing so far as its appearance went, but having paid, it is said, two thousand piastres rather than leave this mean-looking box, a thought came into the head of the merchant. There must have been a diamond in it. In his vexation he went home and told his wife. 'Perhaps it was a talisman,' said she.

" 'O fool!' said his wife's mother, 'miserable dog that

thou art! Doubtless it was Solomon's seal, else why should a Turk, forsooth, pay such a sum for a mean box worth nothing? Thou disgrace to our house, what hast thou done? Hast thou kept a shop in the bazaar so long for this? O small man! A woman, indeed, would have been more awake! Dost thou call thyself a man? Where are thy brains? O man! Say hast thou any brains or not? Hast thou ruined thy family, or hast thou not? What dirt hast thou been eating? Alas that we have married our daughter to an ass! Woe is me! Amaan! Amaan! Amaan!'

"So the poor man had no peace. No words were spoken to him by his family but words of contempt and abuse. Therefore, in the morning, his life being a burden, he went out into his garden and hanged himself."

The Turk was much affected when he heard of the unhappy ending of the merchant. But a Persian dealer in Kermaun shawls observed: "By the name of Ali! I am glad that the merchant hanged himself, but I am sorry that he did not leave me the two hundred piastres in his will!"

Mount Wilson Observatory is one of the wonders of the world. With its great annual income, splendid situation, gigantic instruments, large and able staff, and shops and laboratories where anything required may be constructed, it is not surprising that the hoary science of astronomy has leaped forward at the urge of the tremendous push of such youthful energy. In its quarter-century of existence, Mount Wilson, besides the wealth of steady observations it continually pours forth, has given the world several epoch-making discoveries, such as Hale's magnetism in the sun; Adams's spectroscopic measures of stellar distances; Michelson's determination of the diameters of stars; and Hubble's resolution of the spiral nebulæ into other galaxies than ours at distances requiring of light millions of years to travel. How astonishing that we see these objects, not as they are today, but as they

PLATE 11

Smithsonian solar station on Mount Wilson, Calif.

PLATE 12

Smithsonian solar station on Mount Whitney, Calif., 14,500 feet above sea-level. This firewood costs $60.00 a cord at the summit

were before men existed upon the earth, though the light which discloses them has rushed through 186,000 miles every second since then to reach us!

The two directors, Hale and Adams, are as opposite as the poles in the types of their greatness. Hale represents the romance of discovery. Eager to see phenomena, continually pleased by the beauty of the spectrum, or a microscopic view of the denizens of a drop of ditch water, willing to try anything, he did not shrink from putting into practice a hundred new ideas to the ordinary man's one, of which a goodly percentage proved fruitful. Adams, the steady though brilliant observer, willing to set his goal far ahead, requiring for its attainment millions of observations and years of effort, makes his approaches like the successive moves of the chess player, though ever on the watch to take advantage of the fortunes of the game.

In 1907, no Mount Wilson expedition was made. Volume II of the *Annals of the Astrophysical Observatory* was being prepared for publication. In it the ground-work of solar-constant observing was studied with care. Instruments and their sources of error were described. The numerous measurements made on Mount Wilson and in Washington were set forth. Here was encountered Langley's long-accepted value, 3 calories, for the solar constant. The reasons which required us to reject it were fully explained. In its place was substituted 2.1 calories which, in its turn, was later on further reduced, after the standard scale of radiation measurements was fully perfected in 1913. The evidence for variability of the sun was set forth. It was not yet convincing. Much required to be done before it could become so.

Hitherto, we had perfected to a considerable degree the experimental and computational processes of observing the solar constant by Langley's method of high and low sun, and we had found close agreement between the mean of results determined near sea-level, at Washington, and those determined at over a mile of altitude on Mount Wilson. We now undertook a bolder test. In the years 1909 and 1910, while colleagues observed on Mount Wilson, the writer simultaneously made complete solar-constant observations on the extreme summit of Mount Whitney, at 14,500 feet, some 2,000 feet above the level of Langley's "Mountain Camp." Almost perfect accord was found between the results at Mount Wilson and Mount Whitney, showing, when considered with Washington observations, that from sea-level to an elevation of nearly three miles, the Langley method, as perfected and practiced, gave results independent of the altitude of the observer.

We now undertook still another test. Apparently the sun varied. Were the variations really solar, or were they brought about by obscure local atmospheric sources of error, not yet eliminated? To test this question we needed to carry on a long series of observations in duplicate at stations so far apart that their local atmospheric conditions must be regarded as quite independent. Mexico was first proposed, but the revolution which broke out there at that time made it unsuitable, and Algeria, which had the advantage of much greater remoteness from Mount Wilson, was chosen. An outfit of over 30 boxes of delicate apparatus and photographic plates was taken over there in the year 1911. With the invaluable aid of the vice-consul, M. René Boisson, and with the generous assistance of M. de Mestral in the matter of living quarters and observing ground, a station was occupied at Bassour, some 50 miles south of Algiers, from July until November of the year 1911, and from May until September, 1912.

For the Algerian expedition, the writer and Mrs. Abbot were assisted in 1911 by Prof. F. P. Brackett of Pomona College, California, and in 1912 by Dr. Anders Ångström of Upsala, Sweden. At the same time the station at Mount Wilson was carried on in 1911 by Mr. L. B.

Aldrich, and in 1912 by Mr. F. E. Fowle, my colleagues of the Astrophysical Observatory.

In Algeria we lived in one of a row of five thick-walled houses with tiled roofs. These had been erected by the French promoters in connection with a farm-school for poor children of Paris. Our neighbor, M. Sirioud, had grown up in the school, and was now a prosperous farmer, who rented part of the school lands. He was married to a pleasant, buxom wife, and had two little girls. These neighbors were most helpful to us in every way. Mrs. Sirioud was very quick-witted to understand our blundering French, even rising to the emergency without a smile when in my excitement one day I called a *clef* just what the letters spell in English! The Siriouds had cattle, sheep, and poultry, and raised large fields of wheat. M. Sirioud drove to town occasionally, and did our errands. One can hear him yet shouting his *"Allez vite!"* to the horse, who paid it no more attention than he would the buzz of a fly.

A quarter of a mile in the other direction was a proprietor, M. de Tonnac, who with the aid of his sons and many Arab servants, cultivated his large estate planted to vines and wheat. We had many kindnesses from M. and Mme. de Tonnac while we remained in Algeria, and they have not forgotten us even after the lapse of a dozen years. M. de Mestral, also, who managed the great property of the school, was most helpful whenever we had needs of any kind which he could supply.

All about us were the Arabs, cultivating their smaller farm lands, and serving upon the farms of these French proprietors. The most considerable among them, the Cadi, lived in one of the five houses near ourselves and the Siriouds. He, also, with his family did much for our success and comfort. We naturally were the absorbing feature of interest for the villagers so long as we remained. Scarcely a day passed without nearly a hundred Arab visits, though often it was a few individuals who came

[31]

from ten to twenty times a day. But the Cadi saw to it
that they did not come to our observatory on the hill.
We had a screen door at our house, and hour after hour
it would support just as many little Arab boys and girls
as could flatten their noses against it to see what the
American lady was cooking, or the American men were
making inside.

We found the life of Abraham's time little altered there
in the twentieth century. The Bible took on a new meaning as we saw the oxen treading out the wheat, the shep-
herds watching their flocks, the women grinding at the
mill, and the winnowing of the grain in the wind. "On
the housetops" seemed different, too, when we saw in
the villages how much domestic work goes on upon those
flat-topped mud houses. To a New England boy it had
always been a mystery why Boaz slept upon his threshing-
floor. The boy had conceived of Boaz as sleeping upon the
floor of a great barn, where the grain was being threshed
with flails. He was enlightened when he saw his French
neighbor pass at twilight, with his double-barreled gun
and fierce dog, to sleep under the stars upon the great pile
of grain, which weeks of patient treading by the oxen had
heaped up. Boaz evidently had light-fingered neighbors
too.

As for the work on the sun's radiation, the locality
proved fairly satisfactory, though by no means ideal. Our
little observing shelter was built of box-boards from the
packing cases, and weighted down with a ton or more of
stones piled all about it. For we found that occasionally
a three-days' storm of wind from the Sahara howled
around us with such violence that we feared almost for
the thick-walled house where we lived, and marveled
that our observatory on the hill could stand at all. The
heat during these storms was most oppressive, and they
were the more trying because the air was loaded with fine
sand that drifted through every crack. Occasionally, too,
there were heavy rains against which our beautiful red-

PLATE 13

Smithsonian solar-radiation expedition to Bassour, Algeria, 1911.   Prof. Brackett observing with the silver-disk pyrheliometer.   The instrument shelter is weighted with stones to prevent its being blown away

PLATE 14

The Cadi, at Bassour, Algeria

tiled roof was a poor protection. On one night we were awakened to find the floor all submerged. Quick work was needed to find dry places for the numerous photographic records, books, and instruments of the expedition, not to mention our clothes and beds.

Other things than rain, such as scorpions, centipedes, and some more domesticated members of the insect world, visited us not infrequently from their domiciles with our Arab friends, who lived under our house. More than these, however, we detested the dogs. The Scripture says "Without are the dogs." We came to understand how feelingly the author of this passage must have written. Just behind our house lived an Arab family in a dug-out thatched with straw, through which simple roof percolated the smoke from their cooking-fire of dried cow-dung. One entrance there was, too low for an adult to enter upright. This served for window as well as door. It was guarded night and day by a wolfish cur, eager to set his teeth into anyone who came within reach of his rope. At every pretext, and often, as we thought, at none at all, he barked short quick barks at the (measured) rate of 29 times in ten seconds for a quarter of an hour or more. Once when I hit him with a little stone he speeded up to 40 times in ten seconds. Often at 2 o'clock a.m. he would awaken us, and, all other dogs within hearing joining the chorus, they would keep it up steadily for an hour or two.

In order to get rested at night for the daily work, we had to do something about this dog. Mrs. Abbot had made a conundrum about him as follows: "What is Kadra's door made of?" The answer: "Dog-would-bark." We tried to buy him, but they refused to sell. We offered to pay for his board elsewhere. This was tried a few days, but they missed him too much and brought him home. At length we solved the problem in this way: We paid a regular stipend of 5 francs per month to have him quieted at night. As his owners slept without hearing him, we carried in every night a hatful of stones, and threw them from our window when the dog concert began until the owners awakened. They immediately threw a quilt over the dog and stifled his barking for the remainder of the night.

During our second season, in 1912, Doctor Ångström occupied a little room which we added to the observing shelter. On his way to bed he would pass through the fields near another Arab dug-out, where the dog at once, of course, began to bark. Then all of the dogs in Bassour barked, all of the dogs in Ben-Chicao joined with them, and so on, as we suppose, until all of the dogs in Africa and Asia barked because Doctor Ångström was going up to bed. Possibly this source of atmospheric disturbance may not be altogether negligible for meteorology!

The country about Bassour was in its way very lovely. At an altitude of nearly 4,000 feet, and surrounded by rolling hills with few trees, but many shrubs and cultivated vineyards, the outlook was charming. Especially was this so in spring, when the ground was carpeted everywhere by a most extraordinary profusion of flowers of every color. I have never seen such a gorgeous flower-carpet in any other part of the world. Later in the summer the soil became very dry and hard, but still some desert varieties of plants continued to bloom.

As for the results of the expeditions, we can compare the Algerian solar-constant values with those of Mount Wilson most satisfactorily by a diagram giving Mount Wilson values as vertical, and Bassour values as horizontal distances, on each common day of observation. For if the sun really varies and our determinations of its radiation outside our atmosphere were quite without error, then all of the results in a plot of this kind would be strung out upon a line inclined at 45°. Drawing such a line, we found that the actual observations, though not lying all upon it, because of accidental errors, yet spread themselves along near it, rather than lying within a circle, as they would do if there were no solar change at all.

MEASURING SUN RAYS

The extremes show a range of about ten per cent in the solar constant.

A good many more days would have been available if it had not been for the tremendous eruption of the volcano Mount Katmai in Alaska, about June 6, 1912. Within two weeks after this volcano had belched its dust into the air, we began to notice a peculiar streakiness in the sky at Bassour. Two or three days later the same was seen at Mount Wilson. The sky grew more and more white and hazy, until in August, 1912, fully 20 per cent was cut off from the intensity of the sun's rays at noon. All of the summer's work was injured by these unlucky sky conditions, and many days quite spoiled. However, some new facts about volcanic dust, its diffusion, its behavior with light, and its possible influence on climates were found out and published in a paper in the *National Geographic Magazine*, entitled "Do Volcanic Eruptions Affect Climate?" Other observers in Europe and America noted similar effects, but measurements by Harvard Observatory men in Peru, South America, proved that the Alaskan volcanic dust, although it spread all over the northern hemisphere, never penetrated beyond the equator.

The summer's work of 1912 was brought to an early close, not only on account of the thick volcanic haze, but because a great forest fire east of Mount Wilson ruined the atmospheric transparency there for many weeks. At the conclusion of the Algerian work, the observing party made an auto trip to Bou Saada, an oasis in the Desert of Sahara, accompanied by M. René Boisson, vice-consul of the United States at Algiers.

The governor of Algeria, learning that an American astronomer and party were going to Bou Saada, wired to the military commandant there to show every possible courtesy. As the troops were fighting in Morocco, the commandant arranged with a notable Marabout (holy man of importance) at El Hamel, six miles distant, to entertain the guests at dinner. Accordingly the party, accompanied by the commandant and one or two others, motored to El Hamel.

An escort of honor met the guests about a mile from the town. A carriage was provided for the astronomer and his lady, while the rest advanced on foot, excepting a guard of about twenty horsemen led by the Cadi of the place, who was attired in a scarlet cloak. These horsemen, splendidly mounted, and armed with prodigiously long guns with inlaid stocks, did some fancy riding, discharging their pieces as they dashed by the carriage.

Arrived at the town, the whole male population in their white burnooses were found lining the walls to see the company approach. Dismounting at the mosque, a dance was given by little children and armed men. The long guns were thrown up and caught as they fell. One went off with a tremendous bang, causing us considerable anxiety. However, no one was hurt.

Next, we were invited to inspect the interior of the mosque, our feet shod, of course, with sandals to prevent defiling the place. We saw there the graves of the Marabout's predecessors. The interpreter, indeed, managed to gather for the vice-consul a handful of sand from one of these holy graves. This he sealed in an envelope before handing it to M. Boisson, so as to preserve its sanctity. It was intended for presentation to an Arab lady of Algiers, the wife of a French officer. She had asked the vice-consul to be so kind as to procure it, in the hope that its mighty virtue might cause her to present a child to her husband, for this blessing hitherto had been denied her.

After this visit to the mosque, we saw a large company of pilgrims come from a distance, at this the conclusion of the month of Ramadan, to kiss the Marabout's shoulder. These ceremonies completed, we were invited to the feast. Even the Marabout's brothers failed to qualify for this honor, which was for us a great one. After about six preliminary courses, the table was cleared, and a great brass platter, a yard in diameter, hammered in beautiful

PLATE 15

Up from the Sahara desert with the black tents for the grape harvest, at Bassour, Algeria

PLATE 16

"Thou shalt not muzzle the ox when he treadeth out the corn"

designs, was laid upon it. All of the guests rose up while two men brought in upon their shoulders a long pole with a whole sheep spitted upon it and roasted by turning the pole by hand before an open fire.

The sheep being placed upright upon its legs upon the platter, the etiquette of the feast was for each guest to pull off with his fingers some choice morsel and place it upon his left-hand neighbor's plate. So the Marabout, a benevolent-looking elderly man with a flowing white beard, pulled off some of the skin and fat, thought by Arabs to be the greatest delicacies, and laid these morsels upon the writer's plate. In my turn I helped the million-aire Cadi who sat on my left, and so on around the table.

As we discussed the roast, the Marabout remarked in Arabic, "This is a great day with me. It is a day I shall long remember." This saying, being translated by the interpreter into French and by the vice-consul into English for us, I replied: "However long the Marabout may remember it, I shall remember it much longer!" Considering our relative ages, this seemed very likely. My reply having been turned into Arabic, the Marabout smiled sweetly and said something even more complimentary. M. Boisson, however, discouraged a response on my part, saying that the Marabout was no novice at these polite speeches, and we should be apt to keep the competition going indefinitely.

After we had finished the roast and remaining courses, we inscribed our names in a visitors' book. Then we took leave of the courteous Marabout, receiving a cordial invitation to renew our visit. We in our turn invited him to Washington, a journey which we felt sure would give him great satisfaction. As we were leaving, a gentle rain began to fall, and possibly this was looked upon by these dwellers in a Saharan oasis as a final proof, if more were needed, of the eminence of their visitors. The white-robed company upon the walls was still patiently in attendance as we rode out of sight.

THE SUN AND THE WELFARE OF MAN

One other incident of our Algerian expeditions may be worth relating. In our first journey, in 1911, we had thought to go to Oran rather than Algiers, and to locate our observatory in the mountains to the south of that port. As no steamers from America touched at Oran, we took ship to Gibraltar, hoping to find there some small vessel going to Oran. In this we were disappointed, and so took passage by the North German Lloyd steamer to Algiers. Our man whom we engaged at Gibraltar to arrange matters, got our 33 cases of instruments aboard just before the ship sailed. But as we ourselves went up the ship's ladder, an officer informed us that the vessel could not deliver freight at Algiers, and therefore all must go ashore again.

We protested that this had been regarded as our personal baggage in our voyage from New York. The officer held firm, but said we might see the purser. This official took the same position. From him we appealed to the captain. To him we stated our whole case. We were sent by the United States Government. It was a scientific expedition. These boxes contained our instruments. Our ambassador at Paris had been apprized. He doubtless had arranged for the entry into Algeria.

The captain repeated that he could not land freight at Algiers. It would cost the company over $3,000 to do so. Such were the rules regarding foreign shipping at Algerian ports. However, as we were delaying the ship —we were very sure, were we not, that our consul at Algiers would expect us—very well, as we were delaying the ship, if we would telegraph to the consul to meet us at Algiers, and would agree to have the cases taken on to Genoa if they could not be landed there, he would not send them ashore now.

All this we agreed to, and after a smooth little voyage arrived one morning at Algiers. We waited anxiously for some time. At length M. Boisson, the vice-consul, appeared, looking for us, and was surely a welcome visitor.

MEASURING SUN RAYS

No notice had come from Paris, but with some difficulty he at length succeeded in getting a permit to take the apparatus ashore. From that time until our second expedition was over M. Boisson was our good angel. Our success was greatly owing to him.

We should not have told of this incident but for its sequel. Mrs. Abbot and the writer determined to make a visit to Italy and other European countries, partly in order that a comparison might be made between the silver-disk pyrheliometer carried to Algeria and those which the Smithsonian Institution had furnished a year or two before to Italy, Germany, England, and France.

As it happened, we engaged passage to Genoa upon the very same North German Lloyd steamer which brought us from Gibraltar. Now we found all changed. The captain evidently had heard more about us. He was most attentive, and listened with great interest to our account of the expedition. He regretted that, as we proposed to go to Naples, we should not remain with the ship. He urged us to do so. Unfortunately the best cabins were engaged from Genoa to Naples. He had even been obliged to give up his own to the Duchess of——. However, he could make us very comfortable. Would we not change our plans and go on with him?

We thanked him, but wished to go overland to see Pisa and Rome upon the way. After expressing most politely his regrets, the captain said there was one point that he hoped he might be pardoned for suggesting. Why in the world had we not come with official cards? For example: "Herr Professor Doctor Geheimrath Charles Greeley Abbot, Director of the Astrophysical Observatory of the Smithsonian Institution, member of this, that, and the other learned academy and society, etc., etc." "Why!" cried he, "When you came on board at Gibraltar, and presented that plain card,'Mr. Charles Greeley Abbot,' and brought all of those boxes, I thought you were a drummer!" The next time he went abroad, the writer

[39]

followed the captain's suggestion, and besides carried a letter addressed "To Friends of the Smithsonian Institution" from Secretary Walcott and embellished with the great gold seal of the Institution. It worked magic!

So the Algerian expedition strongly confirmed our impression of the variability of the sun by proving that independent measurements, made at stations separated by a third of the earth's circumference, united in showing simultaneously high and low values of the solar constant of radiation. As a somewhat unwelcome by-product of the second expedition, in 1912, we have found that the volcanic dust from Mount Katmai in Alaska traveled to the south coast of the Mediterranean in twelve days. In our next chapter we shall relate how the Australian Government became interested in the work, but had to postpone a partly formed plan of joining in it owing to the outbreak of the war, and how Mr. Clayton's researches in Argentina led the Smithsonian Institution to devote a tenth of its little income to enable us to obtain a better record of the variations of the sun.

PLATE 17

Music at Bassour, Algeria

CHAPTER III

THE ENDS OF THE EARTH, THE SUN, AND THE WEATHER

WE had now gone far to prove that the sun is a variable star. Suggested by Washington work, the conclusion had been strengthened by observations on Mount Wilson and Mount Whitney. Our expeditions in Algeria and California, in the years 1911 and 1912, had agreed in showing changes of nearly 10 per cent in the intensity of solar radiation. These results, and numerous observations made in the years from 1908 to 1912 at Washington, Mount Wilson, Mount Whitney, and Bassour, Algeria, were published in Volume III of the *Annals of the Astrophysical Observatory*, which appeared in the year 1913. Great improvements in apparatus and procedure were also described there. This publication attracted attention among men of science all over the world. Their comments were not all favorable.

A very definite type of criticism related to the estimation of the losses of radiation in the atmosphere, which forms so essential a part of solar-constant work. It was maintained by some critics that our estimates of these losses were so inadequate that the true value of the solar constant, instead of being about 1.94 calories, as we published it, should be taken at not less than 3.5 calories, and probably over 4.0 calories. Evidently, if our results lay so far below the truth as this, they could give no just proof of solar variation. A small change in these supposed tremendous atmospheric losses, which, as our critics conceived, had utterly escaped our measurements, would account for the apparent solar changes.

We prepared three kinds of experiments to confute these criticisms. It had been our custom to determine atmospheric transparency during a morning period of two or three hours, while the aslant thickness of atmosphere[1] traversed by the solar beam was decreasing from about 3.0 to about 1.3 times the vertical thickness of the atmosphere. Our critics claimed that observation through much greater thicknesses of atmosphere was necessary. To test the matter, we made special experiments on September 20 and 21, 1913, at Mount Wilson. The measurements were commenced at daybreak, just as the sun cleared the horizon, and were continued until noon. In this way the range of observed air-masses, instead of being from 3.0 to 1.3, ran from 19.6 to 1.2. We reduced these observations as a whole, and also as if they comprised three consecutive determinations. There was hardly any difference between the four results. Our critics' objections, therefore, appeared to be groundless.

About this time, my colleague, Mr. Fowle, made a sensational test of our work. He employed our determinations of atmospheric transparency, in a method used first by Sir A. Schuster, to estimate the number of molecules in a cubic centimeter of the air at the earth's surface. We shall explain it more fully in a later chapter. Fowle's result agreed entirely with the generally accepted value, found by Millikan, which rests on electrical data of wholly different character. This close accord strongly confirmed the trustworthiness of our measurements of the atmospheric transparency on which our solar-constant value depends.

Dr. A. K. Ångström now made the fine suggestion that we should lift our measuring instrument towards the sun till the atmosphere lay practically all below the apparatus. If a self-recording instrument could be lifted

[1] Otherwise known as the air-mass.

by a free balloon until almost all of the atmosphere should be left below, the result of a solar measurement with such apparatus would be most interesting because no assumption about atmospheric transparency would have to be made. Accordingly, we devised an instrument of this character, which, in cooperation with the U. S. Weather Bureau, was successfully flown by my colleague, Mr. Aldrich, from Omaha, Nebraska, in July, 1914. It was recovered uninjured in the state of Iowa, having drifted about 150 miles and having reached an elevation of over 15 miles above sea-level. The air pressure at maximum elevation, as measured by an attached recording barometer, had been only 1/25 of that which exists at sea-level.

Our atmosphere is a very complicated structure. Though sharply limited at the earth's surface, there is no upper limit to restrain it other than the attraction of gravity. Being gaseous, all of the innumerable molecules which compose the atmosphere are darting hither and thither. All molecules have approximately equal striking power at equal temperatures, hence the lighter the molecule, the faster it shoots about. Consequently the lighter ones, like hydrogen and helium, besides gravitating to the top of the atmosphere on account of their lightness, are most apt of any to escape altogether, owing to their high speeds, whenever the direction of their motion is away from the earth. These two conditions of tending to high level and proneness to escape, explain why these two gases, both of which are rising from the surface of the earth in amounts which, in the long run, would be considerable, are not found appreciably in the atmosphere.

The atmospheric pressure continually decreases as the altitude increases, because the weight of that which is still higher continually diminishes as we rise. Arriving at various heights, the pressures are approximately as given in the accompanying table which represents the

ascension of July 11, 1914, from Omaha, Nebraska. Up
to a little more than 20 miles, the pressures have actually
been measured along with the temperatures by automatic
apparatus raised by sounding balloons. Above that level
the pressures are estimated from the laws of gases and
estimated temperatures.

THE ATMOSPHERIC CONDITIONS

Height, miles	0.2	1	2	5	10	15	20	30	50	100
Pressure, in.	28.8	24.8	20.5	11.8	3.9	1.3	0.24	0.015	0.004	0.0001
Temp. F.		91°	77°	54°	9°	−54°	−51°	..	..	....

THE ATMOSPHERIC MAKE-UP AT SEA-LEVEL
In Parts by Volume of 10,000

GAS PARTS

Oxygen..............2066.	Ozone..................0.015
Nitrogen..............7712.	Water Vapor...........140.
Argon..................79.	Nitric Acid..............0.08
Carbon dioxide..........3.36	Ammonia...............0.005

The reader will notice how curiously the temperatures
alter with altitude. It would have seemed more natural
to find them continually falling with increasing altitude,
till at last they fell nearly to the level of the absolute
zero. On the contrary, the temperature of the atmosphere
ceases to fall at about 7 to 10 miles of elevation, and
sometimes is found even to rise a few degrees as the
recording apparatus goes higher. This region of nearly
constant temperature, called the "isothermal layer,"
extends to the highest levels yet reached and it is believed
that the temperature of it is sustained by the absorption,
both of the sun's very short ultra-violet rays and of the
earth's long-wave infra-red rays, by the ozone existing
there.

We know the chemical composition of the mixture of
atmospheric gases near the earth's surface, but at high
altitudes the subject is largely given over to speculation.

PLATE 18

Balloon pyrheliometer which in July, 1914, automatically recorded the sun's heat fifteen miles above the earth's surface, where 24/25 of the atmosphere was surmounted

Ozone, to be sure, which is very rare at the earth's surface, certainly exists at high levels, as is proved by its effects in cutting off the solar and stellar spectra in the ultra-violet. Helium and hydrogen are believed to exist there too, for the reasons already mentioned. But it would add much to our knowledge if samples of the very high atmosphere could be brought down for analysis.

It is no longer hopeless to expect that samples of the higher atmosphere, and measures of its temperature and pressure, may be obtained. The great improvements in rockets which have already been made by Dr. R. H. Goddard (with Smithsonian financial support) lead to the belief that soon we may be able to send special apparatus for collecting air samples, and for measuring temperatures and pressures, up to any desired height.

How high does the atmosphere extend? Doubtless there is no absolute outer limit. For practical purposes, however, the atmosphere may be regarded as ceasing at those heights where meteors no longer flash, where northern lights no longer play, and where the sunset glows no longer shine. These heights seem not to reach beyond 150 miles.

Doubtless the scheme employed in the free balloon flights to lift our automatic solar-measuring apparatus above $^{24}/_{26}$ of the atmosphere is familiar to many readers. The balloons are made of India rubber, and are inflated with hydrogen gas. They are flown in pairs or triplets attached together. About a yard in diameter on leaving the ground, the balloons expand severalfold as they rise to higher and higher levels under diminished pressure, until at length the rubber becomes too thin to withstand the pressure of its hydrogen from within. The weakest balloon bursts, and the others which remain are unable to float the weight of the whole system, and so they come softly down with their cargo.

Our recording "balloon-pyrheliometer" deserves a few words of description. It hung by a wire, nearly 100 feet long, from the group of balloons. This long suspension avoided the danger that the instrument might be shaded by the balloons. The sun's rays were received upon a horizontal blackened disk of aluminum. We proposed to measure the sun's heat by the rate at which it could warm this disk. It was surrounded, except from above, by a U-shaped copper-walled vessel, nearly full of water. Many copper plates, passing to and fro through the water, were joined to the inner wall of the vessel. This promoted a uniformity of temperature of the water and of the inner wall which surrounded the aluminum disk. As the instrument reached regions in the atmosphere far colder than the freezing point, the water was continually being congealed, and hence remained at constant temperature until wholly frozen. Thus, the surroundings of the aluminum disk were kept, as far as it was possible to do so, at constant temperature during the higher parts of the flight.

There was a shutter above the disk which was shaped something like an inverted umbrella. It was designed to hide the sun from the disk during half of the time. Its lower conical surface was of polished silver, so that whether the shutter was opened or closed the light of the sky fell upon the disk, either directly or as reflected by the shutter. The upper flat surface of the shutter was double, so that no solar heat could reach the lower surface to affect the temperature of the disk.

This shutter rotated once in 8 minutes around a vertical shaft attached to its outer rim. But the rotation was intermittent. It took place in two quick motions, each of a semirotation. Hence, during 4 minutes the shutter shaded the disk from the sun, and during the other 4 minutes the sun shone freely upon the disk. These motions were regulated by an accurate clockwork.

To record the changes of temperature which were to be determined, there was a thermometer lying horizontally, with its bulb inserted in a hole bored radially into the side of the aluminum disk. This thermometer was of very special construction. Its stem was flat-backed, and its bore very wide and thin. The back of the stem was painted black, leaving only a central narrow slot of transparent glass just beneath the mercury in the bore. Thus, the sun, shining down, could shine through the slot in the stem except where the shadow of the mercury in the bore filled the slot.

A drum covered with photographic paper rotated slowly underneath the thermometer stem, and in this way the sun could print upon it the position of the end of the mercury column. Thus, there was made a zigzag record, corresponding to the warming and cooling of the aluminum disk, as the shutter opened and closed. One more contrivance was necessary, in order to measure the barometric pressure, so as to inform us how much of the atmosphere still remained above the instrument. For this purpose the sensitive part of a so-called aneroid barometer was employed. This actuated a long aluminum index arm adapted to indicate the atmospheric-pressure changes. It was arranged to lie between the photographic paper on the drum and the stem of the thermometer. The weather was so hot that at the start the stem was nearly filled with its column of mercury. But as soon as the balloons rose the temperature fell a little, and there was left free space for the sun to print through the slot in the back of the thermometer stem, excepting where the barometer-arm shaded the photographic paper. In this way a barometric record was made.

Plate 18 shows one of these recording pyrheliometers finished in the Smithsonian shop by our skillful mechanician, Mr. Kramer. The reader will wonder, perhaps, about the purpose of the large horizontal plate which surrounds the instrument. It serves as a wind screen to keep down the swirl of air currents which would otherwise tend to vitiate the readings. The usefulness of it was proved by experiments in measured air currents.

Figure 3 shows a tracing made from the actual record of the successful flight of July 11, 1914. The original record, though readable, is not printed dark enough to reproduce.

These balloon instruments were all tested and com-

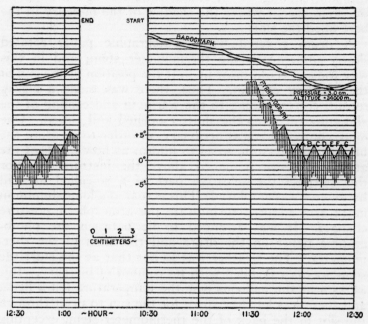

FIG. 3. Automatic record of solar heat and atmospheric pressure from the ground up to fifteen miles altitude made by special apparatus attached to sounding balloons. July, 1914

pared with standard pyrheliometers before the flight. But as that one which made the record was recovered entirely uninjured, many more tests and standardizations were made with it after the flight. It was, indeed, subjected in the laboratory to the actual conditions of temperature, pressure, and air movement which occurred in flight, and many tests were made under these conditions.

As a final result of the experiments, the solar radiation intensity, found at an elevation where the air-pressure was only 1/25 of that at sea-level, came out 1.84 calories per square centimeter per minute. Our best estimate of the atmospheric losses above this level is 0.04 calorie. Adding these figures, we find 1.88 calories for the solar constant. Our determinations by Langley's method, at the various observatories we have occupied, have ranged from 1.80 to 2.02 calories. Thus, the accord between the balloon experiments and our determinations by Langley's method is quite within the error of observation, and also within the range of the supposed real variation of the sun.

Figure 4 gives this automatic balloon observation and several others which have been made by different observers at stations of various elevations. I quote from our description of this illustration in our original paper, as follows:

"We give a plot of the pyrheliometer results at various altitudes, as just collected. It seems to us that, with the complete accord now reached between solar-constant values obtained by the spectro-bolometric method of Langley, applied nearly 1,000 times in 12 years, at four stations ranging from sea-level to 4,420 meters, and from the Pacific Ocean to the Sahara Desert; with air-masses ranging from 1.1 to 20; with atmospheric humidity ranging from 0.6 to 22.6 millimeters of precipitable water; with temperatures ranging from 0° to 30° C.; with sky transparency ranging from the glorious dark blue above Mt. Whitney to the murky whiteness of the volcanic ash filling the sky above Bassour in 1912, it was superfluous to require additional evidence.

"But new proofs are now shown. The figure gives the results of an independent method of solar-constant investigation. In this method the observer, starting from sea-

level, measures the solar radiation at highest sun under
the most favorable circumstances, and advances from one
level to another, until he stands on the highest practicable
mountain peak. Thence he ascends in a balloon to the

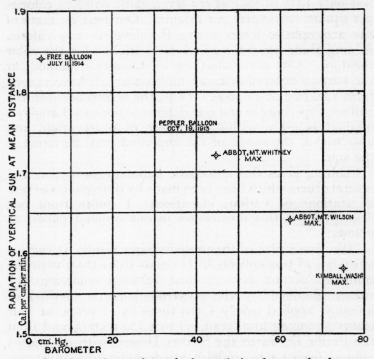

FIG. 4. Direct observations of solar radiation from sea-level up to
fifteen miles elevation

highest level at which a man may live. Finally he com-
mits his instrument to a free balloon, and launches it to
record automatically the solar radiation as high as balloons may rise, and where the atmospheric pressure is
reduced to the twenty-fifth part of its sea-level value.
All these observations have been made. They verify the
former conclusion; for they indicate a value outside the

atmosphere well within the previously ascertained limits of solar variation.

"Our conclusion still is that the solar constant of radiation is 1.93 calories per sq. cm. per minute."

The third type of observations which we undertook in 1913, while not suited to add confirmation to the accuracy of our determination of the solar constant, were designed to search for some other types of changes in the sun's

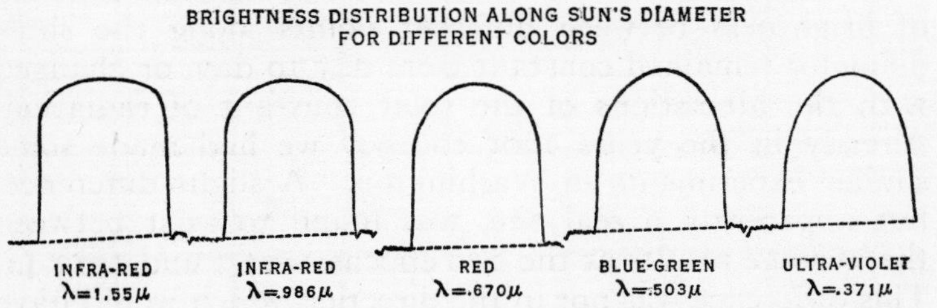

BRIGHTNESS DISTRIBUTION ALONG SUN'S DIAMETER
FOR DIFFERENT COLORS

| INFRA-RED | INFRA-RED | RED | BLUE-GREEN | ULTRA-VIOLET |
| $\lambda = 1.55\mu$ | $\lambda = .986\mu$ | $\lambda = .670\mu$ | $\lambda = .503\mu$ | $\lambda = .371\mu$ |

FIG. 5. The original U-shaped curves which show that the sun's disk has dim edges in all colors

radiation associated with the supposed solar variation. If we could find other kinds of solar variations occurring simultaneously with the one which we had already discovered, and if the new kinds proved to be associated with it, they would enormously strengthen our case. For this purpose we erected above the observing station on Mount Wilson a tower (see Plate 11) upon which we constructed a tower-telescope adapted to form within the observatory an image of the sun about 20 centimeters (8 inches) in diameter. We arranged matters so that this image would drift at a uniform rate centrally across our bolometer. Thus, we could automatically record, in any spectrum color we pleased, the intensity of the solar heat all along a diameter from one edge of the sun to the other.

In this way we produced U-shaped curves like those of Figure 5. They represent the march of brightness

[51]

along a diameter, from edge to edge, of the sun's disk, and are taken in various colors of light. It is very noticeable from these curves that the sun's disk is not equally bright all over, but falls off greatly in brightness towards the edges. The contrast between edges and center of the disk is much greater for blue and violet rays than for red ones. It still decreases as we pass beyond the red to the invisible rays, called infra-red.

What we wished to discover was whether this contrast of brightness between different points along the sun's diameter remained constant from day to day, or changed with the alterations of the solar constant of radiation. Already in the years 1905 to 1907 we had made some similar experiments in Washington. A slight difference, but apparently a real one, was found to exist between the average results at the two epochs 1905-7 and 1913-14. This difference was not in the direction which would have been expected. It would have been natural to suppose that the more hazy sky conditions, the poorer quality of the astronomical "seeing," and the inferiority of the instrumental equipment in our Washington experiments would all have combined to blur the sun's image, and so, by producing a greater shading-off at the edge, to have decreased the contrast between edge and central brightness. The opposite proved true. Washington results showed the edge of the sun fainter compared to the center than those of Mount Wilson.

We continued these tower-telescope solar-contrast determinations until the year 1920. They were made on almost every day when observations of the solar constant were conducted at Mount Wilson. The results were a little disappointing. There seemed, indeed, to be small real variations of contrast, and sometimes these seemed to be very closely associated with changes of the solar constant. But the relation appeared to be complicated by reversals of sign, and although on the whole we believed some confirmation of solar variation was indicated thereby, the matter was far from being a plain case. We had even dared to hope that these easily performed contrast experiments might prove to be a means of indicating the solar variations more accurately than the

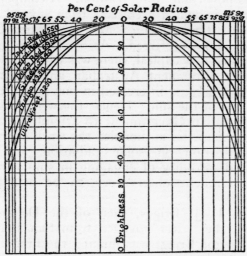

Fig. 6. The sun is dim on the edge of its disk in all colors, but most so in the ultra-violet

far more laborious measurements of the solar constant itself. In this we were disappointed.

Our measurements of solar contrast, however, were greatly appreciated by theoretical students of both the sun and stars. For the sun, they give a means of testing some of the most far-reaching theories as to the condition of the sun's material, and the manner of escape of his radiation. For the stars, they serve as a guide to what may be expected in the important subject of the eclipsing double-star variables.

In the year 1914, the British Association for the Advancement of Science met in the principal cities of Aus-

tralia.   Plans were then already on foot to build a capital
city at Canberra for the uses of the Australian Government.   As a unique undertaking, Australia proposed to
build, in an uninhabited place, a model capital city which,
indeed, has now come to its fruition.   A competition had
been invited, in which architects from several countries
participated.   The plans of Mr. and Mrs. Griffin of
Chicago had been preferred.   As one of the institutions
of the proposed new capital, there was to be a government
observatory.   Prominent Australian and English scientific men had become interested in our measurements of
the variations of the sun.   Hence, the writer was invited
by the Australian Government to attend the meetings,
and to present to the authorities the work of the Smithsonian   Institution   on   solar   radiation,   and   also   to
explain the desirability of engaging in similar researches
at   the   government   observatory   to   be   established   at
Canberra.

With Dr. L. J. Briggs, then of the Department of
Agriculture, the writer voyaged from San Francisco to
Sydney.   Doctor Briggs was making the first trial of his
newly devised apparatus to determine the force of gravity
at sea.   His device was essentially to balance gravity
against a perfect spring.   He used in practice a column of
mercury balanced against the expansive force of a chamber of gas.   Gaseous pressure, of course, is not subject to
"creep" or "fatigue" like steel springs.   The difficulties of
the measurement were all seemingly very little ones, and
associated with the pranks of the liquid metal—its surging
under the rolling of the ship, the electrification and con-
sequent sticking of the mercury to the little index point
which showed its level, and other such vexatious little
troubles.   Of course, the gas and the mercury required to
be kept at constant temperature, but this was accomplished easily by the copious use of cracked ice.

Unfortunately, a leak developed in the apparatus on
the outward voyage, which we attempted to repair in

[54]

our short stay at the Fiji Islands, but without success. It was not until after the instrument was rebuilt at Sydney that Doctor Briggs got a fair trial of the plan. Later he made a voyage from New York to California with an improved copy of the device, and obtained interesting results, but not quite sufficiently accurate to meet the requirements of the problem.

Gravity on land can be measured with pendulums to nearly the millionth part, so great is the accuracy of the method. The fluctuations of gravity over the earth's surface are small, but immensely significant of the condition of the earth's interior. We have hitherto been shut out from the knowledge of them under the oceans, which occupy nearly three-quarters of the earth's surface. An apparatus accurate at least to a hundred thousandth part is necessary. Doctor Briggs's scheme hitherto has fallen somewhat short of this degree of precision. By employing a submarine vessel, little affected by waves on account of submergence, a Dutch scientist has recently gotten fairly satisfactory measures of gravity at sea.

Arrived at Honolulu, we transshipped to an English steamer. Doctor Moseley, the brilliant young discoverer of the atomic numbers, with his mother, were fellow-passengers, along with several other English scientific men on their way to the meetings. We were at sea all unconscious that the mobilization of Europe was taking place, and landed at Sydney on the day that England declared war. The atmosphere of the public mind in Australia was electrical. The Government cabled immediately the offer of twenty thousand Australian troops. The warships in Australian waters departed on mysterious errands. A number of German merchant ships in Australian harbors were seized. Public meetings were held and attended with great outbursts of patriotic fervor.

Nevertheless, the British Association carried out its program in Adelaide, Melbourne, Sydney, and elsewhere, nearly as planned. The generous and cordial hospitality was most impressive. At Adelaide, with Professor Turner of Oxford, I was entertained by Mr. Justice, soon afterwards Mr. Chief Justice, Murray; at Melbourne, along with the Astronomer Royal, Doctor Dyson, by the Attorney General; and at Sydney, at the home of a Senator of the Commonwealth. I shall never forget attending at Adelaide a great patriotic public meeting in the Town Hall, ending with the singing of "Rule Britannia." At that time the German squadron of Admiral Von Spee and the cruiser *Emden* were sinking merchant shipping in the great oceans which separated many of us from our homes, so that we felt more than ordinarily the significance of the song.

At Melbourne, I gave my paper on the work of the Smithsonian Institution on solar radiation. With prominent Australians, and with Sir Oliver Lodge, the Astronomer Royal, Professor Turner, and others, I waited upon the Premier of Australia to urge the desirability of similar work being undertaken at the proposed government observatory. The Premier expressed his interest in the subject, and stated that he had been prepared to promote the enterprise, but, now that the great war had burst upon them, he felt that no new things ought to be undertaken. We, of course, could but acquiesce in the wisdom of this conclusion.

I had intended returning by the Union Steamship Line, by way of Tahiti. But in the condition of insecurity of British merchant shipping on the Pacific at that time, my friends recommended me to transfer my passage to the Oceanic Steamship Line, an American concern. This required me to shorten somewhat my stay in Australasia, but on my return journey threw me in with a most extraordinary ship's company. Among others, there were about a dozen prominent English and German scientific men who had been attending the meetings. The eminent Germans, being guests of the British Association, were

naturally permitted to leave Australia, but under the circumstances there was a certain atmosphere of constraint. There were also the German and Austrian consuls-general to Australia, returning by diplomatic privilege. Among the English group was Doctor Moseley, hurrying back to serve his country as an officer of Territorials. He soon after lost his life in the Gallipoli campaign, a lamentable loss for science.

We had several famous musicians. There were the great violinist, Mischa Elman, with his father and accompanist, and the great pianist, Harold Bauer, with his wife, besides some others who would have seemed great in lesser company. Two world-famous Spanish dancers were also sailing. Still more picturesquely, we included in our company no less than seven eminent prize-fighters, one being then the holder of the world's championship belt for light-weights, all ablaze with diamonds.

As usual on ocean steamships, a committee of amusements was formed soon after leaving port. The committee waited upon our distinguished musicians without receiving encouragement. The scientists were more obliging, probably because scientists are used to serving the world for nothing, and they gave several popular lectures on a very wide range of subjects. A great chess contest was inaugurated, in which Mischa Elman, Moseley, and others took leading parts. The pugilists held two public four-round boxing matches on the forward deck, and the dancers danced for us.

By this time, the strange company had become like one family, and one afternoon Harold Bauer and Mischa Elman, after taking off their coats and repairing the old piano, delighted us with violin sonatas from old Italian composers. The next afternoon, they continued with sonatas of Beethoven. Finally, just after leaving Honolulu, a grand concert was given one evening, with everybody doing his bit. So we ended what perhaps was one of the most extraordinary voyages made in recent years, to learn that the Battle of the Marne had been fought while we were at sea. My friend, Doctor Briggs, returned by the Union Line, as planned, in order that he might have time to complete the repairs of his gravity apparatus at Sydney. His ship just escaped being sunk by Admiral Von Spee's squadron when they bombarded Papeete on the Island of Tahiti.

Cooperation in solar work by Australia being thus postponed, we continued on with our summer expeditions to Mount Wilson, in order to follow in partial measure the sun's variations which we now believed established. Fortunately, these studies attracted the attention of Mr. H. H. Clayton, chief forecaster of the Argentine meteorological service. Mr. Clayton had been seeking means to lengthen out and improve his forecasts so as to make them more and more useful to business men whose affairs depend on weather conditions. Several schemes tried had yielded him but indifferent success. About the year 1915, Clayton undertook, however, to examine whether the variations of the sun produce appreciable effects on weather phenomena.

Our first knowledge of his studies came in a letter from which I quote as follows:

"I inclose herewith a copy of a paper in which are given the results of a comparison of Dr. Abbot's solar measurements with temperature and pressure in various parts of the world. It deals with a matter of considerable importance and if published only in Spanish would be understood or read by few English readers. For this reason, with the permission of the Chief, I am sending you the original English copy to be published by the Smithsonian Institution as one of its bulletins simultaneously (or as nearly so as may be) with the publication of the Spanish translation here.

"Should you be unable to publish it as a 'Smithsonian Miscellaneous Collection,' or otherwise, would you please forward it to the editor of the *Monthly Weather Review*,

U. S. Weather Bureau, and say that I have requested you
to forward it to him for publication?

. . . .

(Signed) "H. H. CLAYTON."

This paper was referred to the present writer who
reported:

"I have examined the paper which Mr. Clayton desires
published by the Smithsonian Institution, entitled 'Effect
of Short Period Variations of Solar Radiation on the
Earth's Atmosphere.'

"I strongly recommend the paper for publication with
all its figures and plates.

"The paper seems to me to be of very unusual value.
It proves beyond question, it seems to me, that the short-
period changes of the sun discovered by the Smithsonian
Astrophysical Observatory affect decidedly the earth's
temperature and the barometric pressure. Not only so,
but the effects are traced all over the world by Mr.
Clayton, and his results may evidently be used for purposes of forecasting, as soon as regular excellent daily
solar-radiation values are available."

A sample of the kind of evidence which induced me to
make this enthusiastic statement is illustrated by Figure
7. Clayton collects the highest solar-constant values for a
period of 4 years in one group, the lowest in a second
group, and the mean values in a third. For each day
found in group 1, he writes down in consecutive columns
the departures from normal temperature for the city of
Buenos Aires, beginning with the actual day of high solar-
constant observation, and going on for each of the twenty
days following. This makes one line of a twenty-column
table. Continuing the same treatment for every one of
the days of high solar constant, he obtains as many such
lines as there are found days in group 1. The mean
values of the temperature departures in each column
being then computed, they evidently express the average

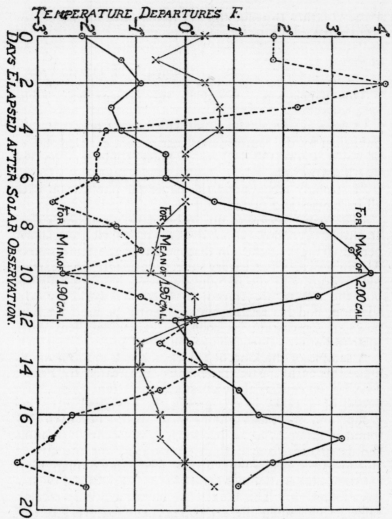

FIG. 7. March of temperature at Buenos Aires attending and following high, mean, and low solar-constant values as measured at Mount Wilson in the years 1913, 1914, 1915, and 1918. Mean results of many observations. (After Clayton)

march of temperature departures at Buenos Aires for the twenty days next following a high value of solar radiation. These data are plotted in the heavy full line of Figure 7.

The dotted line in the same figure represents the similar treatment for days of low solar radiation. The light full line corresponds to average solar-radiation values. It is obvious that the curves representing opposite extremes of solar radiation march oppositely; and the curve corresponding to medium values runs in their mean. Also the widest separation between the extreme curves occurs 10 days after the event, and hence gives promise of forecasting value for at least that interval in advance.

Clayton submitted manuscripts which were published by the Smithsonian Institution as Volume 68, No. 3, and Volume 71, No. 3, of its *Miscellaneous Collections*, under the titles, "Effect of Short Period Variations of Solar Radiation on the Earth's Atmosphere," and "Variations of Solar Radiation and the Weather." From the data included in the second of these papers, the present writer prepared the diagram shown in Figure 7. Results so striking deeply interested us at the Smithsonian Institution, and Secretary Walcott felt justified in employing the income of the Hodgkins Fund to promote the measurements of solar variation on which Clayton's results depended.

Thomas Hodgkins bequeathed to the Smithsonian Institution the sum of $200,000, the income from one half to be used for general purposes consistent with the aims of Smithson, that from the other half for the promotion of investigations relating to the properties of atmospheric air. Our solar-radiation work was believed to be peculiarly harmonious to this restriction. In the first place, our measurements of solar radiation disclosed the transparency of atmospheric air, the quantity of its humidity, and the effects of its dust, clouds, and water-vapor to diminish our quota of the solar rays on which all our concerns depend. In the second place, our discovery of solar variation had proved to be closely associated with important changes of the atmospheric pressure and temperature.

We desired to establish a solar-radiation station at which measurements could be made daily, as far as possible, at all seasons of the year. It was known that great interruptions of continuity would occur in the winter months at Mount Wilson, but it was intended to observe there during the more favorable part of the year. We felt it highly desirable to locate a second station far removed from Mount Wilson. Our outfit of apparatus to equip a second station was finished early in the year 1917, but just at that time the United States declared war. The uncertainties of the outlook deterred us from selecting a station across the oceans, and therefore the location was made tentatively on Hump Mountain in North Carolina.

Here observations were made from June, 1917, to March, 1918, but they were highly unsatisfactory. The humidity of the eastern part of the United States quite unfits it for these studies. By the excellent advice of Dr. Walter Knoche, formerly in charge of the meteorological service of Chile, we chose the region of the Chilean city of Calama as the most favorable one not likely to be involved in the operations of the war. The outfit which had been in use on Hump Mountain was removed to Chile, in June, 1918, and reinstalled near Calama by the efficient hands of my colleague, Mr. A. F. Moore.

The city of Calama, about 7,500 feet above sea-level, lies on the banks of the small river Loa, on the borders of the Atacama Desert in the foothills of the Andes Mountains. The Atacama Desert is one of the most desolate regions of the earth. As rain almost never falls there, it is nearly destitute of plants, animals, birds, and insects. The familiar sparse prickly vegetation of ordinary deserts is absent. Naked earth, swept bare of dust by the winds of many centuries, extends as far as the eye can see. Darwin, in his diary of the "Voyage of the Beagle," tells of a day's journey in this barren desert during which his keen eye saw no living thing but a few flies feasting upon the dead body of a mule.

Amid this desolation, the River Loa, fed by the snows of the towering Andean peaks, makes a ribbonlike oasis. At the crossing of a trade route over this river stands the little city of Calama. A railroad from Antofagasta into Bolivia has a division point at Calama. Some miles eastward, nearer the Andes, lies the mining town of Chuquicamata, where United States capital has developed one of the greatest copper-producing mines of the world. Between Calama and the ocean are the famous Chilean nitrate fields, mainly operated by English companies. Such is the region chosen for our solar-radiation observatory.

The Chile Exploration Company, owning the copper mine at Chuquicamata, and having large offices at Antofagasta, greatly aided Mr. Moore in landing his equipment, getting it through the customs, and afterwards in establishing the observing station near Calama. The Company owned several small buildings on the outskirts of Calama, and placed one of these at our disposal as the observatory station. Furniture for it was also loaned from their surplus stock in another of the buildings. From that time to the present, we have frequently been under great obligations to the "Chile Ex," as it is familiarly called, and to its officers in New York, Antofagasta, and "Chuqui" (as they say for short) for many acts of courtesy and aid, which evidence both kindness of heart and interest in our investigations.

Mr. Moore commenced his solar-radiation measurements at Calama on July 27, 1918, and never missed a day when it was possible to observe until the station was removed to the nearby peak called Montezuma, about

THE SUN AND THE WELFARE OF MAN

August 1, 1920. The station at Calama proved highly favorable, except for occasional drifting of smoke from the mine at Chuqui, and from the refuse-burning by the people of Calama. These nuisances, however, seemed to be on the increase, and in 1920, owing to the generosity and great interest taken by Mr. John A. Roebling, Mr. Moore removed the station to a peak 9,000 feet high about 12 miles farther south. Before dismantling the station at Calama, the new dwelling at Montezuma and the cave-laboratory for the instruments there were fully prepared. So energetic were Mr. Moore's dispositions, that only 10 days were lost for observing owing to the dismantling, removal, and reinstallation.

This was the first solar-radiation station where we made use of the tunnel idea for a shelter to contain our delicate instruments. It was suggested by Mr. Edgar B. Moore, brother of our field director. We have used it invariably, and with great profit, in each of the six installations of solar-radiation apparatus in which we have since been instrumental. The tunnel has great advantages. In a site remote from lumber, and difficult of access, it is the cheapest installation. It avoids all danger by lightning in regions too dry to yield effective earth contacts for lightning rods, and where heavy electrical storms sometimes occur. It requires no repairs against roof leakage, and is unaffected by gales. Above all, the tunnel remains at an equable temperature, night and day, summer and winter; and so is highly favorable to the exacting installation of an apparatus sensitive to temperature inequalities of a millionth of a degree. (See Plates 1 and 2.)

At Mount Montezuma there is apparently no more life than there is on the moon. Perfectly barren brown gravel stretches in every direction. No birds or insects are there except the domesticated housefly, and every expedient has to be taken to discourage him. All provisions and even water itself must be hauled from town, a distance of nearly fifteen miles by road. Fortunately, it

PLATE 20

Smithsonian solar-radiation observatory, Table Mountain, Calif. Director Moore adjusting the coelostat which keeps the beam of the sun in a fixed direction

proved possible to make an auto road of easy grade from Calama right up to the dwelling, at trifling expense. A trip to town about once a week suffices to bring all necessary supplies. Mr. Roebling's generosity has provided a telephone line which not only permits daily communication with Washington by cable, but is a great comfort and protection against casualty besides. A piano, victrola, radio, library, and games help to overcome the loneliness of this isolated desert peak.

We made a change of first-rate importance in our methods in the year 1919. Up to that time, we had employed exclusively the method of Langley, only improved in small details, and simplified by labor-saving computing devices. Let us recall its principal features. Beginning about an hour after sunrise, pyrheliometer measurements of the total intensity of the sun's beam were made at intervals for several hours. At the same time, the bolometer measured the intensities in all parts of the sun's spectrum. By comparing its indications against the measurements of total radiation by the pyrheliometer, the bolometer work was standardized into units of heat. The successive spectrum observations enabled us to form the sun's spectral-energy curve as it would be outside the atmosphere. The standardization against the pyrheliometer, as just mentioned, furnished the data to express this area in terms of total intensity of energy, which, when reduced to mean solar distance, is the "solar constant."

The great objection to this method is that, during the two or three hours consumed, the atmosphere may grow clearer or less clear. If so, an error creeps into the result. A second objection is that only one good measurement can be made in a day, because the afternoon sky is seldom uniform in transparency. Even if good observations could be made both forenoon and afternoon, the reduction of them is so laborious that several computers, additional to the observing force, would be needed in order to keep up the reductions; and the investigation, already costly, would become prohibitively so.

What we long desired was a brief method, independent of changes of the atmospheric transparency. It was this that we found in 1919. We had invented an instrument, called the pyranometer, for measuring the brightness of the sky. It occurred to us that since the sky becomes brighter the less its transparency, it might be possible to find some definite relation between the atmospheric brightness and the atmospheric transmission. As we knew that the humidity has much to do with these matters, we also drew into our new solar-constant method a spectroscopic determination of the total quantity of water-vapor in the atmosphere.

To make a long story brief, we found it possible to plot curves giving the atmospheric transparency in all parts of the spectrum in terms of the brightness and humidity of the atmosphere. Hence, by using these curves, in connection with observations requiring less than 10 minutes altogether, we could estimate the atmospheric transparency as well or even better than by observing for two or three hours, as we had done formerly. Since the computing for the "short method" was very much abridged, it was found possible to observe five times each morning, and yet the regular observers could reduce the work before evening. In this way, the average accidental error of observation was greatly diminished, both by multiplying observations and by avoiding the effects of changes of transparency. However, as the short method is only empirical, it might fail if atmospheric conditions were much changed. Hence, we continued to use the method of Langley frequently, as a check observation.

The year 1919 was notable for another reason, for it was the first year when solar radiation was used in weather forecasting. Mr. H. H. Clayton, then chief forecaster for the Argentine weather service, had become convinced of the probable meteorological utility of solar-radiation

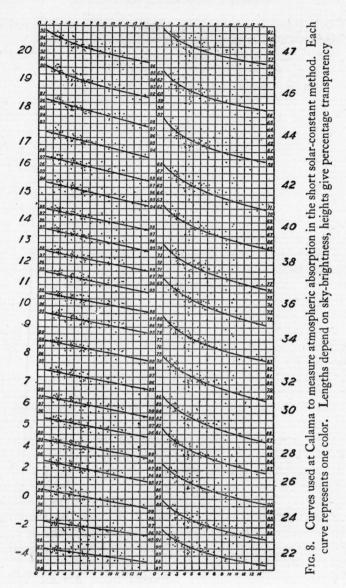

FIG. 8. Curves used at Calama to measure atmospheric absorption in the short solar-constant method. Each curve represents one color. Lengths depend on sky-brightness, heights give percentage transparency

observations. His studies were cordially supported by Chief G. O. Wiggin of the Argentine weather service. It was arranged that a daily telegram in code should go from our solar station at Calama, Chile, to Buenos Aires, giving the observed values of the solar constant. Beginning with December 12, 1918, this information was employed by Clayton to make up a weekly forecast. This is still a feature of the Argentine weather service. These weekly forecasts, gotten out on Wednesdays, indicate by curves the temperatures to be expected at Buenos Aires, both morning and evening, for the seven days beginning the day after the forecast. Rainfall is also predicted. In Figure 9 are shown twelve successive weeks of these forecasts, and also the temperatures and rainfall which actually happened. Although the prevision disclosed is far from perfect, the contractors and other men of affairs who employ these Argentine forecasts have strongly expressed the conviction that they are of real value, measured in financial returns gained by their advance information.

We have mentioned the change of location of our solar-radiation station from Calama to Montezuma, rendered possible by Mr. Roebling's generous aid and counsel. The same valued ally provided means, at the same time, to remove the solar-constant equipment from Mount Wilson to Mount Harqua Hala, in Arizona. This station was selected after a prolonged investigation by special U. S. Weather Bureau observers, arranged for us by Chief Marvin. Mount Wilson atmospheric conditions had proved unsuitable, and seemed steadily deteriorating for these exacting purposes as Los Angeles and neighboring towns expanded. Every day, towards mid-forenoon, the sea-breeze rises there, and brings a haze over the mountain which is aggravated by the smoke and dust of the business of this immense population lying between the mountain and the Pacific.

With the simultaneous removal from Mount Wilson

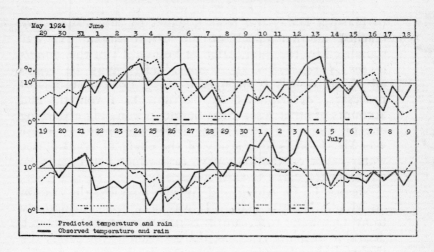

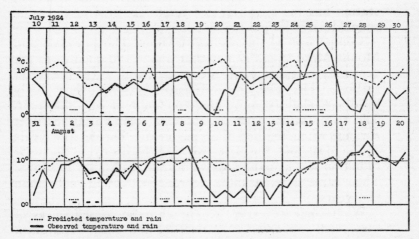

FIG. 9.   Weekly predicted and observed temperature and rainfall at Buenos Aires.   Twelve successive weeks of 1924.   (After Hoxmark.)   Predictions cover eight days in advance, based on Smithsonian solar observations

[69]

to Harqua Hala, and from Calama to Montezuma, we reached another epoch of the investigation. It was signalized by the publication of Volume IV of the *Annals of the Astrophysical Observatory*. Here may be found all of the results from 1912 to 1920, critical studies of processes, descriptions of instruments invented, and accounts of other researches, besides our mainly absorbing one of the sun's variations. Most prominent of these was Mr. Fowle's long study of the effect of atmospheric water-vapor on the long-wave rays which continually go out from the earth toward space.

Messrs. C. G. Abbot and Aldrich installed the station on Mount Harqua Hala. It was occupied continuously from October, 1920, until September, 1925. Though desirable in many respects, the isolation of the place, the frightful thunderstorms of summer, and a less favorable atmospheric condition than had been anticipated, led to a removal to Table Mountain, in California, in 1925. Besides greater accessibility and less cloudiness, this station has the advantage of 2,000 feet greater elevation than Mount Harqua Hala.

Comparison of the results of Mount Harqua Hala and Mount Montezuma shows that about 180 good days per year may be expected at the former, and 260 at the latter station. The average difference between their daily results is slightly more than one-half of one per cent. The two stations unite in showing solar variations over a range of more than four per cent. During the years 1920, 1921, and the first two months of 1922, the solar radiation was generally above normal, as Figure 10 shows. Then came a remarkable depression, lasting more than two years.

What shall we expect as the climatic consequences of these well-supported variations of the sun? That is a question so difficult that the answer is not yet fully known. Mr. Clayton's researches have gone farthest towards its solution. We shall defer consideration of them to a new

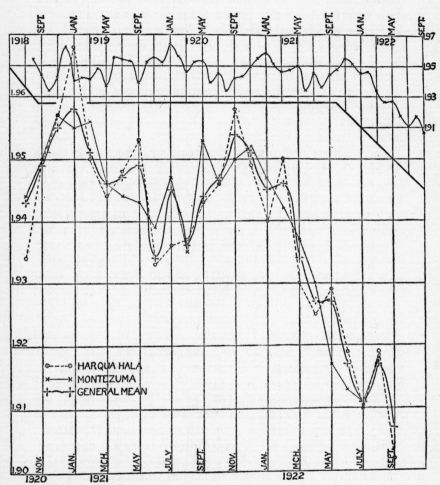

FIG. 10.   Great decrease of solar radiation, March to September, 1922, as measured independently at Mount Harqua Hala, Ariz., and Mount Montezuma, Calif.

chapter. The extraordinary result they lay bare is that a change in solar radiation of no more than one per cent is associated with changes of temperature and barometric pressure which may fairly be called major changes. Yet these effects are very complicated in their distribution, so that an enormous amount of work is necessary to unravel their intricacies. As these discoveries come to light, one cannot but regret that the pioneer in this field, Doctor Langley, could not still be living to see his dream of predicting the fat years and the lean beginning to come true.

If it comes to fruition, the world will be owing much to Mr. H. H. Clayton and Mr. John A. Roebling. It was the result of Mr. Clayton's pioneering studies that gave us at the Smithsonian Institution the incentive to stretch our little means to the limit, in order to install and maintain our station in the Chilean desert. It was Mr. Roebling who saw in the reports of progress which we issued from time to time the promise of worth-while accomplishment, and who lent his powerful aid to keep up the solar work and to enable Mr. Clayton to study North American conditions in connection therewith. No less will the world be indebted to the indefatigable observers, A. F. Moore, L. B. Aldrich, H. B. Freeman, W. H. Hoover and their assistants, who so long supported the perplexities, dangers, discomforts, and tedium of lonely desert observing. Their incentive was loyalty to what was thought by some an unreasonable faith in the future value of the work. Their financial compensations alone could not have retained them for a month under such conditions.

If it be inquired what probability now exists that long-range forecasting will be promoted by solar-radiation observations, it is necessary to point out a consideration, obvious enough when explained. Since the earth's surface is so highly complex, with its mountains, deserts, oceans, and ocean currents, and since the atmosphere is both complex and variable in its constitution and circulation, the problem of theoretically predicting the local effects of small solar changes seems insoluble. Hence we are driven back to the study of the history of the associations between solar and weather changes.

How long a history is needed depends on the interval in advance for which it is desired to predict. If it is only a week in advance, then 500 weeks of history makes quite a background, and it can be accumulated in ten years. But if it is a season or a year in advance, then ten years of history is far too short to test the relations. Accordingly we can not hope in this generation to thoroughly test the value of solar forecasting for seasonal predictions. But unless we patiently and accurately carry on solar observing throughout this generation, our successors will be as much at a loss as we are to determine the question.

CHAPTER IV

MEASURING INSTRUMENTS FOR SOLAR RAYS

OUR observatories are observatories without telescopes. What kinds of instruments, then, must one use to measure the energy of solar radiation, its possible variability, and the influence of the atmosphere on our solar heat supply? We receive from the sun perfectly enormous quantities of radiation. During bright days, while the sun is nearly overhead, there falls on a single square yard of the earth's surface fully one horsepower of solar energy. With such a wealth of heat to investigate, it seems at first thought that the observer must be a dunce if he requires anything but the coarsest of apparatus. But in fact, no one has been able to do much in this field without an instrument sensitive to the millionth of a degree of temperature, and quick-acting enough to give its full response in two seconds of time.

Why is this paradox? In the first place, the rays of the sun are not homogeneous. We see in the rainbow something of the complexity of that which we call white light. Really it comprises not only Sir Isaac Newton's seven primary colors, violet, indigo, blue, green, yellow, orange, and red, with every gradation or shade of color which merges between them, but there are besides great quantities of rays beyond the violet and others beyond the red to which the human eye is wholly insensible. All of these solar rays, the ultra-violet, the visible, the infra-red, suffer losses in traversing our atmosphere. These losses

[74]

are altogether unequal. Even for neighboring rays, the atmosphere differs sometimes by ninety per cent in its transparency. In order really to know the solar radiation as the sun emits it, and the properties of the atmosphere as they affect climate and weather, we require to deal with the individual rays of the spectrum, not merely with them all in mass. Here, then, is one reason for greater delicacy of observing apparatus. For we must stretch out the rays into a long spectrum and observe them severally, not their total intensity only.

In the second place, the optical means for producing first-rate spectra are very costly, and their cost increases much faster than the area of their apertures. Not only does the cost increase with prohibitive rapidity, but the usefulness of large, thick prisms and lenses is interfered with by the absorption of radiation in the glass which composes them. We think of glass as perfectly transparent. It is not. Flint glass, indeed, is almost totally opaque for rays just a little beyond the violet of the spectrum. For such reasons it is impracticable to employ for spectrum analysis very large instruments capable of collecting immense quantities of solar radiation. The observer must be content with a solar beam of only a few square inches. This, too, forces him to employ receiving instruments of great delicacy.

Most of the refined solar-spectrum energy measurement has been done with the bolometer, an electrical thermometer. It is sensitive to a millionth of a degree! Neither the eye nor the photographic plate can be used, though both are far more sensitive than the bolometer for certain rays. They are, however, not equally sensitive for all, as the bolometer is, and indeed are wholly insensitive in some spectral regions. The bolometer was invented and named by Dr. Samuel Pierpont Langley about the year 1878. The name is from the Greek, and means "ray measurer." Though later a pioneer in aeronautics, Langley's greatest interest at that time was the study of the sun. He felt the need of a highly sensitive instrument to supplant the thermopile, which had not reached then the exceedingly small dimensions and great sensitiveness which it now has. Langley in his bolometer, made use of the principle embodied in the device called Wheatstone's bridge, so much used by Sir Charles Wheatstone, the great English physicist, that it is named after him, though really invented by S. H. Christie in 1833.

The diagram, Figure 11, shows the principle of the bolometer. A and B are two very thin and narrow strips of platinum, as nearly equal in dimensions and electrical resistance as possible. Connected at one end to a common junction of copper, C, the free ends are attached through two copper connectors, D and E, to two equal coils of manganin wire, F and G, themselves uniting at H. A storage battery, J, discharges a constant electrical current through the system from C to H. The current branches in two equal parts owing to the exact symmetry of the paths AF and BG. Moreover, since the electrical resistance of A equals B, and F equals G, the two currents arrive at the points of connection, D and E, at equal electrical potential, and no current at all flows across from D to E, or E to D, through the highly sensitive galvanometer K, which is connected from D to E to test this condition.

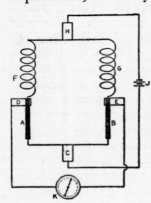

FIG. 11. Diagram of the bolometer, that electrical thermometer sensitive to a millionth of a degree

Both of the platinum strips, A and B, are blackened by painting them (on the front side only) with a thin layer of paint made of lampblack, shellac, and alcohol. This causes them to have an absorptive power of about 97 per cent not only for the visible solar rays of all colors, but also for the invisible solar rays beyond the violet and the red ends of the spectrum. It is arranged that one of the strips, let us say B, is hidden from view by a screen. A ray of the spectrum falling on the other, A, is absorbed. That is to say, its energy of radiation turns into heat, and consequently the strip A becomes slightly warmer than the strip B. But this slightly increases the electrical resistance of A over that of B. On this account there no longer prevails a state of equal electrical potentials at D and E. A current therefore flows from E to D and deflects the tiny needle system of the galvanometer, K, proportionally to the intensity of the radiation falling upon the strip A.

Such is the principle of Langley's bolometer. Now for some remarkable details. As it was to be so highly sensitive, so sharply differentiating of adjacent rays, and so quick-acting, the strips, A and B, had to be short, narrow, and thin. Short, so as to get all of the sensitive parts into small compass to avoid temperature disturbances from without. Narrow, in order that the instrument could distinguish the heating effects of rays very near together in the solar spectrum. Thin, lest the attainment of the final state of steady temperatures should be delayed too long, owing to a capacity to store up heat in the strip. In practice the dimensions came down to these: Length, 12 millimeters (1/2 inch); width, 0.1 millimeter (1/250 inch); thickness, 0.005 millimeter (1/5000 inch).

As the sensitiveness of the instrument increases with increasing electrical current flowing from the electric battery through the system, it is important to use a current as large as conditions will warrant. But this current heats the very thin platinum strips considerably. If the air is free to bathe the strips with its little eddying drafts, increasing current strength soon brings about a condition of unsteadiness of temperature easily noticeable by the wiggling to and fro of the light spot which makes the galvanometer record. To avoid this disturbance, we have in recent years confined the bolometer in a sealed glass vessel, and exhausted the air therein very highly. This is a modern development not employed by Langley. Exhaustion of the air, besides reducing the tremors of the galvanometer is of still further advantage, because it leads to about fivefold increase of sensitiveness.

One readily sees why this is, for the molecules of air, which act as if they were baskets to carry heat away, are mostly removed. The cooling of the strip, in high vacuum, depends almost wholly on the emission of rays of great wave-lengths compared to visible light.

As we remarked, however, whether in air or vacuo, the electrical current is always used as large as circumstances will justify, and it causes the bolometer strips to be at something like 100° C. (180° F.) above the temperature of the surroundings. This fact heightens the astonishment with which we must conceive that a temperature increase, due to radiation, of one millionth of a degree, or even less, can so easily and accurately be measured with the instrument. One would rather be inclined to suppose that, arising from strips as hot as boiling water, there would certainly be such irregularities of flow of heat as would mask entirely influences so insignificant as those which produce temperature changes of a millionth of a degree.

There are still finer details than these, however. Consider the recording galvanometer. It contains four coils of copper wire, each wound in a special shape, and with several wires of graded sizes joined to complete the windings. Two coils are at the top and two below. If one could stick two pins horizontally through a windowpane, one above the other, separated by about 1½ inches, and should hang the four coils, two outside and two inside of the window, the arrangement would be about as it is in the galvanometer, except that the glass and pins must be supposed removed and yet the coils left standing.

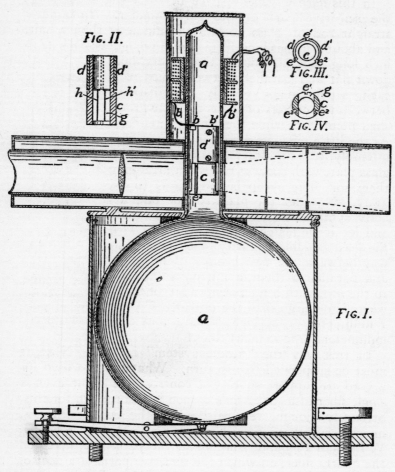

FIG. 12. The vacuum bolometer, which measures the heat of the solar spectrum to a millionth of a degree. The sensitive strips are *h h'*, FIG. II, the balancing coils are *b b'*, FIG. I. The large vacuum chamber, *a*, FIG. I, preserves high exhaustion, even if some air oozes out from the coils after a time

In this narrow vacant space between the coils hangs the sensitive part of the galvanometer. Imagine a straight rod of glass no larger in diameter than a hair, and about 2 inches long. Imagine 12 magnets, each 1/16 inch long and no thicker than hairs, laid down flat and parallel in two groups of 6 each, separated by exactly the distance between the centers of the coils. One group shall point N-S, while the other points S-N. As the little magnets resist such constraints intensely, it is necessary to stick them on a glass plate with sugar syrup when arranging them so. The syrup is afterwards rinsed away. Now let the glass rod be laid exactly symmetrically upon the 12 magnets and let it be fastened to them firmly with the least possible quantity of shellac. Half way between the two groups of magnets, and parallel to them, a mirror is fastened to the rod, with a microscopic bit of beeswax. How large shall the mirror be? Only 1 millimeter (1/25 inch) square, and 0.05 millimeter (2/1000 inch) thick!

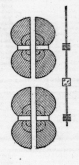

FIG. 13. Coils and magnetic needle-system of the most sensitive of galvanometers

In this way the "needle system" is built. Next, it must be suspended free to turn. What shall be used for a cord to support so tiny a contrivance? Not even a single fiber of a silkworm's cocoon is fine enough for this. Strangely enough, we turn to one of the hardest of rocks, quartz crystal, to furnish the thread. It was Prof. C. V. Boys of England, who, about the year 1890, invented the quartz fiber, on which the sensitive parts of a host of modern instruments now depend. We all know that glass can be drawn out into spidery threads when hot. Quartz has similar properties, but requires a much more intense heat. Hydrogen, or illuminating gas, burned in oxygen, fuses quartz readily.

Professor Boys devised two methods of making fine

PLATE 21

Group of apparatus for measuring the energy of the solar rays, including the bolometer, the spectroscope, and recording apparatus. (From "The Earth and the Stars," courtesy of the Van Nostrand Co.)

quartz fibers, one more picturesque, the other more serviceable. In the first, he employed a little bow and arrow. To the bow and to the arrow were fastened bits of quartz. In the flame they were melted together. The arrow was then sped, trailing a long fiber behind it. The simpler method is to hold the two bits of quartz rod in the two hands. When experience tells that the heat is right, the hands are drawn apart, and the blast of the flame itself shoots out a fiber from one of the rods. It floats in the ascending air currents above the flame, where the sharp-eyed observer detects its free end. This he captures with a wetted finger. Carefully keeping the whole fiber in view, and nearly taut, he places it in the prepared box, where his assistant secures it by sticking it between two cleats an inch or so above a black velvet background.

To such a quartz fiber, about two thousandths of a millimeter (2/25,000 inch) in diameter, and about 15 centimeters (6 inches) long, the magnet-mirror system must be attached. It is only with a certain arrangement of light streaming into an otherwise dark room that such a quartz fiber can be seen at all. Moreover, although as strong as steel for equal dimensions, the finest fibers are so frail that the weight of a bit of writing paper half an inch long and a quarter of an inch wide is too great to be supported by one. Hence, it is easy to understand that even the most skillful manipulator breathes a little more freely after he succeeds in getting his needle system suspended within a tall glass bottle for testing.

It is not enough that the needle system should be built up and suspended as we have described. The six upper magnets must be, as a group, so exactly equal and opposite to the six lower ones, that the combination hardly tends to point either north or south. The reader will readily perceive that if one set of magnets is exactly as strong as the other, but exactly opposite in the aspect of its north and south poles, there is nothing for the earth's magnetism to lay hold upon, or for changes of its intensity or direction to affect. There must be so little directive force that the system can be turned around, despite its strong magnetic quality, by the torsion of the fragile quartz fiber. Many times must the almost invisible construction be lifted out of its testing bottle, slightly altered in magnetism, and the two sets of magnets slightly twisted with respect to each other about the glass rod, before this almost unreachable state of adjustment is arrived at. The object of so much trouble is to prevent the daily changes of the earth's magnetism from having any perceptible objectionable influence on the position of the needle system when it hangs within the galvanometer.

Now a word as to the enormously high sensitiveness of the galvanometer. We all have a general idea of the amount of electric current used to feed an ordinary incandescent electric light. Let us say it is about 0.3 ampere. A sensitive galvanometer, as used with the modern example of Langley's bolometer, will measure an electric current a hundred billion times smaller!

To record the indications of this marvelous combination of instruments we employ photography and sunlight. Most electrical testing instruments have a fine metallic needle for an indicator, that swings along the scale and tells how many volts or amperes the instrument is exposed to. But this is far too coarse a pointer for our galvanometer. We must attach to it a beam of light, that weighs nothing at all, and can be as long as we please. To do this, a tiny sun ray is reflected into the darkened chamber where the galvanometer stands. It falls upon the bit of a mirror which is attached to the needle system, and by this it is reflected back through a horizontal slit into a camera. There, as a tiny spot about as big as the period ending this sentence, it imprints itself on a photographic plate.

Whenever a ray of the solar spectrum warms the strip which we called "A" of the bolometer, the little mirror of the galvanometer is rotated slightly, owing to the reaction between the magnets and the electric current which the heat tends to set up in the coils. Hence, whenever this occurs, the recording spot of sunlight moves a little horizontally across the photographic plate. The distance it moves is exactly proportional to the rise of temperature of the bolometer strip, and so measures the energy of the solar spectral ray. But meanwhile an accurate clockwork is steadily moving simultaneously both the spectrum and the photographic plate. New spectral rays fall on the bolometer strip, causing new swings of the galvanometer needle and its recording shaft of light. But they are not confused with the former ones, because the photographic plate has meanwhile moved a little way downwards, and now exposes a fresh surface to the recording light-spot.

In this way we pass through the solar spectrum, and in about 7 minutes of time we produce an automatic curve of its energy. This includes all colors, and extends also far beyond the limits of the region to which the eye is sensitive. Such spectral energy curves as we have described are given in Figure 14. We must consider their significance in the next chapter.

We have described the most sensitive parts of the apparatus, but there are several others scarcely less interesting, and just as necessary for the investigation of the solar radiation.

Such a group of apparatus as the spectroscope and the bolometer demands a very steady mounting, and very uniform temperature conditions. These would be hard to secure if the combination of instruments should be mounted like a telescope and swung about an axis to follow the sun in its daily march from east to west. It is much better to force the sun's rays to stand still, as Joshua did of old, so that the instruments can remain stationary inside of a carefully protected laboratory, which may be a horizontal tunnel in a hillside.

THE SUN AND THE WELFARE OF MAN

For this purpose we use the coelostat, which, as its name signifies, fixes our view of celestial objects and so gives us stationary sunbeams. The instrument is shown in Plate 20. It requires two good-sized mirrors to accomplish its purpose of sending a fixed sunbeam into

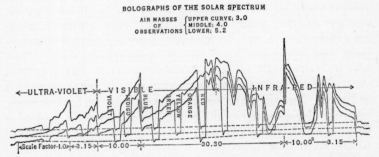

BOLOGRAPHS OF THE SOLAR SPECTRUM

AIR MASSES OF OBSERVATIONS { UPPER CURVE: 3.0 MIDDLE: 4.0 LOWER: 5.2

FIG. 14. The energy of the solar spectrum. Three curves taken at different elevations of the sun, the highest nearest noon. Note how rapidly the rays strengthen in the ultra-violet as the path of sunbeams in the atmosphere decreases. Great depressions in the infra-red are due to atmospheric water-vapor

the observatory. The first mirror to confront the sun is parallel to the axis of the earth. This mirror is caused to rotate by clockwork just half as fast as the earth, as one can readily see that it ought to do. For simplicity, suppose oneself at the equator on March 21, and desiring to reflect a sunbeam vertically upward all day long. At sunrise, the mirror must be inclined 45° east of the vertical, and at sunset, 45° west of it. Hence the mirror rotates 90° while the earth rotates a half way round or 180°.

In the Northern Hemisphere, the rotating mirror of the coelostat as usually set reflects its sunbeam southward, as well as upward. The reflected light falls obliquely on the second mirror, from which it is again reflected horizontally northward into the laboratory. Things are, of course, opposite at observatories south of the equator.

[84]

PLATE 22

Electrically driven rotating sectors which graduate the intensity of the sunbeam to suit our instruments

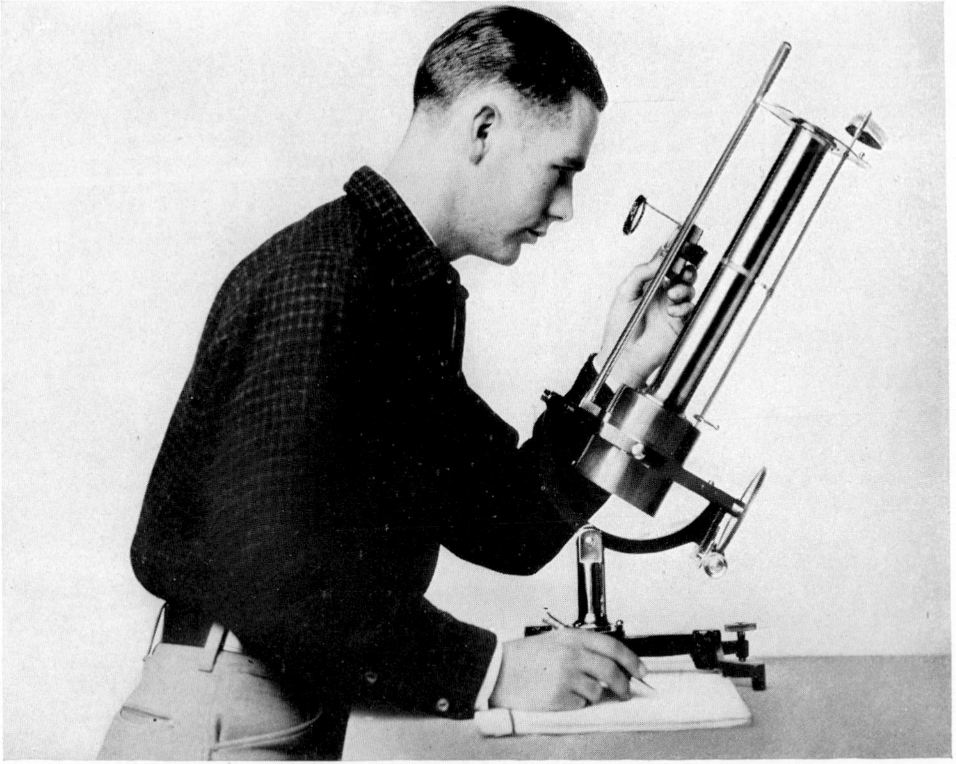

PLATE 23

Assistant Baughman measuring the intensity of the sun's total radiation with the silver-disk pyrheliometer

It will be noticed from the illustration that the moving mirror is mounted upon a double carriage, so that it can be rolled to east or west, or north or south. These adjustments are necessary for two reasons. Firstly, because the sun seems to move from north to south at different seasons of the year, and stands in the celestial equator only in March and September. On this account the moving mirror must be farther north in July than in January to reflect sunlight fairly upon the fixed mirror. Secondly, when (in the Northern Hemisphere) the moving mirror is farthest south, it is shaded at noon by the mounting of the fixed mirror. Hence, it must be moved either to the east or the west to avoid this inconvenience.

So the coelostat fixes the sun rays, avoiding for us the necessity of moving our sensitive measuring apparatus. There is yet another thing to be attended to before the solar beam reaches the spectroscope which disperses it into colors. We find that the intensity of the rays furnished by the different parts of the spectrum differs enormously, being very slight in the violet and ultra-violet compared to that in the red and infra-red. Hence, if the bolometer is sensitive enough to record well in the violet, the red and infra-red indications are much too great to measure. An equalizer, of exactly measured influence, must be provided. We use for this purpose a group of rapidly rotating sectors as shown in Plate 22.

We have all heard that jugglers fool us because our eyes are too slow to follow their hands. The rotating sectors for dimming light depend on a similar principle. Three toy electric motors are placed symmetrically about an axis fixed to the wall of the observing chamber, and a little to one side of the slit through which the sun rays are to pass to the spectroscope. Each motor is provided with a circular disk of aluminum. From the first disk have been removed, on opposite sides of the center, two sectors of 60°, or 120° in all, one-third of the circumference. From the second, similarly, have been removed two sectors, each of 20°, and from the third, two sectors, each of about 7°. Either one of the three mutilated disks can be swung into position exactly in front of the slit which admits sunlight. But on the instant that one of them almost arrives in position, an electrical contact causes its motor to start in swift rotation, carrying with it the disk. Rotating so swiftly in front of the slit, the sector of aluminum cuts off the light a majority of the time. To the bolometer or even to the eye, the instants of total obscuration are imperceptible, and the light seems to be continuous and merely dimmer. The intermittent quality of it cannot be distinguished. The consequence is that the quantity of sun rays admitted is 1/3, 1/9, or 1/27 of the full intensity of the beam, according to which disk is inserted.

So much for the fixed sunbeam, its intensity control, the spectrum, the bolometer which measures it, and the astonishingly sensitive galvanometer by means of which the distribution of energy in the spectrum is automatically recorded. All of this complex apparatus could be dispensed with if we could observe from the moon, beyond the interference of our atmosphere. We should need then only a device to measure the heat in the solar beam as a whole. On the earth we have indeed to use such a device for observing the total intensity of the sunbeam, but in addition to it we are obliged, as we have said, to measure the heat of the different spectral rays separately, so as to be able to study the different absorptive effects of our atmosphere upon them.

Let us consider the instrument used to measure the total energy of a solar beam. It is called by a name chosen by Pouillet, an investigator of a century ago. He invented such an instrument and called it by the Greek name "pyrheliometer," or "that which measures the heat of the sun." At the Smithsonian Institution we have used Pouillet's principle, but our instrument, which we call the "silver-disk pyrheliometer," is very unlike his. It is shown in the accompanying illustration.

As this instrument points directly towards the sun, it requires a special adjustable mounting. The instrument is mounted on a tripod stand which supports a semi-circular piece carrying two bearings. In these bearings lies the main axis whose central part is a circular hoop, within which, on a second set of bearings at right angles to the first, rests the "silver-disk pyrheliometer." The main axis is tilted up parallel to the earth's axis, and a worm-screw and wheel is attached, so that the observer can readily move this axis in slow rotation to follow the sun's march through the heavens. The pyrheliometer itself can swing on the second axis to suit the sun's march between its extreme north and south positions of June and December. In this way we may point the instrument exactly at the sun at any time of the day or year,

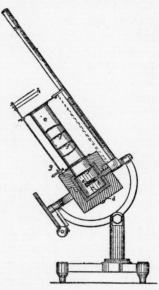

FIG. 15. Abbot's silver-disk pyrheliometer for measuring the heat of sun rays

and a little indicator is provided to show when this adjustment is exact.

The solar beam enters through a tubular vestibule, *e*, which is provided with diaphragms, *f, f, f*, to prevent the wind from entering too. The rays fall at right angles upon the blackened surface, *a*, of a silver disk (shown sectionally). Being absorbed there almost completely, they tend to warm it. A cylindrical bulb thermometer, *b*, is inserted in a radial hole in the silver disk. This hole is lined with a thin steel thimble, and filled up with mercury to make a good heat connection with the bulb. The

[87]

thermometer stem is bent at right angles to make it safer from breakage.

Above the vestibule lies a triple screen or shutter made up of three thin polished metal leaves. This is employed to cut off the solar beam. With watch in hand, the observer notes the thermometer reading at a certain instant. The shutter still remaining closed, he records the temperature again 100 seconds later, and immediately afterwards opens the shutter to admit sun rays. He then notes the rise of temperature during 100 seconds and closes the shutter. Another observation, after 100 seconds, with closed shutter completes the determination. The rise of temperature during the sun exposure, plus the average fall of temperature in the two intervals before and after it, gives the corrected solar effect. It is proportional to the total energy of the solar beam.

But yet the measurement is incomplete. One would need to know the capacity of the silver disk for heat, and the loss which it experienced by incomplete absorptive property. As these factors would be very difficult to measure accurately, we use another expedient. It is to construct another kind of pyrheliometer called the "standard water-flow pyrheliometer," not so easy to use, but whose theory is simpler. Figure 16 shows its sensitive part. As before, the rays are admitted through a tubular vestibule, BB, containing diaphragms, to keep out air currents. The last diaphragm, C, is of precisely measured diameter. After leaving it, the solar rays enter a tubular chamber, A, which is blackened within, and fall upon a blackened cone, at the back of it. Here they are about 97 per cent absorbed and changed to heat, but if any vestiges of radiation remain not absorbed, they are reflected to and fro upon the sides of the chamber, which absorbs at each encounter 97 per cent of what remains. Thus the conversion into heat becomes practically total. The problem now is to measure all of the heat thus produced.

For this purpose, the walls of the tubular chamber are

made hollow. A spiral watercourse runs through the hollow walls from end to end and continues round and round in the back and in the conical receiver. To maintain the waterflow, a tube, E, connected to a reservoir at a much higher level, brings in a steady stream of distilled water at constant temperature. This enters the chamber wall through the spiral ivory piece at D_1, and leaves it by the similar ivory spiral at D_2. Through each of these two ivory spirals is threaded to and fro, from end to end, in many parallel piercings, a measured length of hairlike platinum wire. As the water flows round and round in the ivory spiral channels, it bathes these platinum wires and forces them to assume the exact temperature of the water. They are connected up just as the bolometer wires are to form a delicate electrical thermometer. One wire is in the inflowing stream, the other in that which flows out after having bathed the chamber walls which

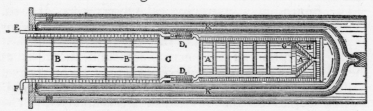

FIG. 16. The water-flow pyrheliometer, world-standard instrument for measuring solar radiation

are warmed by the sun rays. Hence, there is a difference of temperature between the two platinum wires, which exactly measures the rise of temperature of the water stream, due to its continuously absorbing the solar radiation.

Here we have all the elements for the measurement. For the heat of a solar beam of known area of cross-section is thereby found to produce continuously an observed rise of temperature in a current of water which flows at a measured rate.

However, this is not all. Lest there might be a mistake somewhere, we provide a check on the determination. A coil of wire, H, is inserted far back in the receiving chamber, lying close to the blackened cone on which the sun's rays fall. Through this coil of wire we may pass a measured current of electricity. This will produce in the coil a certain well-known amount of heat. By the same means, involving the waterflow, that measure the solar heating, we measure this test quantity of electrical heating. Many trials have shown that our measurements recover 100 per cent of the electrical test-heat. Hence, we infer that it is the same with sun-heat, too.

Having thus provided the well-proved "water-flow pyrheliometer," which measures the total heat furnished by the solar beam, we use it as a standard and compare with its results the indications of the "silver-disk pyrheliometer" used in every-day experiments.

The Smithsonian Astrophysical Observatory devised, constructed and fully tested these pieces of apparatus for measuring solar radiation. In the year 1913, we published a full description of the instruments and the tests of them. They were recognized everywhere as authoritative. A demand arose from all parts of the world for standardized copies of the silver-disk pyrheliometer. The Smithsonian Institution has constructed, tested, standardized, and sold at cost to investigators in all the continents, over fifty of these instruments. They are regarded everywhere as furnishing the true scale of solar-radiation measurements. In the publication of solar observations made with other types of pyrheliometers, authors almost invariably apply the necessary corrections to express their results in terms of the Smithsonian scale, which thus has become, by almost universal consent, the standard solar-radiation scale for the world.

Not all of the sun's rays that reach us are contained in the direct beam. A part which reaches 5 to 25 per cent, or even more sometimes, comes indirectly from all parts of the sky. It is scatteringly reflected by the dust, haze, clouds, and even the molecules which compose our atmosphere. As it comes from all directions within a complete hemisphere, we cannot measure it as we do the direct beam, but require a special instrument. Such an instrument was devised, constructed, tested, and has been much used by the Smithsonian Astrophysical Observatory. We call it by the Greek name "pyranometer," which means "that which measures heat from above."

In order to understand it thoroughly, we must go into an explanation of some properties of radiation which are seldom thought of because they concern rays which the eye cannot see, lying, as they do, far beyond the visible end of the red spectrum. Look upon the sparkling white-hot iron as the blacksmith welds it. After he has made the weld and is shaping the piece with his hammer, it grows yellowish, reddish, and dull red as it cools. It altogether ceases to glow about the time he plunges it into water, but as he lifts it out, steam comes from the water drops, so that we know it is still warm. But it no longer emits light. Does that mean that it no longer emits rays similar to light? By no means! All bodies, however cold, unless indeed they could be reduced to the absolute zero which lies even below the temperatures of frozen hydrogen or frozen helium, emit rays similar to light, but of longer wave-lengths of vibration, to which the humors of the eye are not transparent.

The hotter a body, the shorter become the prevailing wave-lengths of its emission. This does not mean that it loses the rays of longer wave-length. They even grow in their intensity, but the more rapid growth of intensities of rays of shorter wave-lengths gives a prevailingly shorter and shorter average wave-length character to the beam. This is why the blacksmith's iron, as he heats it, passes from dull red to yellow, to white, and if he could reach much higher temperatures, we should see a tinge of blue.

[91]

THE SUN AND THE WELFARE OF MAN

The sun is so hot that a very large proportion of its rays are in the visible region. Some stars, much hotter than our sun, seem distinctly blue. Others, much cooler, seem reddish. The earth, much cooler than red stars, sends out rays, all invisible to our eyes, but nevertheless capable of communicating a very considerable amount of heat to a blackened surface. So also with the materials which compose the atmosphere. They emit rays of long wavelength, invisible, but nevertheless of so much intensity as to be quite comparable in their heating effects with the solar rays of shorter average wave-length which the atmosphere reflects. In the case of the moon, the long-wave rays which it emits are so intense as to overmatch by severalfold the intensity of the solar rays which it reflects.

With this explanation, the reader will understand why it is that in measuring scattered sun rays with the pyranometer we are obliged to use some kind of a screen impervious to rays of long wave-length, such as mainly compose the beams emitted by the atmosphere, but transparent to those of the sun which the atmosphere reflects to us. It is unnecessary to resort to this device in the silver-disk pyrheliometer, first, because that instrument sees but a very little part of the sky, and, second, because the sun rays of the direct beam are usually ten or twenty times as strong as those reflected from the whole sky. Thus the influence of long-wave rays under these circumstances is negligible.

Plate 24 shows the pyranometer. Flush with the surface of a brightly polished metallic plate there is inserted an electrically insulated, black-painted, short strip of the alloy manganin, as thin as gold leaf. This is the sensitive part, which is designed to absorb the sun rays scattered from all parts of the sky. To prevent it from absorbing long-wave sky rays too, a hemispherical cup of glass, optically polished within and without to exact spherical curvatures, is placed on the metallic plate, ex-

PLATE 24

Abbot's pyranometer, the instrument which measures heat in the rays of the whole sky or of the sun alone

actly concentric to, and covering over the thin absorbing metal strip.

Underneath the thin strip there is fastened with shellac a device called the thermoelectric couple. It is a junction of two metals, which produces a difference of electrical potential when warmed. In our case, we use the metals tellurium and platinum for this combination. When the absorbing strip is warmed, a current of electricity flows from their junction, and deflects a galvanometer proportionally to the rise of temperature of the strip. It is arranged, however, that a separate current of electricity may be caused to flow through the strip. As this produces a known amount of heat in the strip, we are able in this way to set up a precise measure of the heat of the sky, by exactly matching with electrically introduced heat the sky effect upon the thermoelectric couple. This ingenious means of measurement was first invented by K. J. Ångström and is used in the excellent Ångström pyrheliometer.

In using the pyranometer the observer levels the plate, if he intends to observe the entire sky. A polished cup-shaped shutter covers the glass hemisphere. As the observer pulls a cord, or pushes an electric button, the shutter opens, and exposes the strip. A swing of the galvanometer index on its scale results. Closing the shutter, the observer duplicates the galvanometer swing by the electrical heating, and so the measurement is made. Sometimes only a special portion of the sky is to be observed. In this case the glass hemisphere is partly covered over and the instrument is inclined as may be necessary.

The pieces of apparatus we have described are not very common ones. Langley's bolometer, indeed, is used in some laboratories. But it is regarded by many observers as highly difficult to manage, so that they are apt to prefer the simpler "thermopile," which has come to perfection in recent years. Much of the formidable reputation of the bolometer arose from Langley's own accounts of its behavior in the early days, before it was fully perfected. One of these experiences was as follows:

As we have said in an earlier chapter, Langley, in 1881, conducted an expedition from Pittsburgh, Pennsylvania, to Mount Whitney in California, for the purpose of measuring sun rays under the pure sky surrounding the highest peak of the United States. It was a part of his plan to observe first at the comparatively low altitude of Lone Pine, just east of the mountain, before ascending to conduct the observations near the summit. The town of Lone Pine is an oasis of the Inyo desert, depending on the waters of Lone Pine Creek for its existence. At the time of the year when Langley was there, it is apt to suffer temperatures well above 100° F.

At Lone Pine, Langley's laboratory was a small tent, in which sweated the devoted observer, surrounded by the bolometer, galvanometer, and spectroscope. There was no attempt at photographic registration. Instead, the observer read off the positions of the recording spot of light upon the scale, one meter (over a yard) long. What with the large daily range of temperature, the necessity of so lining the tent as to secure darkness for the observations, and the high winds, the temperatures in this extemporized laboratory varied enormously. With this condition of affairs it is not surprising that so delicate a device as the bolometer responded not only to the heat of the solar spectrum, but far more also to the changes of temperature of its surroundings. Hence, the recording spot of the galvanometer galloped about, and, as Langley used to say to me in conversation, often traversed the whole scale, a meter long, in a single minute.

The observer, therefore, could by no means tell whether it was solar heat or desert heat that was causing the changes he read off. All he did was to call out the position of the spot of light upon the scale, at definite intervals of a few seconds, to the recorder, who also set down the data about the spectrum and its exposure. From thousands of such observations the solar effects had to be culled out, as best they might be, from the much larger accidental ones due to the abominable conditions for observing.

At the present time, all is changed in our field stations. We build our laboratories under ground to secure constant conditions. With a far more sensitive bolometric outfit than Langley's, and with photographic registration of every change that occurs, it is seldom indeed that so much as a centimeter (3/8 inch) of movement due to outside causes takes place in the record during the 7 minutes required to explore the solar spectrum, starting far beyond the visible violet and ending far beyond the visible red. Much more can be observed, and far greater accuracy can be attained, in 7 minutes under present circumstances, than in several hours in the olden days. The bolometer, outgrowing the wild coltish antics of its youth, has settled down now to a plow-horse steadiness comparable to an ordinary mercury thermometer!

We have remarked that the coelostat mounts two plane mirrors for the purpose of reflecting a sunbeam into the laboratory. There are also mirrors in the spectroscope. In most observatories, mirrors for such purposes are of silvered glass, but not, like household mirrors, of silver-backed glass. It is entirely inadmissable in first-rate optical work to allow the light to pass through the glass and return. Hence, the silver is deposited chemically on the front surface of the glass, and then highly polished with a chamois-leather pad, covered by the finest rouge-powder. The rouge itself is first carefully prepared by stirring it into a uniform suspension in water, from which it is separated into fractions, because the coarser parts settle first. For the finest polishing, only the grains which have remained in suspension for several hours are employed.

The glass surfaces, of course, are prepared with extreme care. Two first-rate plane mirrors, if laid face to face, would nowhere be separated by 0.00005 millimeter (1/500,000 inch). In the making of them thick glass of good quality is employed. The thickness of an astronomical mirror should not be less than 1/6 the diameter. After it has been ground as perfectly as possible with finest abrasive powders, the mirror is at last polished for many hours with a tool of brass covered by pitch and fed with rouge-powder and water.

Although silver is by far the best reflector for solar rays, excepting in the extreme ultra-violet, it is continually tarnishing. We see this in the tea-table silver, which must be polished from time to time. So, also, with astronomical silvered mirrors. But the silver coat is almost inexpressibly thin, certainly far under the millionth of an inch. After a few polishings, it wears away and must be replaced. This, in itself, is not a serious drawback. But for the solar studies which we are about to describe, the tarnishing of the silver, even in a single day of exposure to sun rays, is a serious source of error.

We made several trials of other substances to take the place of silver, so as to avoid this tarnishing. We tried speculum metal, a mixture of copper and tin, also magnalium, a mixture of magnesium and aluminum. Neither of these substitutes proved very satisfactory. Success came, however, with the alloy called stellite, which on account of its excessive hardness is principally used for lathe and cutting tools. This substance, indeed, is so very hard that even with a high-speed carborundum wheel it can be ground away only very slowly. Imagine, then, the difficulty of grinding and polishing a large plate of such a substance to a perfect optical figure! Processes that take hours for glass drag themselves out to as many days for stellite.

Notwithstanding this excessive difficulty of preparation, there have been made for the use of the Smithsonian Institution no less than twenty large stellite mirrors. These are now being used in California, Arizona, Chile,

The late Lord Rayleigh, whose experiments and theories illuminated the subject of radiation. (Courtesy of the Royal Society of Great Britain)

Argentina, South West Africa, and Australia. So entirely permanent are these stellite surfaces, that mirrors polished as much as 10 years ago are quite as bright, and in every respect as perfect now, as when they were new. In reflecting power, however, they do not approach silver. They give an average reflecting power of about 65 per cent, where silver gives nearly 95 per cent. But in the region of ultra-violet rays, where silver is not reflecting but transparent, stellite still retains a reflection coefficient of nearly 40 per cent.

Having given some of the curious facts connected with our apparatus, we shall turn in the next chapter to consider some extraordinary properties of our atmosphere.

CHAPTER V

THE ATMOSPHERE. WHAT HAS IT TO DO WITH SOLAR RADIATION?

PAINTERS speak of atmosphere. Other people rarely consciously see it, although on windy days they readily appreciate its buffeting. Rain and snow, too, fall down from its clouds, and the blue of the sky ought to be a perpetual reminder of its existence. There are other properties of the atmosphere, which are known to few and seldom discussed, but which separately or in combination profoundly affect our lives.

First of all, since we have mentioned the blue sky, let us understand how this beautiful canopy of our world is tinted. It used to be supposed that some one of the constituents of the air was intrinsically blue and therefore the sky was blue, just like water with bluing in it. But the late Lord Rayleigh showed, over half a century ago, that all gases have a tendency to be blue because they are composed of molecules which are small compared to the lengths of the waves which transmit light. Yellow light, for example, contains about 17,000 waves per centimeter (over 40,000 per inch), and for violet light the numbers are about 1½ times larger. Compared to light-waves, the diameters of molecules are very much smaller, something like 30,000,000 diameters per centimeter (75,000,000 per inch).

Lord Rayleigh's theory indicates that when light passes through a medium made up of particles which are small compared to the wave-length, there will be a scattering from every particle in every direction, though not uniformly so. The amount of light scattered increases very rapidly as the wave-length diminishes, so rapidly, indeed, as to be proportional inversely to the fourth power of the wave-length. As blue light is roughly but 2/3 as long in wave-length as red light, the scattering of blue is nearly as 81 is to 16, or about five times as great as the scattering of red. Hence, when the sunbeam comes through the atmosphere, it loses on its way far more of blue than of red. However, the rays which are stolen from the direct beam are partly restored to us by scattering from all parts of the sky. As we have just seen, the scattered rays are mainly blue and so the sky seems blue. This is also the reason why painters see the distance as purple. It is because the long intervening stretch of air is scattering to us predominantly bluish light. Thus the atmosphere is really blue, not because any one of its constituents is like a dye, to color the whole compound, but because all of its gases join to make the sky blue, although having themselves inherently no dyeing properties at all.

Yet while we speak of dyes, which seem from common experience to have such simple properties, it is far from obvious, after all, just what property a dye imparts to a piece of cloth to give it color. Before the time of Sir Isaac Newton, white was considered to be the simplest color of all. But Newton showed by his prisms that white light really consists of a mixture of colors, of which he distinguished seven, as follows: violet, indigo, blue, green, yellow, orange, and red. These shade into one another by indistinguishable gradations in the spectrum, so that the number of hues is infinite. Morever, if mixed in special combinations and proportions, groups of these colors which are found in white light make up other colors such as old-rose pink, which is not found at all in the spectrum.

The colors of dyed cloths, paints, and flowers come about

in the following way: The chemical substances of which they are composed and which are responsible for their colors, absorb some varieties of the white light which plentifully bathes all objects in the glare of day. That is to say, these varieties of light are destroyed as wave-energy more or less completely by these color-substances, and are transformed into the energy of heat, which is merely the irregular darting hither and thither of the molecules of material substances.

The remainder of the white light, not thus absorbed, is partly reflected by the texture of the substance, and partly transmitted through it to those objects which lie beyond. Lacking the parts absorbed, the reflected and the transmitted rays are no longer the white light of day, but exhibit whatever color is proper to the mixture of the portions remaining after omitting from the spectrum the absorbed parts. This process is a somewhat different means of producing color from that which we have described as producing the blue of the sky. In the case of dyes, absorption forms definite gaps in the spectrum of the reflected rays. In the case of the sky, no colors are lost; all colors are diffused, but in unequal profusion, so that the prevailing impression is of blue.

Here again comes up an interesting consideration. The eye itself is no impartial judge of color. Obviously this is so in the case of the color-blind. But even in the normal eye the efficiency of perception differs enormously as we pass the spectrum in review. Of violet and of red it takes far more of radiant energy to produce equally intense sensations of brightness than is the case with yellow green, and beyond the violet and beyond the red lie rays the eye cannot see at all. Individuals differ in these sensations, but the efficiency of the average eye to see the spectrum colors is indicated on the accompanying diagram. We should assign the hues of objects very differently if our eyes were equally sensitive to Sir Isaac Newton's whole gamut of the seven primary colors, for the

PLATE 26

Three eminent American scientists. From left to right: A. A. Noyes,
G. E. Hale, and R. A. Millikan

PLATE 27

Snow Crystals. Photographed microscopically by Wilson A. Bentley. (From "Everyday Mysteries," by courtesy of the Macmillan Co.)

mixtures would then seem to us entirely changed. Daylight, indeed, would seem to us what now we call deep

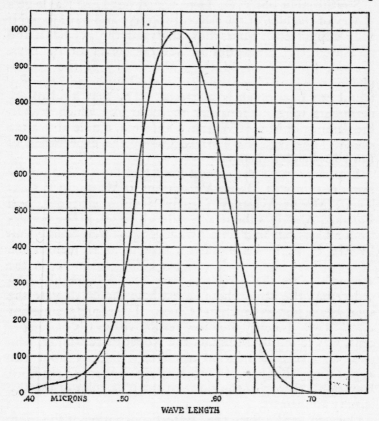

FIG. 17. The efficiency of the eye for light. Wave-length .50 is green,
.60 is orange-red. So the maximum is in the yellowish green. It takes
over ten times as much energy of blue as of yellow light to affect the
eye equally

blue, for our appreciation of the blue and violet parts of
it would be enormously intensified. Furthermore, as the
eyes of individuals differ so much in their sensitiveness to

different colors, you differ from your companion in your impression of what, for instance, is green or blue in nature.

Smithsonian observers have tested out Lord Rayleigh's theory of the blue of the sky in two ways and have found it fully supported. First, they analyzed the sky-light, and measured the intensities of several colors of its rays. Second, they measured the transparency of the atmosphere for solar rays of different wave-lengths and thereby found out how much is scattered. The first kind of experiments were made under the clear sky which crowns the summit of Mount Wilson, California, a mile above the ocean. The results confirmed closely the expectation of Lord Rayleigh's theory.

Experiments of the second kind had been going on for years not only at Mount Wilson but at Washington (sea-level), Mount Whitney (nearly 3 miles altitude), and Bassour, Algeria (about 2/3 mile altitude). The results from all stations and for all wave-lengths were worked up by Mr. F. E. Fowle in such a fashion as to furnish the count of how many molecules per cubic centimeter in the atmosphere at the earth's surface would be required, in order that the atmosphere as a whole should deplete the solar beam just as much as it does. His result [1] came out 2.70×10^{19}. Exactly the same result, within 1/5 of one per cent, was found by Millikan, the Nobel Prize winner, who used an electrical method absolutely distinct from any application whatever of Lord Rayleigh's theory. So Lord Rayleigh's theory of the cause of the blue color of the sky is fully confirmed.

One can hardly form the faintest conception of the enormous number of molecules just mentioned. It is said that the number of living people in this world is nearly two billions. If there were as many inhabited worlds as there are human inhabitants on ours, and if each of them also contained two billions of inhabitants, the total census

[1] We shall use this system of notation to avoid writing many ciphers. The number here given means 27 followed by 18 zeros.

figure for the population of the universe would be less than one-fourth as great as the number of molecules in a bit of air no larger than one of the dice used in playing backgammon! This shows one of the marvelous properties of the atmosphere, and how trifling an influence each single molecule must have separately in the scattering of light which produces our lovely sky.

But oftentimes the sky seems to fade and lose its charm, becoming whitish and soiled-looking. This appearance is apt to be caused by a combination of water and dust. The heat furnished by the absorption of sun rays is continually evaporating water from the oceans and the fresh waters, and from the surfaces of plants and animals. Hence, the lower part of the atmosphere is charged everywhere and always with a load of water-vapor. Sometimes this load exceeds the limit that the atmosphere can retain at the temperature prevailing. Rain or snow then falls. So long as the water-vapor remains in the form of separate molecules it is indistinguishable, because it merely adds a little to the scattering by the molecules of the atmospheric nitrogen and oxygen, and thus tends merely to deepen the blue color of the sky.

When the air becomes very humid, however, the molecules of water run together, forming their groups by preference about particles of dust, such as smoke and the winds keep forever soaring. Oftentimes in the space of a few moments, these centers of condensation become large compared to the wave-lengths of light, though still too small to be seen individually. But particles of larger diameters than light-waves no longer scatter the blue rays with so much preference over the red. Their effect is nearly equal on all rays of the visible spectrum. Hence, when the air is loaded with these grosser particles, its scattered light differs little in quality from direct sunlight. We say then that the sky is hazy. But as the dust tinges the quality somewhat, and as the haze, if very thick, weakens the intensity of the rays a good deal, there is produced that depressing dinginess characteristic of the seaport city sky. How strongly it contrasts with the exhilarating influence of the pure blue of a clear mountain day !

We have already noticed an effect of this kind, in our account of the Algerian expedition of June, 1912, when the high-thrown ash from the volcano of Katmai in Alaska drifted across the world to our Mediterranean station in 13 days, and to our California station in 15 days. Though this volcanic dust was so fine in texture that the last vestiges of it stayed in suspension at least until the end of the year 1914, it was nevertheless so coarse compared to the wave-lengths of light as to produce a milky, whitish sky, very depressing to the astronomers accustomed to the deep mountain blue of ordinary years. We shall have occasion in our chapter on eclipses to speak of the unparalleled violence of the volcanic eruption of Krakatoa in the Strait of Sunda, August 27, 1883. The dust of Krakatoa rose fully 17 miles in our atmosphere, and, blanketing the whole world, remained several years in suspension, producing, besides the dimming of daylight, the dusky reddish long-drawn sunsets so notable at that period. Dr. W. J. Humphreys has proposed an hypothesis of glacial climates based on the influence of volcanic dust in former ages.

Quite opposite in its psychological influence to the formation of haze is the formation of the fluffy, rolling, brilliant, white clouds. Even the astronomer, demanding clear skies for his work, can hardly resist hailing these beautiful objects. Clouds are classified by the meteorologist according to appearance, and these of which we are speaking are called cumulus, or heaping. Their formation is due to the cooling of masses of air below the dew-point. As we were saying, air at a given temperature can dissolve only a fixed proportion of molecules of water. The lower the temperature, the less the proportion. When the sun, having by its heat evaporated into the air at the earth's

PLATE 28

The cloud-banner on Mount Assiniboine. Photo by Walcott

surface nearly all of the water-vapor which it can hold, by its continued shining warms the air, and hence tends to expand it, rising air-currents are formed. These are particularly likely to flow up the slopes of mountains, much as water follows a stick when one pours from a pitcher. This is because the mountain sides themselves are warmed, and start rising currents which lead the way upwards. Soaring birds know of this, and love to play on the wind at the crest of a bluff, where the rising air currents are tumbling upwards.

As the warm surface air rises, carrying its load of water-vapor, it continually expands as it goes higher and higher where the atmospheric pressure grows less and less. By expanding, the air cools. Soon it may grow too cool to retain so much water-vapor, and a cloud is formed. We are apt to see such clouds resting on or above the peaks of high mountains, which serve as chimneys to guide the rising air currents.

These clouds, too, are apt to form at night in low places, but we call them fog. At such times, the air is too full of moisture to retain all of it during the cooler night hours. The fog-cloud is apt to form first in the coolest spots, where hills shade the ground from the declining sun. But it flows down into the lower levels, and forms there too, as the night grows cooler. Being heavier than air, the water globules fall, and, therefore, fog usually fails to cover the hills.

It may seem strange at first thought that the fleecy cumulus clouds, also made up of heavy globules of water, do not fall down to the earth. There are several reasons why they remain floating high above us. In the first place, rising currents of air prevail where they form. In the second place, if they fall, they come continually into air-regions of greater atmospheric pressure. So the air which they carry with them becomes denser and warmer, just as the air in the tire of an automobile becomes warmer while being pumped. If they fall, therefore, their globules of liquid water again evaporate. So the cloud is being continually dissolved at its bottom, and renewed at its top. It is not the same cloud two moments in succession, though it remains as a cloud wherever the conditions of the atmosphere are right to cause one to form.

This idea of the importance of the state of the atmosphere on the formation of clouds may be carried further in regard to rainfall. When we see on weather maps of successive days the march of a huge cloudy area from the Gulf of Mexico up the Atlantic Coast till rain pours down in Washington, we may be apt to suppose that the rain that falls in Washington was carried up there by the cloud from the Gulf of Mexico. Is it then just as if the cloud were a huge bucket, that had been filled in the Gulf and emptied all along the Atlantic Coast? Not so! Much of the rain that falls in Washington existed as water-vapor in the air above Washington while the sky was clear before the rain. It is the state of the atmosphere favorable to cause rain, not the cloud bearing its water drops, that moves along. As fast as the atmospheric disturbance reaches new localities, it brings down the vapor already existing there. Of course there is some qualification to this, for there seldom exists directly above a place enough humidity to produce a very unusually heavy rainfall. Some of the water-vapor flows in from the sides of the disturbance, but not much from hundreds of miles away, where the cloud may first have formed.

In cloudless summer weather at the seaside, there is frequently as much water-vapor contained invisibly in the atmosphere as would make an inch and a half of rainfall. Probably very much more than this may be loaded into the air in stormy times when clouds have formed. The invisible water-vapor of the air, although it does not usually contribute more than a twentieth of the total weight of the atmosphere, and at many times and localities much less than this, is nevertheless of prime

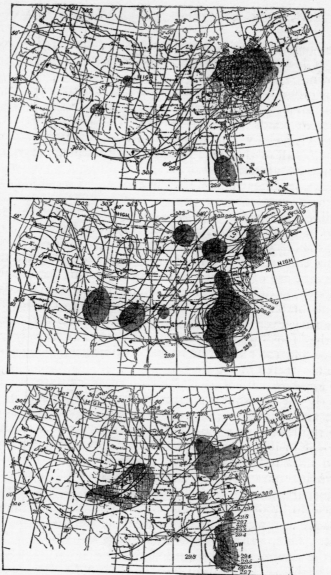

FIG. 18. The march of a West Indian hurricane up the Atlantic Coast,
August 27, 28, 29, 1893. (U. S. Weather Bureau)

importance to us. For not only is it the source of rain, but it blesses us in another fashion much less generally known.

In order to understand about this matter clearly, we must amplify the remarks we have already made about different kinds of rays. Although X-rays, ultra-violet rays, visible rays, infra-red rays, and Hertzian or radio-rays are all of the same nature, being nothing other than transverse vibrations or waves, they differ in wave-length. X-rays are of extremely short wave-length, as short, some of them, as 0.00000001 centimeter (1/250,000,000 inch). Visible rays run from 0.00004 to 0.00007 centimeter. Almost all of the energy of sun rays lies between wave-lengths 0.00003 and 0.00025 centimeter. But earth rays, being emitted by a body of much lower temperature than the sun, are of no importance for wave-lengths less than 0.00050 centimeter. They reach their maximum intensity at about 0.0010 centimeter but continue in considerable intensity even to 0.0100 centimeter. Radio messages—as the "fans" well know—are propagated at wave-lengths exceeding 100 meters, or 10,000 centimeters. These facts are illustrated in Figure 1.

Our eyes cannot reveal all of these rays to us, and partly for the simple reason that the front parts of the eye are opaque to most of them. Glass, also, although we think of it as almost perfectly transparent, is only so for the visible rays, and for a small extent of ultra-violet and infra-red lying closely on either side of the visible rays in the spectrum. Glass begins and ceases to be transparent just about where the sun's rays begin and cease to be of considerable intensity, and it is almost as opaque as a piece of metal for rays such as the earth sends out. This, although perhaps he does not realize it fully, is the reason why the gardener uses glass windows over his hotbed. They admit the sun's rays with little loss, and not only hinder the winds from carrying off the heated air underneath, but also cut off altogether the direct radiation

PLATE 29

A sea of fog below Mount Wilson.   Photo by F. Ellerman

PLATE 30

Alto-cumulus and cumulus clouds near Mount Wilson.   Photo by F. Ellerman

of the soil, which would tend to cool the seed-bed both by day and night.

Somewhat similar is the rôle of water-vapor in our atmosphere. Not quite as transparent as glass, still the atmospheric water-vapor is seldom sufficient to absorb more than 15 per cent of the direct solar rays which would otherwise fall upon the ground. We may say that usually in cloudless weather about nine-tenths of the solar rays are transmissible through the atmospheric humidity. But it is far different with those outgoing rays, of great wave-length, which the earth's surface continually emits. According to the investigations of Mr. Fowle, conducted at the Smithsonian Astrophysical Observatory, in cloudless weather only about 20 per cent of the earth's sea-level surface radiation can go straight through the atmosphere to space. The remainder is absorbed by water-vapor. Hence, the cooling of the earth by day and by night is greatly retarded by this invisible blanket which hinders the escape of earth-heat through the atmosphere.

Clouds are even more effective. According to the observations made in California by Dr. A. K. Ångström,[2] a cloudy atmosphere cuts off completely all radiation from the earth's surface outwards towards space. As the earth is, on the average, 50 per cent cloudy, this means much for the efficiency of the atmospheric blanket. But on the other hand, a cloudy sky cuts off entirely the direct solar rays, and allows to pass, as scattered solar light, only from a tenth to a third of the whole solar contribution. The exact proportion depends on the denseness of the cloud. Thus, clouds, since they reduce solar rays so greatly while they stop outgoing earth rays completely, are not much more efficient to keep the earth warm than is invisible water-vapor in the atmosphere.

Of course, earth-heat escapes despite these obstacles.

[2] These observations were financed by the Smithsonian Institution from the income of its Hodgkins Fund.

Air currents carry the heat upwards. Rays rising from the earth's surface and absorbed by water-vapor and clouds, warm these constituents of the atmosphere. They themselves, in consequence, radiate more freely outwards towards space than they would otherwise. By such processes, the heat at length gets up to the layers which are free to radiate, and then it can escape. But we must recollect that these higher atmospheric layers are cooler than the earth's surface. Hence, their radiating power is less. So the atmospheric blanket of water-vapor and clouds works effectively and steadily to keep the temperature of the surface where we live higher than otherwise it would be, just as the gardener's glass makes of his forcing place a "hot-bed."

It is hard to determine exactly how much the earth's surface temperature is increased by the atmospheric blanket. If it were removed, clouds and all, the sun rays available to warm the surface would be materially increased. This would go far to counteract the increased rate of cooling which would then prevail. But if the quantity of sun's rays reaching the surface of the earth could meanwhile remain constant, the removal of clouds and humidity from the air would probably lower the mean temperature of the earth to near the zero of the Fahrenheit scale in place of the present mean earth temperature, which is near 60° of that scale.

On one point there can be no question at all. The equableness of the earth's surface temperature would be destroyed by removing the atmospheric blanket. We have only to refer to the moon for the proof of this. Situated at the same mean distance from the sun as is the earth, her sunlit surface is shone upon continuously for two weeks at a time, because the moon rotates only once in about 29½ days, as seen from the sun. Without any clouds or atmosphere of any kind to intercept the solar rays, the moon's surface attains a temperature not far from that at which water boils. But occasionally the moon is eclipsed. The earth comes squarely between the sun and moon, and cuts off the solar rays almost entirely. The observations of Lord Rosse, Langley, and later observers all agree in showing that within an hour after the lunar eclipse becomes total the moon's surface no longer gives the slightest indications of warmth. Our atmosphere prevents an accurate estimate, but it is certain that within one hour the fall of temperature of the temporarily darkened lunar surface greatly exceeds 100° C. (212° F.).

Similar would be the condition of our earth without its atmospheric blanket. Life would be impossible, merely on account of the freezing of vegetation during every

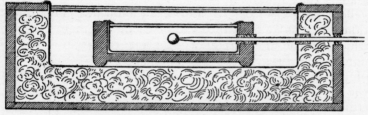

FIG. 19. Langley's "hot-box." Sun rays are trapped under glass and raise temperatures above boiling without lenses or mirrors

night, even at the equator. Water, as of course we always realized, is indispensable to both plants and animals. But we do not always consider that water in the atmosphere is just as indispensable to all forms of life as water on the ground.

It is surprising to find how high a temperature can be gotten by a simple application of the hot-bed principle. Figure 19 shows a contrivance to illustrate this. A tin pan is painted inside with a mixture of lampblack, alcohol, and a little shellac. It is covered by a clean sheet of window glass which is made to prevent the easy escape of air from the interior by the device of inserting a thick ring of felt against the edge of the pan underneath the glass. A spring behind the pan presses it forward against the glass. All is surrounded by a bed of feathers or cotton packing several inches thick, and enclosed by a flat wooden box. A thermometer lying in the pan indicates the result. With such simple means, the observers at the Smithsonian Astrophysical Observatory in Washington, practically at sea-level, frequently measured temperatures much exceeding the boiling point of water. Care was taken, however, to adjust the apparatus so that the sun shone upon it nearly at right angles. This plan has even been used successfully to produce power from sun rays, as we shall describe in a later chapter.

Reverting to the subject of the color of the sky, some readers may inquire why the sky is all aflame with vivid yellows and crimsons at sunrise and sunset. This question takes us at once into the heart of our main subject, which is the measurement of solar radiation. As we noted very briefly in earlier chapters, the transparency of the atmosphere for solar rays differs very much with the wave-length. There are limited regions of the spectrum where the gases and vapors of the atmosphere nearly extinguish the solar rays. For instance, oxygen is powerfully absorbing at several places in the red, where it produces the two curiously constituted series of dark lines named by Fraunhofer B and A.

In the neighboring spectral region of the infra-red quite invisible to the eye, lie the great absorption bands of water-vapor called by Langley, ρ, ϕ, ψ, Ω. These will be found indicated by great depressions in the bolographic energy curve of Figure 14 where they may be compared with the band A, just mentioned. It will be seen that water-vapor is far more effective than oxygen as an absorber, even though much less plentiful in the atmosphere. The reader may be surprised that the bolographic energy curves of the band A show no such detail as the photographs. This is because the bolographic spectrum is on a very much smaller scale. It is possible to feel

PLATE 31

Scarf cloud over cumulus, Mount Shasta, Calif. (After Humphreys.)
Photo by C. A. Gilchrist

PLATE 32

Tornado from two successive exposures near Elmwood, Neb., April 16, 1919. (After Humphreys.) Photo by G. B. Pickwell

out many of the individual lines of A with the bolometer in a spectrum of sufficient dispersion.

Besides these bands of special absorption by individual gases and vapors of the atmosphere, there is a general weakening all along the spectrum caused by the scattering of light, which Lord Rayleigh first carefully investigated. This effect is very small for deep-red and infra-red rays. Thus, at our station on Mount Montezuma, in Chile, we find that for this infra-red region of the solar spectrum the loss of the direct solar beam due to atmospheric scattering, when the sun is directly overhead, is but two or three per cent. However, as we pass along to the other parts of the spectrum, the yellow, the green, the blue, and the violet, we find the losses greater and greater, and reaching 40 per cent for rays somewhat beyond the last visible violet. These figures are suitable to a mountain station nearly 10,000 feet in elevation. At Washington, near sea-level, we found much greater losses, ranging from about 8 per cent in the infra-red to more than 70 per cent in the ultra-violet.

We shall have occasion, in a later chapter, to explain how we measure the atmospheric scattering. Here we merely desire to point out the fact that red rays "carry" farther, as one would say of a rifle, than blue ones do in the atmosphere. The sun at sunrise or sunset shines very obliquely through the layers of air. The course of its rays in the atmosphere is nearly 20 times as long as it is when the sun is vertically overhead. Hence, we easily understand why the sun looks red near the horizon, for the blue rays have been scattered out of the direct solar beam by the air molecules along the way.

Next to the red, the orange and yellow are best transmitted by the atmosphere. These colors have, too, an advantage, because the eye is more highly sensitive to them than to any others. Figure 17 gives a chart showing the intensity of the effects produced on the eye by equal amounts of energy of different colors in the spectrum.

THE SUN AND THE WELFARE OF MAN

With nearly as favorable atmospheric transmissibility, and with so much greater eye-effectiveness than red rays, it is not surprising that orange yellow predominates during the earlier moments of the grand illuminations of the western sky which come at sunset when the clouds are favorable. A little later, when the sun is altogether set, and its beams illuminate the clouds which we can see only by reflection from others still more distant, the path of the rays in air becomes so very long that even the advantage possessed by yellow rays in their eye-effectiveness cannot overcome the handicap of air losses. Thus, we see only the red in the last sunset glows. Neither green nor blue are noticeable in the sunset because the long path of the sun's rays in air quenches them.

There is still another curious color effect sometimes seen at sunrise or sunset, called the green ray. In order to see it, the sky must be exceptionally clear, and the observer preferably on a mountain where he can look down to his horizon, several thousand feet below his level. In these circumstances, let him avoid the dazzling sun rays until only the thin crescent of the sun remains. It is safer, in order to make sure of this, for him to have a friend to tell him when to begin to look. As the last rim of the crescent sun disappears below the horizon, it looks, not red as just before, but emerald-green. Sometimes the same fine color is seen in the rays of Venus as she sets in like favorable conditions. The green ray may be seen quite as well at sunrise as at sunset, only that one must know just where to look, for then it is seen only just at the instant when the sun's rim begins to peep above the horizon.

The explanation seems to be this: Of all the spectrum rays, light green, after yellow, is next most effective upon the eye, and, though much inferior to red and yellow, yet next after yellow, the atmosphere transmits it best. Hence, if there was some device to cut off for us the red, orange, and yellow for an instant, we should certainly expect to see near the horizon a green sun, not a blue or violet one. There is such a device. It depends on that bending of rays called atmospheric refraction.

Just as an oar seems bent where it passes from the rarer air to the denser water, so the sun rays are bent for us in passing from the rarer upper to the denser lower atmos-

FIG. 20. Apparent oar-bending by water refraction

phere. There is no bending at all for rays in the zenith, but more and more the further we go from it. This bending is noticeable for red rays, but grows more and more considerable as we pass along the spectrum through orange, yellow, and green to blue and violet. When the sun goes below the horizon, its crescent would therefore remain visible longest in violet and blue, if it were not that the eye is so insensitive to these colors. Green, however, next to blue most highly refracted, affects the eye strongly. Hence, we see the sun last in green, after the red and yellow are quite beyond the horizon. So we have the "green ray," but only if the air is transparent enough to let green rays through to us, and if the horizon is low enough to give a pronounced atmospheric refraction. We have spoken several times of the transparency of the atmosphere and how it alters from ray to ray in the spectrum. This subject is so fundamental in the studies of the variation of the sun which we are about to describe that at the risk of being a little tedious we must tell how it is measured. We wish to know, of course, how much the solar beam loses in its pathway through the air.

As evidently one can never ascend above the atmosphere to compare the intensity of the sun's rays there with that which they still retain when they reach the earth's surface, our first thought might be to send a beam of light

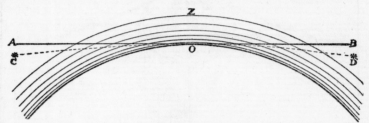

FIG. 21. How atmospheric refraction bends the rays and shows us the sun and stars when they are below the horizon

horizontally between two stations separated so far that the quantity of air between them equals that above us. But this expedient will not do, because the quality of the lower air differs greatly from that which lies above. In the lower air-layers occur all of the dust and nearly all of the water vapor. At higher levels, the air becomes purer and clearer. The transparency of lower layers is no index at all for those which lie above.

The scheme which was invented nearly a hundred years ago for measuring atmospheric transparency depends on the change of length of the path of sun rays in air between morning and noon. In Figures 21 and 22 we represent the scheme crudely. Though the atmosphere is known to extend over a hundred miles high, because meteors and twilight glows are seen there, yet the layer having enough density to scatter light appreciably is not over 40 miles thick. Compared to the earth's radius of over 4,000 miles, this is so thin that in order to show it at all as a covering of a spherical earth, one must represent the curvature of the earth in gross exaggeration in the diagram. But the principle will be understood.

The observer at O (Figure 21) sees the sun rise through the very long path of air, OC. As noon approaches, the path becomes shorter and shorter, and attains its minimum, OZ, when the sun is vertically overhead. This minimum is never fully reached in latitudes outside the tropics, but everywhere the sun shines through the shortest possible path for that station at noonday. In the gradual shortening of the sun's path from sunrise till noon, every layer of air (Figure 22), from the earth's surface to the limit of the atmosphere, takes part. Neglecting a couple of minor corrections depending on the curvature of the earth and atmospheric refraction, the shortening proceeds in the same proportion in all of the horizontal atmospheric layers. Everywhere the length of path is proportional to what mathematicians call the secant of the angle, Z, called the "zenith distance," which measures the separation of the sun from the zenith.

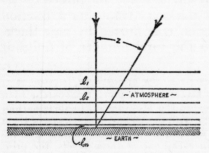

FIG. 22. How the atmosphere scatters light

When the angle of zenith distance is 60°, the atmospheric path, technically called the "air-mass," is twice as long, and at 70° 30′ three times as long as for vertical sun. Now if we can express mathematically the growth of intensity of the solar ray in terms of the decrease in the atmospheric length of path or air-mass, we have found the means of exactly measuring the losses due to the effect of the air.

Nearly two centuries ago, two natural philosophers, Bouguer and Lambert, independently found the expression for loss suffered by light in traversing the atmosphere. They began by considering the progress of light through any homogeneous transparent medium. Suppose the block of the medium to be divided into layers of unit thickness. Let the first layer, l_1, transmit a fraction, a'. This will be very nearly, but not quite, equal to unity. Since the medium is homogeneous, no reason can be assigned why each succeeding layer of unit thickness will not transmit exactly the same fraction of the light which reaches it. Hence, if there are 2 units of thickness, the transmission must be $a' \times a' = a'^2$. Similarly, if there are n units of thickness, the result is a'^n. In this way we find that a layer of any thickness transmits a fraction found by raising the fraction transmitted by unit thickness to a power equal to the total number of units of thickness in the layer.

We cannot apply this law directly to the atmosphere, because it is not homogeneous. The upper layers are far more transparent than the lower ones. But let us divide the atmosphere, in imagination, into so many layers, all concentric with the earth, that each one of them is so thin that no appreciable error is introduced by regarding it individually as homogeneous. In every one of these layers, the principle that we have just developed holds. That is: If a' now represents the fraction of a vertical ray transmitted through one such layer, then for a ray making the angle Z with the vertical, the length of path being secant Z, the transmission fraction becomes $a'^{\sec Z}$. In the next layers, the fractions are similarly $a''^{\sec Z}$, $a'''^{\sec Z}$ . . . up to $a^{n \sec Z}$. The final intensity of the beam after passing obliquely through the entire n layers composing the atmosphere is $a'^{\sec Z} \times a''^{\sec Z} \times \ldots \times a^{n \sec Z}$ or simply $(a' \times a'' \times \ldots \times a^n)^{\sec Z}$. But $(a' \times a'' \times \ldots \times a^n)$ is a quantity which represents the fraction of a ray remaining after being transmitted vertically through the entire atmosphere. We call this α, and name it the "atmospheric transmission coefficient." Hence, if R_0 is the intensity of the beam outside the atmosphere, and R_Z its observed intensity as received at the earth's surface, after oblique transmission, at angular distance Z from the zenith, we have:

$$R_Z = R_0 \, \alpha^{sec\,Z}$$

This is the Law of Bouguer and Lambert, and the key to all of our knowledge of the sun's energy of radiation.

Suppose, now, we have measured R_2 and R_3, corresponding to secant Z = 2 and secant Z = 3, respectively:

Since $R_2 = R_0 \, \alpha^2$ and $R_3 = R_0 \, \alpha^3$, we find immediately by division:

$$\frac{R_3}{R_2} = \frac{\alpha^3}{\alpha^2} = \alpha$$

$$R_0 = \frac{R_2}{\alpha^2}, \text{ in which } R_2 \text{ and } \alpha \text{ are both known.}$$

Here, then, is the way to measure the transparency of the atmosphere, and the intensity of sun rays outside the atmosphere. We have merely to measure the intensities of the rays as they get through to the earth's surface at two different zenith distances of the sun.

There is yet one more complication. The solar beam is not simple and homogeneous. It is made up of rays of widely different penetrating powers for the constituents of our atmosphere. Our formula does not hold good for this complex beam. One can easily see why. There may be one ray which is totally absorbed by some rare gas lying high up in the atmosphere. Ozone, for instance, cuts off utterly all rays of wave-lengths shorter than a certain limit. Such rays never reach the earth's surface at all, and therefore no change in their intensity occurs when the zenith distance diminishes. If they be combined with other rays which do come through, the growth of intensity of the combined beam can never truly indicate to us what was the intensity outside the atmosphere. Other cases of differences of transparency less extreme than this are always occurring. If we should employ Bouguer's formula with complex rays containing

THE SUN AND THE WELFARE OF MAN

constituents of unequal transparency, our coefficients of
atmospheric transmission must always be too high, and
our values of the intensity of the sun's beam outside the
atmosphere too low.

This difficulty can be met only by treating the several
rays composing the sun's spectrum each by itself. This
is why we must employ the bolometer. It is only by
observing the growth of intensity in every part of the
spectrum separately, as the sun mounts in the sky, that
we can come to a true knowledge of the transparency of
the atmosphere and of the sun's contribution of radiation
to our earth.

The Smithsonian Institution has conducted measurements of the sun's radiation and the transparency of the
earth's atmosphere at many stations, and under greatly
differing conditions. From sea-level in the City of Washington to the summit of Mount Whitney at 4,500 meters
(14,500 feet); in the United States, Algeria, and Chile; in
humid mid-summer at Washington and in the driest
winter conditions of a high mountain in the Atacama
Desert in Chile; at temperatures so oppressively high as
almost to stop the work owing to the exhaustion of the
observers, and again so low that fingers and toes were
actually frozen in making the observations; in the purest
of mountain skies and underneath the thick haze cast up
by the volcanic outburst of Mount Katmai; year after
year throughout a period of almost a quarter of a century
these measurements have been continued. In Chapter VII
we shall examine where the investigation is now leading.

CHAPTER VI

A DAY IN THE FIELD

WE are upon Mount Harqua Hala, Arizona, over a mile above the sea. The sunlight streams through our eastern windows and awakens us to a new day. As we look out from our desert mountain camp, there is not a cloud to be seen. Standing just above the horizon, already the sun has lost the redness which clings to its face so long in murky city atmospheres, and the sky is deep blue, not whitish, as it almost always is, even on the fairest of days, in the Eastern States. A little later in the morning, if one hides the solar disk by holding the tip of a single finger at arm's length before his eyes, the deep blue sky color holds right up to the edge of the sun itself.

While one observer prepares a bit of breakfast, the other gets ready the instruments. The coelostat is uncovered. Its mirrors are breathed upon and polished off with clean hospital cotton, to remove the trace of cloudiness that forms upon them, even though they are of stellite. A beam of sunlight is reflected into the observing chamber. It is carefully adjusted until a single ray forms its pinhole image of the sun within a little circle, drawn with India ink on a bit of cardboard, ten feet back on the wall of the observing chamber. This is our guiding image. All through the observations, we must take care to keep it exactly central with the inked circle, so that the main sunbeam will enter the spectroscope squarely.

Before attending to the adjustments within the observatory, we carry out of doors the stand holding its two silver-disk pyrheliometers and its pyranometer, and train these instruments also upon the sun. The theodolite, for observing the sun's altitude above the horizon, is also

[121]

made ready for measurements. All of these out-of-door instruments, as used at all our stations are shown in Plate 29. Having connected the wires which lead from the pyranometer to the electrical instruments inside of the observatory, we make a preliminary trial of the pyranometer. This we do by opening its shutter to let in the sky rays which fall within its limited field of view surrounding the sun. The galvanometer responds with a swing of about 50 divisions. All is well.

Next, we open the spectroscope, and having set it upon the head of great "A," the oxygen band in the extreme red spectrum, we look to see that this dark band falls centrally upon the sensitive strip of the bolometer, that the focus is correct, and that the band is sharply defined. Occasionally, but not often, a slight improvement in these respects is possible.

Now we close the shutter before the spectroscope slit, and go back to the farther end of our observing chamber, where stands the galvanometer. A little beam of sunlight enters the corner of this chamber, passes through a slit there, is twice reflected, and falls upon the tiny galvanometer mirror. We look for its reflection on the scale of the plate-carrier. Ah! There it is, just a bit off below the zero. We bring it on with the magnet. Next, the switch is closed to connect in the bolometer, but very gingerly! If anything has gone wrong, the spot of light will fly away as if on the wings of the wind, and as likely as not the needle system of the galvanometer will turn quite around on account of this rude shock to a thing so sensitive. But no! Hardly on one day out of fifty is there more than a hundred divisions' swing of the light spot upon the scale when we close the switch. Think what this means. No change of temperature of one bolometer strip with respect to the other as great as $1/10,000$ of one degree has happened in the 24 hours since yesterday's observing. Yet both strips are heated by the electric current to fully 60 degrees above their surroundings.

A DAY IN THE FIELD

We make a small change in the balancing resistance. The spot of light swings back to zero. Then we set the third rotating sector to spinning in front of the slit, and open the shutter of the spectroscope. The spot of light swings out. We turn a wheel of the clock slowly and note the largest excursion. It is 7.5 centimeters. This is exactly what we desire at this early hour of the morning, for it presages 9 or 10 centimeters later on, at highest sun, which will be just right to accommodate six bolographic curves to our photographic record plate.

The exacting stage of the preparations is now past. We close the shutter, stop the rotating sector, and insert a photographic plate to record the galvanometer. We swing the light-spot across it near one end, to mark its axis of ordinates, and set the plate up to the top position, ready to begin. Finally, we set the spectroscope to the place in the spectrum where we wish to start.

All being in readiness, we go in to breakfast, which has meanwhile been made ready by our colleague. He has also found time to set the page in the record book, placing over it another sheet and carbon-paper, so as to get not only a fixed record in the book, but a movable one which is to be mailed to Washington.

As soon as breakfast is over, it is time to observe. The sun now stands about one hour high. From time to time, one observer takes exact altitudes of the sun at carefully recorded instants, in order to know the lengths of atmospheric path of the sun rays throughout the period of measurement. The same observer reads the two pyrheliometers.

Our habit of reading for these instruments involves noting the temperature on the following numbered minutes and seconds: $0^m 20^s$; $2^m 0^s$; $2^m 20^s$; $4^m 0^s$; $4^m 20^s$; $6^m 0^s$. This series of six readings makes one complete observation, but often we duplicate or triplicate it by going on at $6^m 20^s$; $8^m 0^s$; and so on. The reader will see that the intervals between readings are 100^s, 20^s, 100^s, 20^s, 100^s, and so on, with long and short intervals alternately, while the instrument is first shaded, then exposed, then shaded, in alternation, over 2-minute intervals. No use is made of the short 20^s intervals. These are introduced merely in order to permit the thermometer to pass its turning points and come to regular conditions of steady change at the boundary instants of the defining readings. As it is possible to read another pyrheliometer on the odd minutes without conflicting, we are able to obtain in this way a fine check on the work. The same observer, therefore, reads the second pyrheliometer at the instants 1^m20^s; 3^m0^s; 3^m20^s; 5^m0^s; 5^m20^s; 7^m0^s; and as much longer as desirable.

A novice does not make a great success of silver-disk pyrheliometer observations. It seems to him as if the seconds gallop by. Things go wrong. When he should open the shutter to the sun, he perhaps leaves it closed, while when he ought merely to read the thermometer, he inadvertently closes the shutter. All the more vexatious are these slips if they happen towards the end of an observation, after four or five minutes of reading, for then one must begin all over again, though the proper time to begin has passed away forever. The sun will never occupy again on that day the place in the sky where it should have been during that observation. It is not only necessary to read the thermometer, record the readings, open and close the shutter, but the instrument must be kept pointing exactly towards the sun, or the results will be too low.

Far more trying than all of these preoccupations is the extreme accuracy that must be attained. The head of the mercury column is rapidly moving in the thermometer stem. Its total rise of temperature during 100 seconds is usually less than 3.5 degrees. This rise of temperature requires six readings to determine it, and must be fixed to an accuracy of about 1/3 of one per cent, or 1/100 degree. The theory of error tells us that the individual readings must have accuracy to the order of 1/250 degree, in order that a combination of six of them can be accurate to 1/100 degree. Moreover, the observer must get this accuracy by reading a thermometer graduated only to tenths of degrees, and observing on a rapidly moving mercury column. Furthermore, the exact instants of making the readings must be correct to about 1/5 second, in order to get the desired accuracy in the final result.

It looks impossible. A foreign scientific writer has lately written a paper in criticism of our work in which he says outright that it is impossible. Yet comparisons of pyrheliometers by skilled observers, working exactly simultaneously, show that it is not impossible, but that actually it is usual to get observations accurate to 1/3 of one per cent with the silver-disk pyrheliometer. The reader unaccustomed to scientific observing may ease his mind in accepting so astounding a claim, by reflecting upon the perfectly well-known ability of pianists and pipe-organ players to read at sight, and execute unerringly, music of staggering difficulty, involving a perfectly astonishing cooperation of brain, eyes, and hands. Admirable, indeed, is the capacity of the human organs, and wonder-working is the virtue of practice in all of the arts!

Five sets of pyrheliometer observations are usually made on each observing day. The earliest ones are separated by short intervals of about 10 minutes, for then the length of the path of sun rays is changing rapidly. Later on, the intervals are longer, and at last a full hour elapses between sets. The other observer has done his share, too. Each time the pyrheliometer series is made, there is also a 7-minute run of the spectroscope, producing its spectral energy curve, or bolograph of the solar spectrum. Here, too, care must be taken. The pinhole solar image must stand exactly central in the guide-circle. Shutter closing and opening, the insertion of rotating sectors, and the starting and stopping of the runs, must all be done exactly at the right instants.

Altogether, there are about sixteen of these exact instants, within the 7 minutes of run, when something has to be done, and always the right thing, else a more or less unfortunate consequence will occur. But this is not the whole story, for during the run this observer must also make and record electrical measurements. These determine the sky brightness with the pyranometer about five times successively. These measurements also have to be carefully timed so as to avoid encroaching on the exact instants for making the dispositions above-mentioned. In all of this complexity of duties, one must be sure to remember to keep guiding the little pinhole solar image exactly on its circle, for otherwise all is in vain.

There are many satisfactions to the interested observer in these routines. It is like a game or a puzzle to see the observations work up into a perfect whole. Every pyrheliometer reading affords its moment of expectancy and gratification if it falls in nicely with the series. The bolometric observer has rather less to carry along his interest during the observations, although for him the agreement among pyranometer readings is always to be looked for. At the end of the morning, when he develops the photographic plate, and sees his five or six curves beautifully superposed, with never a mistake marring their similarity, he has a little moment of exultation.

During the intervals between observations, there are always some camp duties to attend to. The hens, the dog, the horse, all have their demands. Then there is wood and water to be gotten, and probably some little repair job that needs attention. We must never forget, either, that "all work and no play makes Jack a dull boy." A little game at throwing the horseshoes, with the excitement perhaps of some double-ringers, puts a zest into the mind which is very needful to support us in the rather dull grind of calculation, which must be taken up at once, after the observations are ended.

Maybe someone has found a story, and cheers the company just at this time by repeating it. For instance:

There was once a poor weaver in the Orient who was dragged before the Cadi charged with having put a man's eye out. The Cadi examined the law. It was very plain: "An eye for an eye, and a tooth for a tooth." So he directed that one of the weaver's eyes should be sacrificed. The poor man pleaded hard. He said he had many children and was obliged to push the shuttle this way and that very diligently to support them. He needed both eyes for his business, but his neighbor, the gunner, needed only one, and could spare an eye as well as not to meet the law's demands.

The Cadi directed that the gunner should be called, and asked him to illustrate his profession. Sure enough, the gunner closed his left eye as he squinted along the barrel of his gun. So the Cadi saw that the weaver was right, and directed that the gunner's left eye should be removed. He saw also that the gunner's eyes were nearly of the same color as his own. Now it happened that the Cadi himself had lost an eye and, not to waste so good an opportunity, he directed that, when removed, the gunner's eye should be inserted in his own head, to replace the one he had lost.

The surgeon made ready the head of the Cadi, extracted the eye of the gunner, and was about to insert it in the head of the Cadi, when by mischance he dropped it upon the floor. A cat, which was going by, seized the eye and made off with it. Though the surgeon quickly chased the cat, he was too late, for just as he overtook the cat it swallowed the eye. Yet, being a man of quick wit, the surgeon extracted an eye of the cat, and inserted it in the head of the Cadi and bandaged it.

After a suitable time had elapsed, the surgeon unbound the head of the Cadi and asked him how he saw. "Why, excellently well," said the Cadi, "and yet with certain peculiarities. For whereas with the eye I had formerly I see just as before, with my new eye I see nothing but rat holes!"

This story was recently told to a gentleman in a certain city, who appeared much interested, but not at all amused. "How remarkable!" said he at the end. "I was not aware that surgery, especially in the Orient, had reached such excellence as to attain success in transplanting the eye."

If a fundamental or "long-method" solar-constant observation is to be worked through, in addition to obtaining the five short-method values, it requires the whole remainder of the day from 10 o'clock a.m. to 7 o'clock p.m. for computing, excepting the time needed for getting dinner and supper, and eating them. This long test occurs at least one day in a week, if sky conditions warrant. On other days of "short method" only, the computing is over soon after noon. Reports, correspondence, study, improvements of the apparatus and buildings, or special observations of various sorts fill the daylight hours.

There are some computations which are done alike for all days, whether the fundamental long method of Langley is being used, or the short method based upon it. In the first place, there is the pyrheliometry. One subtracts his readings made at the beginning and end of the hundred-second periods, adds to the rise of temperature during sun exposure the average fall during shading before and after, and checks every figure of his work. Then, corresponding to the mean temperature indicated by the thermometer during sun exposure, there is a small correction depending on the irregularities of the thermometer bore, the variation of the capacity for heat of silver, and other considerations. These little corrections are found in a table which is provided with each pyrheliometer. Finally, there is a correction depending on the eccentricity of the second-hand's circle of the observer's watch relative to the second-hand's pinion.

The next task is to find the length of path of the sun rays in air, which we call the air-mass. This is given

PLATE 33

Field outfit, two pyrheliometers and pyranometer, for measuring sun and sky rays. Left to right, Messrs. L. B. Aldrich, C. G. Abbot, and A. Kramer, the latter the instrument maker of the Astrophysical Observatory

PLATE 34

Director Moore using special time-saving instruments to reduce observations at the Smithsonian observatory on Table Mountain, Calif. The plate-measuring instrument is at the left, the slide rule extrapolater at the right with all corrections for curvature of the earth, atmospheric density, and so forth, in a prepared table. In that table one has to find the values corresponding to the observed heights of the sun, and make therefrom an accurate curve to represent the air-masses of the day in terms of time of observation.

While one observer is attending to all the foregoing computations, the other, using India ink, draws upon the glass record plate, or bolographic plate as we call it, smooth curves representing the unaffected height of the bolographic curves. For these spectral curves contain characteristic indentations, caused by the absorption of several kinds of gases existing in the earth's atmosphere and the sun. We should call some of the little nicks "Fraunhofer lines" in an ordinary photographic spectrum, and the greater ones would be called "absorption bands." In our work, we are desiring to get measures of the intensity all through the spectrum, as it was in free space, before atmospheric gases and vapors produced absorption bands.

After this is done, the observer next takes the plate to a special measuring machine which we have devised for this particular purpose. He measures thereon the heights of all the curves, usually six in number, at nearly 40 evenly spaced intervals. It makes about 240 measurements in all. This seems a large task in the telling, but compared to the innumerable readings of the galloping spot of light on the galvanometer scale of Langley's Mount Whitney expedition, it is simplicity itself.

All of the readings having been entered in their appropriate columns, opposite the air-masses which were derived from the observations of the height of the sun, the next step is to correct each reading to what it would have been if the optical apparatus had been equally transmissive for every color and ray of the spectrum. All of the numbers in the columns must be multiplied by certain known factors of instrumental loss.

This done, a summation of each corrected column is made. This gives the approximate area which would have been included under each bolographic curve if it had been taken with perfectly transmissive apparatus. We determine these areas because they are proportional to the total energy of the solar beam at the earth's surface. They are proportional because they sum up the average intensities of the radiant energy of all wavelengths. After removing the corrected areas included in the absorption bands under the "smooth curves," they should also be proportional to the reduced observations of total energy which were made with the pyrheliometer. Hence, by dividing pyrheliometer readings by corrected areas, we find a quantity which should be nearly constant. It is this factor by which any bolographic area of the day is to be multiplied to reduce its indications to the units of energy called calories.

There are, however, small departures of these factor-ratios from equality. These departures indicate slight alterations of sensitiveness of the bolographic apparatus during the morning. They, in fact, yield us little corrections to be applied to every reduced measurement of height in the bolographic curves.

Formerly, we used to apply these little corrections individually to all of the 240 numbers, take logarithms of them all, and plot, on immense cross-section papers, all of the logarithmic values so obtained against corresponding air-masses. About the year 1917, a better plan was devised. We prepared an instrument with 8 sixteen-inch slide-rules, such as the engineers use. As their scales are logarithmic, we no longer require to take logarithms. By using their little sliding pieces as our defining scales, we can even apply the little corrections to all of the observations automatically. In this way about 16 hours of computing are saved for every day of observation.

By setting up all of the observations on this wizard-like slide-rule instrument, we can determine in one hour just what disposition of spectral energy the bolometer would have indicated if we could have used it outside the atmosphere altogether. At the same time, we determine the coefficients of atmospheric transparency at all of the forty places in the spectrum.

Not to be tedious with further details, we shall merely say that we sum up the area of the bolographic curve which thus we make outside our atmosphere. Of course, we can never go there in the flesh to observe it, but the mind, that magic carpet, has easily transported us with our observatory to free space. Multiplying the extra-atmospheric area by the factor of energy of the bolometer, as above explained, we obtain in calories the intensity of the sun's heat as it is outside our atmosphere. Making allowance for the position of the earth in its elliptical orbit, we reduce this value to mean solar distance, and obtain the "solar constant of radiation."

Such is the fundamental, or, as we say, the long method. It requires about three hours of observing and seven hours of computing by two observers to complete a single solar-constant determination. That makes a very full day. In 1919, we introduced our short method, based on the long one, but cutting down the time of observing for a single determination to 10 minutes, and of computing to one hour. In 1923, we made a further abbreviation of the computing. Two observers can now make five complete sets of observations, and fully reduce them, all within 4 hours.

We gain thereby in many ways. Five independent measurements per day instead of one; the measurements independent of gradual changes of the transparency of the sky; the opportunities to make errors in computing diminished nearly tenfold; inaccuracies of marking and measuring of plates minimized—with such advantages it is no wonder that the final accuracy of our results has been greatly augmented. Yet the brief methods are not fundamental. If the atmosphere should suddenly be altered in its character, as when Mount Katmai belched forth its charge of volcanic dust over the whole Northern Hemisphere, in 1912, the foundations of our new method would be swept away. Hence, we do not forsake the old, but use it once or twice each week, so as to keep a check on the accuracy of the new one.

Occasional visits to town must be undertaken. At Mount Harqua Hala, these required a two-hour journey down the steep trail, and a one-hour auto ride. The return journey during the night hours required even more time and exertion. At Montezuma, the journey is all by auto, and done in a little over an hour each way. But there the water supply as well as the purchasing of provisions must always be attended to. Water is transported in barrels, filled at the ranch of the friendly Mr. Drummond in Calama. The return auto trip at night, when the clear mountain atmosphere has chilled the desert, is always, even in summer, a cold drive, and in winter a very uncomfortable one.

Solar observers are not angelic always. But with music, books, periodicals, and games, there is much to keep life interesting in our desert stations besides the work. The radio helps greatly. Men of the right sort, realizing their duty, try to be as companionable and entertaining as they may. They endeavor to recall a good story, or a quaint recollection from the cells of memory, to start a laugh at dinner.

Once in a while something funny happens all by itself. In the early days at Harqua Hala, the writer shot a skunk that was wandering about the premises. Mr. F. A. Greeley, who knew how, skinned the animal. Its flesh looked so attractive that the writer proposed cooking it. So we cleaned it with extreme care, avoiding entirely any disagreeable odor. The proper dish seemed to be a stew, which was prepared with potatoes and seasoning, as if made of rabbit or chicken. During the evening, the stew was cooked slowly over the reading lamp for hours, and warmed up on the next day for dinner. I helped Mr. Greeley to a nice piece of the meat, with a generous dish of gravy and potato. As he tasted the first mouthful I asked him if he liked it. I am not likely to forget the expression of his face as he replied, "I can't really say that I do." After trying a mouthful myself, I entirely agreed with him. We threw the remainder as far as we could over the edge of a cliff for less squeamish animals than ourselves to feast upon.

On these high peaks, where the horizon is far away, the colors of sunrise and sunset contribute a lovely embellishment to crown the day. I have tried to put a description of such a sunset into a sort of blank verse, which I offer with apologies for its poetical character, but a claim for its accuracy of statement. It is as follows:

SUNSET FROM MOUNT HARQUA HALA

The sun stoops low upon his course
And silv'ry clouds are tinged with gold.
The east is faintly rose-suffused,
Like pleaséd blush on faded cheek,
Surprised by loving praises earned.
Stand sharp the purple-shadowed peaks
'Gainst desert background softly brown.
The sinking sun's last ray of green,
Like em'rald glitters through yon notch.
Exub'rant glory westward spreads;
On blue the gold-touched crimson blends.
The little clouds have fairy forms.
Attired in iridescent hues
They rollick side by side.
But see! there creeps above the east
The shroudlike shadow of old Earth.
No longer glow the rose-tones there;
The west has lost its gold in red.
As darker nears the night apace
A second recrudescent gleam,
Like Indian summer after June,
Brings colors richer, quieter.
At length 'tis gone; the twilight fades
To night, and stars in glory shine.

We have described an ordinary observing day, but in such places as our observatories must be located, in order to get the necessary sky conditions, there sometimes arise emergencies that call for work quite out of the ordinary. Such a case happened in December, 1920, at Harqua Hala. The building there had been erected of "adobe" or dried mud bricks, made upon the top of the mountain, in order to avoid the great cost of transporting building material up the dangerous trail. At the south end of the observatory, the wall is two stories and a half in height. The building was erected in July and August, 1920, occupied late in September, and by November the south wall had cracked away from the side walls at the corners, owing to the drying out and settling together of the mud bricks.

At that time, we used to communicate with Wenden, 16 miles away, by flashing signals, either of sunlight by day, or brilliant lamplight by night. We employed the telegraphic code of dots and dashes. About November 20, a message came in the night requiring my immediate return to Washington. After observing briefly the next morning, I ran down the trail, caught the freight train at Wenden, and arrived in Washington on Thanksgiving Day. Returning, I arrived in Wenden on December 13.

My young assistant, Mr. F. A. Greeley, met me at Wenden station, having walked the whole 16 miles from the top of Mount Harqua Hala. He was very dispirited. During a great wind, the outside plaster covering had fallen from a large section of the south wall of the observatory, had tipped over the theodolite, which was standing nearby, and broken off its main axle, besides bending other parts. While observing with the wet and dry thermometers, the chain had broken as Mr. Greeley was whirling them, and the thermometers had landed in fragments, 20 feet away. To cap all, Mr. Ellison, our kind miner-neighbor, had left the mountain for the winter, so that Greeley had been up there all alone for over two weeks, with no one nearer than Wenden.

A DAY IN THE FIELD

After a night's rest, we started for the top. We transported to the foot of the mountain a lot of ten-foot steel rods, intended to tie the two end walls of the observatory together, but we did not attempt to carry them up the trail on that day. We reached the top before noon. As I entered the south room of the living quarters, which occupy the floor above the observatory, a bird flew out through the crack between the south wall and the ceiling! In my twenty-day absence, the wall had sagged outwards, leaving a crack nearly 3 inches wide at the top of the building. Obviously there was little time to lose before bringing up the steel tie-rods. However, as I wished very much to observe the sun on the next morning, I spent the afternoon and evening in repairing the theodolite.

With a breast-drill, I made two large screw holes endwise through the broken axle, tapped them, and screwed the axle together with two long machine screws. I had first "tinned" the broken ends, and also filed a groove all around the break, so that I could strengthen the job with soldering. But the mended axle was not straight at first. It had to be connected to other parts, tested, pulled apart and adjusted, and this again and again for fully a dozen times, before the levels ceased to drift when rotated. Patience and care at last prevailed, and a little bending and dressing of the other injured parts put the theodolite by evening in very good shape, so that it has served well ever since.

After observing the sun on the next morning, we ran down the five-mile trail to get the steel. There were no animals of burden on the mountain, so that we were proposing to lug the load up ourselves. We started bravely, each shouldering his bundle of 80 pounds of steel, and trudging up the steep trail. But it was not to be done so. Giants might have been able to do it, but not astronomers!

After a quarter of a mile we gave up that method, and tried each carrying one end of the combined bundles.

[135]

Much worse! So we left half and carried the rest of the steel a hundred steps, laid it down and returned for the balance. It was discouraging to have to walk back after a trip forward over that steep trail. However, in this way we kept up until 4 o'clock of the short December day. We had reached a point only about one-third of the way up the five-mile trail. So I said to Greeley, "We must leave the steel and come back tomorrow, if we are to sleep on top tonight."

We did so, but long before we reached the top I was completely exhausted. The reader must recollect that for a middle-aged man of sedentary life to climb a mountain a mile high on one day, run down it, and carry his half of 160 pounds of steel one-third of the way up on the next, is pretty fatiguing. At any rate, being "all in," I had to lie down in the trail every one hundred steps. It became dark and cold. We had still nearly a mile to go. Greeley offered to go up and bring me some hot soup, and I agreed. But after he had been gone some time, a little strength came to me, and I reached the observatory just before he was ready to return.

That night, a scheme occurred to me. Fortunately, the next morning was cloudy. Instead of observing, I made a loaf of graham bread. We took cocoa, bread, meat, and apples, and two ropes with us, and started down again about 10 o'clock. The food we hid at the spring, about half-way down. Arriving where we had left the steel, we made it into two bundles, and fastened them together at each end with a length of rope between. The slack rope was just long enough to go over a man's shoulders and support both bundles of steel, one on either side, just at arm's length. Thus, with one man at each end, standing between the bundles slung from his shoulders, we started upward. We rested every 100 steps, and now we began to be encouraged with our easy progress. We reached the spring at noon, had a fine hot lunch, and full of courage started up the steep upper half of the trail.

PLATE 35

The Earl of Rosse, who constructed the great telescope at
Parsonstown, Ireland, where important studies of the nebulæ
went on nearly a century ago. (Courtesy of Sir William
Parsons)

A DAY IN THE FIELD

All went well. We reached the observatory at 4 o'clock, ate supper, and then felt so keen for enterprise that we drilled two holes through the south wall by moonlight, before going to bed. The next morning was fair, and we observed the sun. Immediately afterwards, we drilled the north wall, and just before noon we had the satisfaction of screwing up the turn buckles, and bringing back the south observatory wall to plumb, thus closing the crack through which the bird had flown two days before.

This is but a sample of doings, quite apart from ordinary observing, which have fallen to the lot of my colleagues and myself in carrying on the solar-radiation work. Far away from the services of mechanics or servants, the observer must make his own repairs and serve himself. He must be scullion, cook, housekeeper, chambermaid, laundress, wood-chopper, carpenter, tinsmith, mechanic, and instrument maker, besides being a highly skilled observer and exact computer. Above all, he must be a good companion, and keep up a cheerful courage. Far away, sometimes, from Washington headquarters, and in alien lands, he must conduct himself so as to make friends by his tact, squareness, and companionableness, and uphold at the same time his dignity and the continuity of his work.

CHAPTER VII

SOLAR VARIATION AND WEATHER

THE earth is kept warm by the sun. Its snows and showers are produced by that gigantic distilling plant in which the oceans furnish the crude liquid, the sun supplies the heat, and the earth's revolutions and rotations bring about the differences in temperature. As for the barometer, it too responds to the sun's heat-changes in the regular march of day and night, summer and winter, as the atmosphere warms and cools. Because the earth is very complex, with its oceans, deserts, mountains, clouds, winds, ocean currents, and all sorts of obscure interrelations, even these regularly recurring changes produce in the weather elements, temperature, precipitation and barometer, a perfect maze of fluctuations far too complicated to unravel by theory. Yet on the top of all these, as we now know, the sun's radiation, the prime mover in the whole complex reaction, is itself variable through a range of several per cent. Are these solar variations important in weather control? If so, are they predictable?

As there are still some scientific men of eminence who are unconvinced that the sun really varies at all, we shall defer the answer to these questions long enough to assemble some of the proofs of solar variation. They are numerous and mutually support each other, so that when brought together they make up a bundle of evidence very difficult to gainsay. We can refer to only a few of them here.

To begin with, Figure 23 shows the march of monthly mean values of the so-called solar constant of radiation ac-

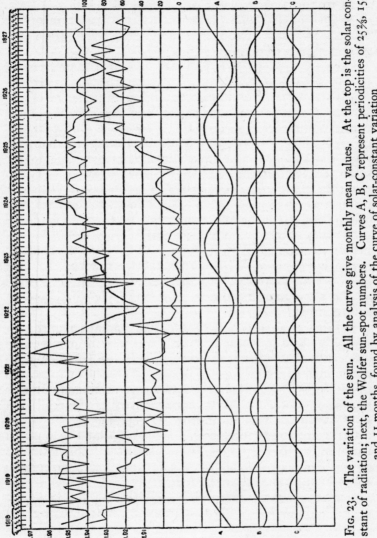

FIG. 23.   The variation of the sun.   All the curves give monthly mean values.   At the top is the solar constant of radiation; next, the Wolfer sun-spot numbers.   Curves A, B, C represent periodicities of 25⅔, 15, and 11 months, found by analysis of the curve of solar-constant variation

cording to Smithsonian observations in Chile for the years 1918 to 1927. The wavy curve, now rising, now falling, shows very well, as we believe, the real variation of the solar heat which has been available to warm the earth during this period of over nine years.

Let us compare these fluctuations with the progress of visible activity seen telescopically on the sun's surface. The second curve of Figure 23 shows the change of the Wolfer monthly mean sun-spot numbers for the same period. We seem to see that during these nine years increased solar radiation attends increased numbers of visible sun-spots. We have much more evidence to the same effect. Figure 24 shows the relation between monthly mean solar-constant values observed from our Chilean stations and the Wolfer sun-spot numbers corresponding, covering the years 1918 to 1927. The curve shows increased solar radiation with increased numbers of visible sun-spots. The relation is not a simple or, as we say, a linear one. When sun-spots are few the curve of radiation rises rapidly, but its rise grows less and less rapid as the sun-spots grow more and more plentiful, and at length slowly declines.

A third comparison between solar radiation and sun-spottedness is given in Figure 25, which is confined to observations made on Mount Wilson, in California, in the month of July, 1910 to 1920.[1] This shows increased radiation attending increased sun-spot numbers. It also shows something still more confirmatory of the reality of solar variation, which will now be explained.

Critics of the Smithsonian conclusion that the sun is a variable star based their objections on their conviction of an insuperable difficulty in allowing for atmospheric absorption. The observer, they truly said, stands underneath an ocean of atmosphere, containing haze, water-vapor, and other variable constituents. Not only do these

[1] The years 1912, 1913 are omitted because of the influence of volcanic dust from Mount Katmai, Alaska, which erupted furiously in June, 1912, and enveloped the Northern Hemisphere with a turbid atmosphere.

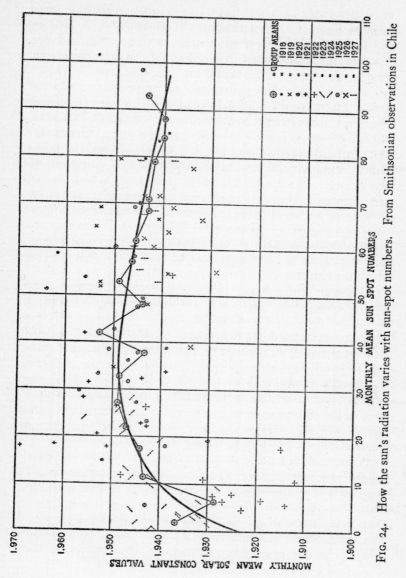

FIG. 24. How the sun's radiation varies with sun-spot numbers. From Smithsonian observations in Chile

vary from day to day, but even in the same day, be it ever so fine, and even though the station be located on the best-selected desert mountain in the world. Hence, changes in atmospheric transparency, these critics contend, may vitiate solar-radiation measurements. Apparent solar changes, they claim, may really be atmospheric.

For many years we had pointed out many evidences tending to support the reality of solar variation, but without fully convincing our critics. In May, 1925,[2] however, a new and simple test was applied which seemed to many minds conclusive. To understand this test, suppose the observer could take his stand on the moon, which has no atmosphere to dim the sun rays. He would then require only daily accurate measurements of the total intensity of solar heating to reveal any solar changes. These measurements he could readily make with the silver-disk pyrheliometer, always assuming that he could live and observe at all on the moon.

Although the observer on the earth has not these advantages, and must look through an atmosphere, it would be of no disadvantage to him provided it retained always unchanged transparency. For though the total heat of the solar ray would in that case be reduced in passing through the atmosphere, it would be reduced every day in the same proportion. Accordingly, pyrheliometer measurements on the earth, if taken at moments of equal atmospheric transparency, would still exhibit the same percentage of variation from day to day as if they had been made on the moon, where there is no atmosphere.

While it is not possible to find any station on the earth where the atmosphere remains absolutely unchanged in transparency forever, it is possible to select moments during a great many days when it has equal transparency. Again we may select moments of still other days when the atmospheric transparency, though less or greater than prevails in the first group of days, is still uniformly less,

[2] See *Monthly Weather Review*, May, 1925.

or uniformly greater. Thus a large part of the days of observation can be arranged in a number of series, and within each series, taken by itself, the pyrheliometric readings will exhibit truly the percentage change of the sun from day to day.

In the selection of a series of such moments, we of course confine ourselves to one station of observation, and the first care is to have the sun at the same altitude above the horizon, so that the thickness of the atmosphere will be unchanged. The next is to restrict ourselves to the same month of the year, so that the temperature conditions of the atmosphere and of the apparatus will be nearly the same. The third consideration is that the atmosphere contains the same quantity of water-vapor. To insure this we must restrict our choice to days when the spectrum shows equal water-vapor absorption, that is equality of form in the great infra-red bands due to moisture, for identical solar altitudes. Finally, the haziness of the at-mosphere must be unchanged. To insure this we reject days, though passing the other tests, when the successive observations taken during the day show unequal increases of transmission for equal decreases of air-mass.

This program is so exacting that it can be followed only on excellent mountain stations. Our first trial of it was made with Mount Wilson observations for the month of July of the years 1910 to 1920. It was quickly found that the years 1912 and 1913 must be omitted, because the erupting Mount Katmai rendered the atmosphere too hazy to compare with other years. The remaining years proved available, and for them the final average march of the values of the selected pyrheliometric readings in the successive July's is as given in the single full-line curve of Figure 25. Taking the average march for the same days, as shown by our published solar-constant results, we obtained the dotted curve. Except in 1914, when a discrepancy of about 1 per cent is seen, the two curves are in excellent agreement, and both show a solar variation of over 2 per cent, very harmonious in form with the curve of sun-spot numbers, shown by the double full line.

Thus the simple test of observing with constant atmospheric transparency supports well the evidence of solar variability, which had already been obtained for the

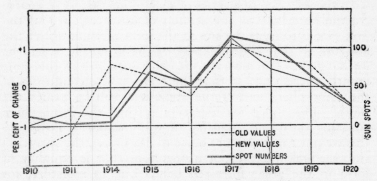

FIG. 25. Ten years of solar variation from Mount Wilson observations, and the corresponding march of sun-spot numbers

month of July, 1910 to 1920, on Mount Wilson. We next applied the same test to every month of the year, with Montezuma observations from 1920 to 1926. Again the selected pyrheliometry supports remarkably closely the solar-constant work already published. There is, besides, a certain similarity of variation as compared with the sun-spot numbers, though not (for all months) so close as in the July series of 1910 to 1920.

These results being so satisfactory, we may next consider an entirely different confirmation of solar variation. Believing, as we have for many years, that solar variation really exists, we desired to know whether the energy of rays of all colors partook of it in equal proportions, or whether solar changes inclined to larger percentages in short-wave rays than in longer ones, as theory would lead us to expect. I say theory would lead us to expect this, because, if the sun increases its brightness sometimes by virtue of a higher temperature, and sometimes by virtue of a more transparent exterior, in either case the percentage effect would be greater for shorter wavelengths. Laboratory experiments on temperature and radiation, and Lord Rayleigh's explanation of the blue of the sky show this to be true.

Accordingly we selected two groups of days for which the solar-constant values were respectively high and low, and differed in their means by 2.3 per cent. Our observa-

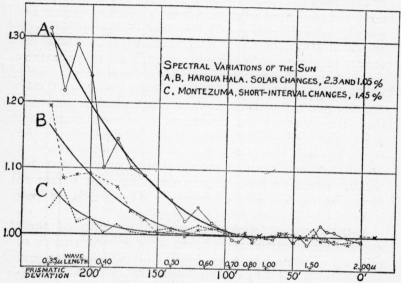

FIG. 26. The solar variations increase towards the ultra-violet

tions yielded the relative intensities of radiation in all wave-lengths outside our atmosphere for each day. Taking the average of these indications for the high group and the low group separately, we divided the former set by the latter, and so obtained the percentage of change from low to high solar condition for each wave-length separately. These percentages are given in Figure 26. Evidently the percentage change grows greater the shorter the wave-length, and is almost nothing at all for rays of longer wave-length than the yellow. Our curve extends considerably beyond the limit of the spectrum seen by the eye in the violet, but stops quite a little short of the extreme limit of the solar spectrum observable on the earth. We should therefore predict still greater changes in this farthest region of spectrum.

In this ultra-violet region beyond our observing limit, Doctor Pettit of Mount Wilson Observatory has lately determined the solar variation. He has employed to form his solar image a silvered quartz lens, opaque to all other rays except the narrow band of ultra-violet rays whose intensity he observes. We should expect, if our own observations of the solar variation are sound, that Pettit would not only discover solar variation in the ultra-violet, but find its percentage change very much greater than our own determinations of change in total solar radiation. We might even predict, considering the rapid rise of the curve towards the violet, that he might find changes of about 100 per cent. Yet we should expect that his results would confirm ours by showing high values of ultra-violet solar-radiation intensity when we found high values of total solar-radiation intensity.

Pettit's results give confirmation of both of these expectations. Although dealing with a solar change of only 1.5 per cent, as against Pettit's ultra-violet change of 60 per cent, yet when our monthly mean curve and his are made to the same scale of height, their general correspondence is very obvious. Details differ, but not more than the difficulties of the work might fairly lead us to ascribe to accidental errors. Individual days, as Pettit found, show changes exceeding 100 per cent.

In view of all these evidences, it seems unquestionable that the sun really varies, and that in the mean monthly values over a series of years the range of total solar radiation reaches at least 3 per cent. Highest values occur when sun-spots are most numerous. Solar radiation increases faster with increasing sun-spots when the total sun-spot numbers are small, than when they are large. The change of solar radiation increases towards shorter wave-lengths. Indeed, if our eyes could see the ultraviolet rays measured by Pettit, we should find the sun nearly twice as bright in some months as in others.

So much for average monthly results. We next inquire whether the march of solar change is gradual or irregular, and, if the latter, whether daily changes may not even exceed monthly mean changes. At first thought, one is apt to suppose there can be nothing but gradual changes in total radiation of a body so tremendous as the sun, which is over 800,000 miles in diameter. But to conclude this is to lose sight of the possibilities attending solar rotation. The sun rotates on its axis in about four weeks, so that we look every day on a new twenty-sixth part of its surface, and see all the visible parts in a changed aspect. Remembering the irregularities of the outer solar envelopes, as photographed at eclipses (see Plate 67), it is reasonable to expect some variation of total solar radiation as these irregularities turn in succession towards the earth in the course of the solar rotation.

Our solar-constant observations show on their face an irregular solar variation from day to day as given in Figures 27 and 28. In Figure 27 we may compare the progress of daily solar-constant values with the position of the great sun-spot group of March, 1920. Is it a mere accidental coincidence that the observed solar radiation gradually diminished as the sun-spot group came on, fell 5 per cent at the time when the largest spots were central on the solar disk, and returned to normal as the group passed by? To test this by other instances, see Figure 28, in which the daily values of the area covered by flocculi within 15° of the center of the sun's disk, as measured at the Spanish Observatory of Ebro, are compared with our solar-constant values for several months. Although

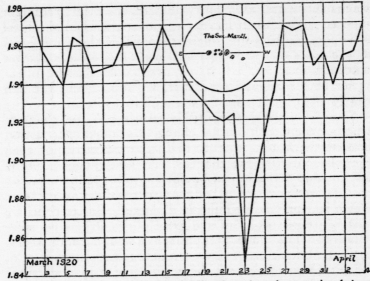

FIG. 27.   How the sun's radiation falls when the solar rotation brings
sun-spots to the center of the disk

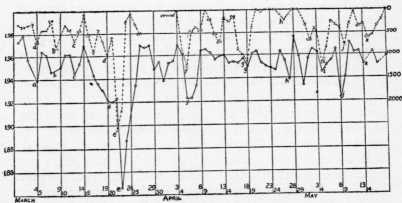

FIG. 28.   Daily variations of solar radiation (lower curve) associated
with variations of flocculi near the center of the sun's disk, March,
April, and May, 1920.   The upper curve is displaced one day forward

[148]

some of the days which one would have wished to consider unfortunately failed of observation at one station or the other, we see many cases where an outbreak of flocculi at the sun's center is attended by a low solar-radiation value.

Mr. H. H. Clayton has numerically studied the value of the solar constant as sun-spots cross the center of the sun's disk in the course of the solar rotation. He finds for the mean result of 36 of the larger spots, occurring between July, 1918, and July, 1924, that on the average the solar radiation was depressed by three-tenths per cent on the day following their central passage. However, not all sun-spots are thus attended by a depressed solar radiation, any more than all sun-spots are attended by northern lights or magnetic storms. Hence the average depression found by Clayton for all large spots is less than the average depression attending active spots only.

It has been a little tedious, I fear, to cite all these evidences of the close association between visible solar disturbances and changes of solar radiation. Yet some critics so persistently discredit the reality of these effects that it seemed necessary to confirm them before passing on to matters relating to weather and to weather forecasting based on solar-radiation measurements.

To sum up the whole discussion, there are many evidences that the sun's radiation varies in two typical ways. Firstly, associated loosely with the numbers of sun-spots and the intensity of the visible activity of the sun, is a gradual change of the total solar radiation, so that the sun emits about 3 per cent more radiation when sun-spots are most numerous, attending the march of the eleven-year cycle of solar activity. This effect is produced, not by a uniform increase of the intensity of all solar rays, but by a disproportionately great increase of intensity in the shorter wave-lengths, culminating in the ultra-violet. Secondly, associated with the rotation of the sun, go changes of several per cent in the total solar radiation, due to the successive turning towards the earth of regions of the solar surface of unequal radiating or absorbing power. Minima of solar radiation are apt to follow, but do not invariably follow, one day after the passage of a sun-spot across the central meridian of the solar disk. Although the proofs of it have not been submitted here, it may be added that maxima of solar radiation frequently attend outbreaks of sun-spots and faculæ (or bright solar regions) at a little distance from the edge of the solar disk.

The first of the two types of solar variation, having long periods, is caused by increasing effective temperature of the sun's surface, as greater agitation takes place in the solar mass. The more active the sun, the more intense its radiation. It is like raking out to the front fresh coals in a fire, and thus sending out from it more heat. The second type of irregular short-interval variations is due to the rotation of the non-uniformly bright sun.

We come back, now, to the question of how the solar changes affect the weather. There are some who say "not at all." "It is," they say, "as if one were in a hall, illuminated by a hundred lamps. If one or two of these lamps should be put out, the illumination would not be changed enough to notice it at all." So, they conceive, it must be, too, if the sun's total radiation changes by one or two per cent. No noticeable consequences ought, they think, to follow in the weather.

There are at least three replies to this argument. Firstly, if the mechanism which turns out one or two lamps in a hall also operates curtains which alter the light reflected from the walls of the room, a very great change of illumination may attend the extinguishing of only two lamps. This analogy has its counterpart in our problem. For curtains we must read atmosphere, for walls of the room we must read outside space and terrestrial surface, and for illumination we must read solar and terrestrial radiation adapted to control weather conditions. We must recall that our atmosphere has changeable elements like clouds, water-vapor, and ozone, all apt to be affected by solar changes. The earth's income and outgo of radiation are both governed by these atmospheric ingredients.

Secondly, if there were processes very sensitive to illumination of a certain intensity, and for which the illumination of 98 lamps would be just below the operative minimum, then the extinction of two lamps would be important, though to the eye unnoticed. For analogy consider the many valuable fruits and grains whose profitable cultivation depends on certain indispensable conditions of temperature and moisture. A change of but a single degree, in North or South latitude, of the outer limits of the zones suitable to these crops, such as might be caused by a slight change in the sun, would alter immensely the world's production of them.

Thirdly, if it were shown that the extinction of two lamps in the hall was always attended by consequences of importance, it would not prevent the forecasting of such consequences if we were unable to understand the connecting links between the two events. In what follows I shall show that there appear to be, in fact, very considerable weather changes following observed changes of solar radiation, and that systems of forecasting based thereon seem already measurably successful.

Hitherto, investigations of the dependence of weather on solar variations have been carried on chiefly by Mr. H. H. Clayton, the well-known meteorologist. He was for many years a colleague of the late A. Lawrence Rotch, a pioneer in studies of the upper air by means of kites. Later, for about 10 years, he was chief forecaster of the meteorological service of Argentina. It was while in the Argentine service that Clayton became interested in Smithsonian work on solar variation. Seeking to improve his official forecasts, he adopted the idea of solar variability as a working hypothesis, and sought to see what came of it.

In what follows I shall give a summary of Clayton's

principal published results, though warning the reader that these are reconnoissances of a new field. Later work may lead to their essential modification. We speak first of his work in Argentina, 1913-1921.

At that time we had only the Mount Wilson observing station, where we made solar measurements once a day on fine days in summer, by Langley's method. It is a weakness of this method that, if the sky gradually clears during

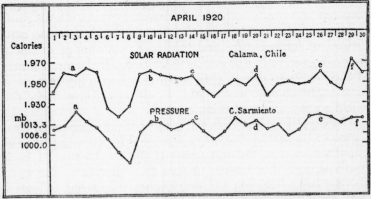

FIG. 29. How the barometer at Sarmiento, Argentina, follows the variation of the sun. (After Clayton. From "World Weather" by permission of the Macmillan Co.)

the several hours of observing required, the result is too high. It is too low, on the other hand, if the sky grows gradually hazy. Clayton appreciated the weakness of our individual results, and therefore he worked with mean values of large numbers of them.

It was not long before his studies convinced him that solar changes have a real bearing on weather in all parts of the world, but, unfortunately, through relations quite as complicated as the complex surface of the earth, with its oceans, deserts, mountains, and clouds, would lead one to expect.

In Figure 29 we see clearly a case of remarkably close

PLATE 36

Mr. F. E. Fowle of the Smithsonian Astrophysical Observatory

correspondence between solar and barometric changes. During the period covered by the chart, a direct correlation coefficient of 75 ± 6 per cent expresses the dependence of the atmospheric pressure on solar variation at Sarmiento, in Patagonia. The waves of pressure move northward from Sarmiento, reaching Buenos Aires, more or less modified, nearly two days later.

Quite as striking a comparison, and this time between solar radiation and temperature departures, is shown in

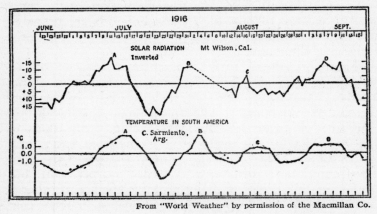

From "World Weather" by permission of the Macmillan Co.

FIG. 30. How the temperature at Sarmiento, Argentina, varies in winter in the opposite direction to the variation of the sun's radiation. (After Clayton)

Figure 30. Here, again, we include the station at Sarmiento, in Patagonia. It shows a negative correlation coefficient of −82 per cent at 2 days after the solar changes. Other stations lag behind more and more, until when the waves of temperature change reach Cuyaba, in Brazil, the maximum negative correlation coefficient of −76 per cent occurs 10 days after the solar changes.

Such results as these convinced Clayton that the sun's variation might give a basis for long-range weather forecasting. He first reduced the new system to practice in

[153]

Argentina in December, 1918. The Smithsonian Institution having established its solar station at Calama, Chile, a few months previously, very readily permitted the Argentine Government to arrange for a daily telegram. Solar results thus became available at Buenos Aires on the morning after they were observed at Calama. From that time till the present, the Argentine weather service has continued to furnish to interested clients official long-range forecasts of the temperatures to be expected morning and evening at Buenos Aires, and also predictions of the times and intensities of rainfall. These bulletins are prepared on each Wednesday, covering the week beginning with the following Thursday.

Figure 31 shows three consecutive weeks of official Argentine forecasts by Clayton, and Figure 9 shows twelve consecutive weeks of such forecasts by his successor, Mr. Hoxmark. The Smithsonian Institution has published a paper by Hoxmark giving verifications of his forecasts for 131 consecutive weeks from July, 1922, to December, 1924. During some of the weeks the positive correlation coefficients exceeded 90 per cent, but unfortunately there are many negative coefficients almost equally high. These latter predictions, so exactly contrary to the event, are thought to have a meaning quite as real as the highly satisfactory correct ones. Further study may teach how to convert these negative forecasts into positive ones. If so a great step will have been taken.

After Clayton's retirement from the Argentine weather service, in 1922, he published a notable book entitled "World Weather,"[3] in which he gave many instances of the interesting relations between solar variation and terrestrial weather. Thus far we have been considering only the responses of the temperature and pressure at individual stations to the solar fluctuations. A broader aspect is exposed in this work of Clayton's. He seeks to observe the

[3] Macmillan Co., New York, 1923.

changes in the world's weather-map corresponding to different levels of the solar radiation.

As the month of July is one in which Smithsonian observers had measured solar radiation for many years,

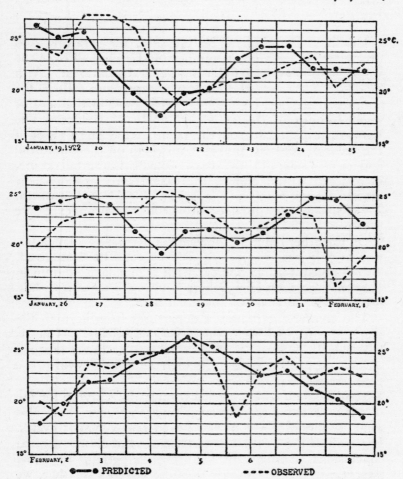

FIG. 31. Weekly predicted and observed temperatures of Buenos Aires. Three successive weeks. (After Clayton)

Clayton makes up a series of mean July solar-constant values as follows:

Year	1917	1905	1906	1911	1910
Mean solar constant...	1.989	1.972	1.962	1.917	1.913
Departure from normal	+0.051	+0.034	+0.024	−0.021	−0.025

He then investigates the pressure, temperature, and precipitation for a great number of stations, all over the world, and finds the following general relations: With increased solar radiation in July the pressure falls in the equatorial regions, over Central Asia, and in the oceanic regions south of Australia and north of Ireland. The temperatures are low on the polar and western sides of the areas of deficient pressure, but high on the equatorial and eastern sides of these areas. Excessive rainfall occurs, in general, within and to the east of areas of deficient pressure, and between the areas of cold and warmth. Areas of deficient rainfall occur within the belts of excessive pressure.

On the other hand, in the years of decreased solar radiation in July nearly opposite pressure conditions occurred. As for precipitation, whereas with high solar radiation in July the Northern Hemisphere land masses are wet, they become dry for years of low radiation.

The greater the radiation departures from normal, the more accentuated were these various effects. What is particularly important, as we shall see later, the latitude of high-pressure regions shifts more and more towards the poles as the solar radiation increases.

Similar studies were carried through by Clayton for the months of October, January, and February, and also some in connection with the eleven-year sun-spot cycles. From all of these investigations he derived certain general conclusions, of which the following are perhaps the most important. As barometric pressure governs weather, we need only deal with it here, omitting discussion of temperature and precipitation. Clayton maintains:

SOLAR VARIATION AND WEATHER

1. Every increase of solar radiation lowers the pressure within the tropics and increases it in latitudes 40° to 60°. This conclusion holds in all cases, whether the solar change is of only a few days' extension, or covers months, or extends over periods of years.

2. The air which leaves equatorial regions on this account raises pressures over continents in winter, and over oceans in summer. In other words, it produces at all times its counterbalancing pressure effects in the *colder* regions.

3. The great permanent low pressures, near Iceland and near the Aleutian Islands, are intensified at all times of increased solar radiation.

4. The more intense the solar radiation, the greater the fall of pressure within the tropics, the wider the tropical belt of diminished pressure, and the higher the latitude of increased pressure.

5. With solar radiation below normal, the reversed effects occur.

6. Hence, there are three variable elements which govern radiation influences upon weather in any one locality. First, variations of pressure attending solar variations; second, an annual periodicity of effects, which reverses them in some localities as between summer and winter; third, a movement of the centers of action to north and south, depending on the absolute intensity of radiation.

Hence, the solar radiation affects weather in a highly complicated way, requiring much study to unravel.

7. From the centers of action there go out waves of effect, which in general travel from higher toward lower latitudes, and from west toward east. "It may be stated as a general law that in each cycle of change in solar activity, whether of long or short period, the effect in the temperate zone begins in high latitudes, progresses eastward and equatorward with a velocity . . . [decreasing with] the length of the solar cycle, and dies out in low

[157]

latitudes. The more intense the solar outbreak, the higher the latitude in which the effect begins, and the greater its intensity."[4]

Such were Clayton's results derived while in Argentina. They interested us at the Smithsonian Institution, and also deeply interested Mr. John A. Roebling. After several conferences, it was arranged that under Smithsonian auspices, and with financial support from Mr. Roebling, Clayton should undertake to investigate more particularly the weather of North America in its relations to solar changes. Engaging one assistant, Mr. E. C. French, and with the cooperation of the Historical Society of Canton, Massachusetts, in the free use of office room, these studies were begun in the early summer of 1923.

Everybody recognizes that there is nothing so convincing of discovery as ability to forecast. Hence, it was agreed that as soon as a proper groundwork of data could be laid, Clayton should undertake forecasts of maximum temperatures for the great city of New York, somewhat similar to those which he had inaugurated for Buenos Aires. He was ready to begin preliminary forecasts in October, 1923, and on October 15 of that year the Smithsonian Institution commenced to receive daily telegrams from its two stations in Arizona and Chile, and to transmit them to Canton, Massachusetts, for Clayton's use. Receiving these advices about twenty-four hours after the solar observations were made, he prepared his forecasts for 3, 4, 5, and 27 days in advance, and transmitted them the same afternoon to the Smithsonian Institution.

After over a year of these forecasts had accumulated, they were compared at the Smithsonian Institution with the actual maximum temperatures at New York as published by the Weather Bureau. The 27-day forecasts showed nothing, but all of the others indicated prevision. As an example of what was found, consider the 4-day forecasts. Let us divide them into three groups made

[4] "World Weather," p. 269.

up of the days when Clayton predicted departures of plus 4°, or more; minus 4°, or less; and between these limits, respectively. The result shows that he hit the day; that days forecast plus were 2.3° F. above the minus ones; and that the forecast normal days averaged nearly normal.

On Friday of each week Clayton wrote to the Smithsonian Institution, predicting how many degrees above or below normal the average maximum temperature of New York would be for the ensuing week, beginning on Sunday. Also, on about the 27th of each month, he communicated a similar forecast for the ensuing calendar month.

In the event of 51 weeks forecast, 31 were given with the correct sign. The average observed temperature departures of the weeks predicted plus exceeded by 2.2° F. the corresponding values for the weeks predicted minus. Of 12 months forecast, 7 were given with the correct sign. A difference of plus 4.4° F. occurred between the average observed temperature departures for months predicted plus compared to those predicted minus.

These are provisional results. For several reasons, the correlations could not be high. Firstly, the individual solar values were not accurate enough. Secondly, in the forecasts for exact days, an error of half a day in the time of an event predicted to occur several days in advance, may mean large differences of temperature, though a rapid rise or fall at about that time has been truly forecast. Thirdly, considering the complicated character of solar weather influences, it is quite too much to expect that all of the important variables governing in North America can be mastered in the course of only a few months of study.

What stands out clearly is this: (1) Probable prevision of weather conditions is shown. It is based on a new element, the solar variation, which, except in Argentina, has hitherto never been taken into account by the weather services of any of the governments of the world. (2) The

accuracy apparently attained, 1923–1925, was sufficient
to make Clayton's forecasts of the weather of next week,
or next month, notably better in the long run than a
mere guess.

It is not, however, in this preliminary success in long-
range forecasting that the greatest merit of the work lies.
Foundations have been laid for further advances. Progress
has been made in the general study of the relations of
the temperature and pressure of North America to solar
radiation.

Having plotted the frequency of solar-constant values of
definite magnitudes, Clayton found that, for the period
1919 to 1922, inclusive, 1.945 calories could be set as
approximately the mean value, and that considerable
numbers of values exceeded 1.960 or fell below 1.931,
respectively. Of 1,118 days of observation, 202 values
exceeded 1.960, 252 fell lower than 1.931, and 664 lay
between these limits. Calling all values above 1.960
high, all those below 1.931 low, Clayton tabulated the
march of barometric pressures for 18 stations of the
United States and Canada, from 2 days before, until 12
days after each event. Separating the high group from the
low, and the winter half-year from the summer half-year,
he computed from these tabulated data the mean march
of the barometric pressures for each of the four conditions
thus distinguished.

Figure 32 exhibits winter results for Winnipeg, New
York, Salt Lake, and Jacksonville. We easily notice
that, excepting Salt Lake, the curves of barometric pressure departure run oppositely for excessive and defective
conditions of solar radiation. For Salt Lake there is,
indeed, a wide absolute difference. Certain well-marked
maxima and minima succeed each other. These nearly
coincide in time at Winnipeg and Salt Lake with the
solar maxima and minima, but lag three days behind at
New York and Jacksonville. In summer there is a similar
quick response in the Rocky Mountain regions, but the

drift to the Atlantic Coast requires about double the time.

Having the data in detail for 18 well-distributed stations

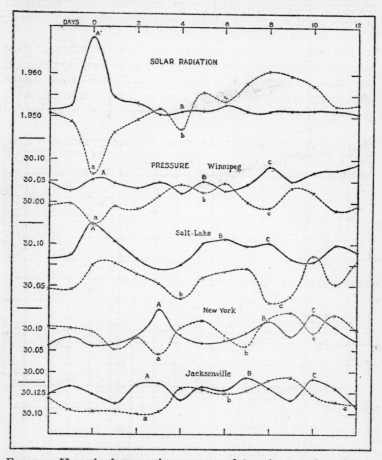

FIG. 32. How the barometric pressures of American stations follow changes of solar radiation. (After Clayton.) Full curves correspond to high solar values, dotted curves to low ones. Curves show the average marches of radiation and pressure for twelve days after high and low solar values have occurred

[161]

Clayton mapped the lines of equal barometric pressure for the successive days after the event. In this way he was able to trace very definitely the areas of high and low pressure associated with high and low solar-radiation values, and to follow their drift towards the Atlantic Coast in successive days.

The next consideration was yet more searching. Not content with rough separation of the solar values into high, medium, and low ranks, Clayton subdivided these ranks into a progressive series of nine groups, beginning with 34 days of values above 1.980, and ending with 69 days of

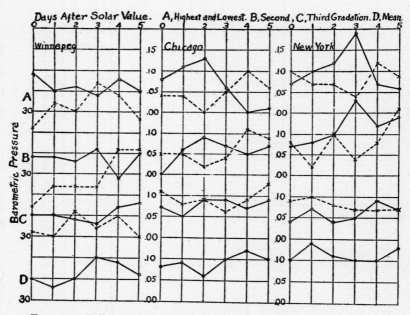

FIG. 33. Full and dotted lines show the march of the barometer attending and following plus and minus departures of the solar constant. From mean results of large groups of observations. Maximum separation of plus and minus curves on zero day at Winnipeg, second day at Chicago, and third day at New York. Separation decreases as solar constant departures diminish

values below 1.911. In Figure 33 we give values for three of these stations. From these groups, he selected winter conditions lying 2%, 1%, and 0.5% above normal, and 2%, 1%, and 0.5% below normal, respectively, for illustration. His figures show plainly how definitely the areas of high barometric pressure shift southward, change into lows, and return northward with decreasing values of solar radiation; how the areas drift eastward in successive days after the event, and in particular what definitely opposed states of the atmosphere attend departures towards higher and lower solar radiation.

Different details, but with persisting opposition of barometric effects, follow steps toward high and low solar radiation in the summer half-year. We need not penetrate further into these intricacies here, for we have seen enough perhaps to indicate that the sun influences the weather by its day to day changes. Yet it is in so complex a manner that anyone who should expect cool weather to follow at every place merely because of low solar radiation, would be very wide of the mark. A tremendous study of tabulated effects must first be made before general solar forecasting becomes practicable. This work is only just begun.

We must not conclude, however, without pointing out a few more facts of interest. According to Clayton's new evidence, the centers of high barometer move towards the equator with decreasing solar radiation. This accords completely with Clayton's earlier studies in Argentina to which we have referred. But he goes two steps further in the same direction. First, by selecting a series of winter months, in which the average monthly values of solar radiation pass through a gradation of steps, there results the series of isobars and isotherms for North America of which some examples are shown in Figure 34.

Not only is the southward drift of areas of high pressure attending decreasing solar radiation confirmed, but the configuration of areas of heat and cold is most suggestive. Consider the state of temperature prevailing in January,

[163]

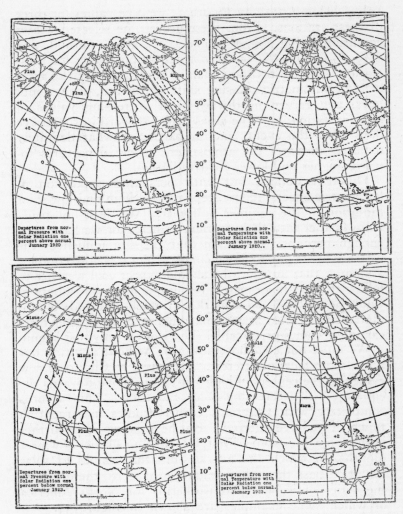

Fig. 34. Effects of increased and decreased solar radiation on the pressure and temperature of North America (Clayton). Note the reversal of areas of positive and negative departures with increased and decreased solar heat

1920, when solar radiation was 1 per cent above normal. Compare it with Figure 35 which gives the glacial map of North America during the great Ice Age. May we not with interest consider Clayton's suggestion that a temporary *increase* in the output of solar radiation perhaps led to that great glacial advance?

We have followed the southward drift of areas of high pressure attending decreasing values of solar radiation, both when these solar changes were of day-to-day occurrence, and when they persisted for complete months. Previous figures show plainly that the solar radiation passes from high to low values as the activity of the sun revealed by sun-spots diminishes. Clayton therefore worked out the pressure charts corresponding to conditions of maximum and minimum sun-spot numbers, and again he finds this important phenomenon of drift of high pressure areas toward the equator.

Consider the magnitudes of the meteorological changes associated with solar variation. A mere tendency would be only of theoretical interest. To be of practical importance, the effects must be sizable. Let us see. As between average solar-constant values below 1.930 and above 1.960, a change, let us say of 2 per cent, Clayton finds the winter barometric pressure in northwestern United States and neighboring Canada increases approximately 1/10 inch. For the same rise of solar radiation, the winter temperature of Winnipeg decreases 12° F. and that of New York 5° F. The southward shifting of areas of maximum pressure and minimum temperature, corresponding to a decrease of 2 per cent in solar radiation, is no less than 30° of latitude, or 2,000 miles. If such substantial effects as these apparently involved should be substantiated in future research, we need offer no excuse for pursuing the study of the sun's variations.

But, some one will say, how is it possible that such small percentage changes of the solar radiation can produce such large effects? We do not yet know fully the reasons for this seeming paradox, but we can see several possible ones. In the first place, the earth is not like a blackened spherical shell of silver, whose surface would

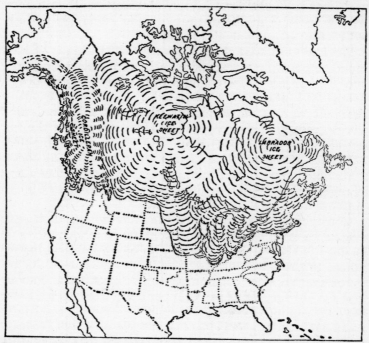

FIG. 35. Glacial areas of North America in the great ice age. Compare upper right hand diagram of FIG. 34. (After Salisbury.) From 'Elements of Geology," by LeConte, courtesy of D. Appleton Co., New York

respond everywhere in unison to changes of radiation from without.

The temperature observed at any continental meteorological station is largely governed by the direction of the wind. This, in turn, is governed by the distribution of barometric pressures. The winds circulate about centers of high and low pressure. Hence, it depends on whether a station is east or west, north or south of such a center as to whether it is bathed by cooling polar winds, or by warming tropical ones.

We must, therefore, look to the influence of the sun upon the barometer to unravel the influence of the sun upon the temperature. And yet this barometric influence is an indirect effect of the primary operation of temperature. Let us solve this riddle. The atmosphere absorbs much solar heat, more in hazy, dusty, cloudy places than in clear transparent regions. Since the atmosphere has little capacity to contain heat, compared to solid or liquid masses, the consequence is that small increases of solar heating raise the temperature of the atmosphere much more than they do that of a body of land or water. Moreover, these effects are different in different places, depending on the obliquity of sun rays and the transparency of the air.

Thus it happens that every rise of solar radiation produces a rush of air from regions where the air is adapted to be most heated to those where it is least warmed. In this way, barometric changes arise. Like sound, such waves of rarefaction and compression may travel very rapidly. At the velocity of sound, an atmospheric wave could travel from the equator to the poles in a few hours.

Here, then, is a mechanism. But are the solar changes we have spoken of adequate to operate it? Again there is another word to say. Figure 26 indicates that the rise of the solar constant of 2.3 per cent is not an equally distributed effect for all rays of the spectrum. It localizes itself preponderatingly among shorter-wave rays, and is larger and larger the farther we look towards the region of the ultra-violet. Instead of 2.3 per cent, the effect becomes 30 per cent in this region. Other investigators, Dobson of England and Pettit of Mount Wilson, have independently observed even larger changes, up to 80 or 100 per cent in the more extreme ultra-violet rays.

Now it happens that just beyond the spectrum region

where these men observed, occurs a remarkable effect of solar chemistry. At great altitudes, certain of the ultra-violet solar rays produce ozone out of atmospheric oxygen, and certain neighboring ultra-violet solar rays tend to re-convert ozone into oxygen again. A balance of these effects occurs. Corresponding to the state of the balance, there always exists a certain amount of ozone in the upper at-mosphere. But, as the intensities of the solar rays alter, the balance is disturbed. After observing but a few days, Fabry had detected changes as large as 20 per cent in the quantity of atmospheric ozone.

This would be interesting but unimportant, if it were not that ozone absorbs powerfully the particular spectrum rays, far beyond the red, which the earth and its atmos-phere constantly emit. Here we have a new factor, there-fore. Let us trace the probable train of the effects: Solar changes, apparently minute yet powerful, alter the ultra-violet rays. Thereby these solar variations change greatly the density of the earth's blanket of ozone. The temper-ature of the atmosphere responds. The barometric pres-sures are disturbed. Profound meteorological effects are thus produced.

Such, it may be, is the complex train of events by which the variability of the sun affects our weather.

What is to be the future of this research? May we en-tertain reasonable hope that, passing from a stage where predictions, of barely sufficient accuracy to be of some use, are being made for a week or a month in advance, solar forecasting will eventually, as Langley hoped, foretell the good and bad seasons and years? It is impossible, as yet, to answer with certainty. As we have remarked, the factors which govern weather conditions are so excessively complex that we cannot hope to master theoretically the problem of the effect of solar-radiation changes thereon. It is like the case of the tides, which so great a man as Lord Kelvin despaired of predicting by theory, and fell back on the expedient of long-continued observations.

SOLAR VARIATION AND WEATHER

So with solar weather-forecasting. If successful it must depend on a study of the variations of weather which have hitherto attended solar changes of the past.

It is only since the year 1918 that a fairly continuous series of solar-radiation measurements exists. If one focuses attention on intervals of a few days or a week, this background, embracing several hundred weeks, may be sufficient for forming a forecasting basis. But if intervals of seasons or years in advance are in view, then a much longer history is indispensable. It is only by a continuous, patient amassing of the facts of solar variation in this generation that the application of them may be prepared for posterity. Unless we lay such a basis of observation, meteorologists of the next generation will be as much at a loss as we are as to whether the sun variations affect weather in a predictable way.

Yet, assuming that the solar changes are of importance in weather control, and assuming further that as a result of a generation of solar measurements the details of the dependence of weather on solar variation became known, is it not improbable that predictions of a season or more in advance would be justified? In short, are not the solar variations so incorrigibly irregular that they can only be found as they occur, and is not the weather so immediately affected by them that no interval for long prevision will remain?

As to the latter query, we must await further evidence. While it appears that the weather effects of short-interval irregular solar changes persist for as much as one or two weeks, it is not yet certainly known what degree of permanence attends the weather changes which may follow a condition of increased or depleted solar radiation persisting over months or years. This information must await many more years of solar and climatological research.

Even if it should be found, however, that the climatological effects of solar variation do not extend as much as a season beyond the duration of the solar changes which cause them, the case for long-range solar forecasting would not be hopeless. For although, as we look at the ragged curve of monthly mean march of solar variation, it looks hopelessly irregular, and as if absolutely without regularly recurring features of any kind, in reality it is not so. Taking the interval of 77 months from May, 1920, to October, 1926, Prof. Dayton C. Miller has been kind enough to analyze it by aid of the wonderful machine with which he has made so many analyses of complex sound waves. The result is that, as Figure 23 shows, the apparently haphazard curve of solar variation is found to be made up, to a large degree, of a combination of several regular periodicities taken in known proportions.

Assuming, then, that we know how to allow for the sunspot periodicity of 134 months, we can build up the whole curve of monthly mean variation of the solar radiation for the years 1920 to 1926 by superposing thereon three curves having periods of 77/3, 77/5, and 77/7 months, perfecting it if we please by adding, in less prominent measures, the several overtones of these periodicities.

It is yet too early to know if these newly found regular periodicities will persist, so that one can surely rely on them for purposes of forecasting. But another decade of solar observation will ascertain. If they should be found to persist, the reader will perceive that, so far as solar change affects the seasons, we shall be in position to forecast them, whether solar changes of several months' duration produce long-continuing weather effects or not.

Our confidence in the periodicities having intervals of 77/3 and 77/5 months is confirmed by the fact that they have long ago been pointed out in weather, and even in crop phenomena.

Our general conclusion, after this survey of the variation of the sun and the weather, is that there is a strong hope of progress to be found in it. Even now an Argentinian contractor, whose business is affected by the weather of

Buenos Aires, will gain advantage by consulting the imperfect weekly official forecasts based on Smithsonian solar researches. As time goes on, and a more thorough study of world weather is made in connection with a constantly growing and improving body of solar observations, it seems reasonable to expect that far more valuable utilities will be found therein.

CHAPTER VIII

A SOLAR OBSERVATORY AMONG THE HOTTENTOTS

As the earth is warmed appreciably by only one sun, the other billions of suns which we call the stars being much too far away to matter, it makes no difference in studying solar variations and weather whether we measure the sun's energy above the atmosphere of California or above that of Africa. One correct determination per day of the intensity of the sun's rays, as they were when they reached the outer confines of our atmosphere, no matter where on the earth's surface it should be made, would enable us to learn, for the use of the whole world, all we need to know of the solar variation. The trouble is to obtain this one correct determination. For we are handicapped by the variable ocean of atmosphere, loaded with humidity, dust, and clouds, not to mention the atmospheric gases which produce a nearly constant screening effect on solar rays.

As we have seen, the Smithsonian Institution, aided by Mr. Roebling's generosity, sent its observers to very isolated desert-mountain sites in the southwestern United States and northern Chile, to reduce as much as possible this atmospheric difficulty. Not content with one daily measurement of solar radiation, the observers at each station are accustomed to make five of them on each good day, in order to enhance the accuracy of the mean result. Yet even with all this painstaking, the measurement proves not fully satisfactory.

[172]

PLATE 38

A street scene in Bombay. (Courtesy of the National Geographic Society)

PLATE 39

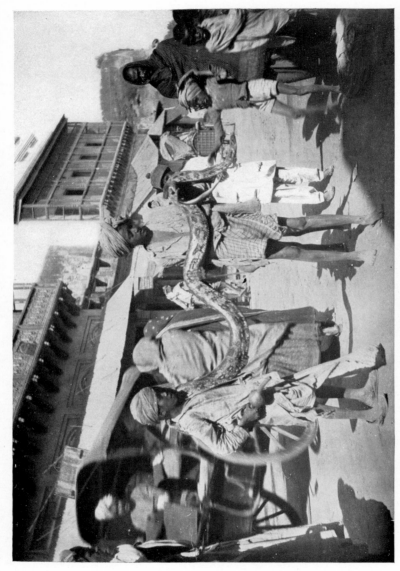

Posing great snake at Agra.   (Courtesy of the National Geographic Society)

On many days, especially in the months of December, January, and February, neither observatory gets satisfactory results because of cloudiness. On many other days, the observations are satisfactory at one station only. Even for satisfactory days, when both observe, the two stations differ, on the average, one-half per cent in their estimate of the intensity of solar radiation outside our atmosphere. If the average discrepancy is one-half per cent, the theory of errors tells us that no small proportion of the days will show a discrepancy of one per cent or more. How then can we guess the right values amid such discrepancies?

Our standard, at which it seems necessary to aim, is the satisfactory observation of the sun on every day of the year by at least two stations, with an average discrepancy not exceeding one-third of one per cent. With a fair approach to this ideal, maintained continually for twenty years, a sufficiently good basis of solar observation would be laid so that the next generation could answer the question: How does solar variation affect weather?

As we were far from reaching this aim, the National Geographic Society, realizing the world-wide interest and value of the work, on March 10, 1925, granted the writer a fund of $55,000 to find the best site in the Old World for a third observatory; to equip there a new station; and to maintain it for a period of four years, or as long as the funds should last. It is hoped that at the end of that period the Smithsonian Institution will have funds available to continue the work. As the affair was to be under Smithsonian direction, and intended to supplement our other work, President Grosvenor called the new project, "The National Geographic Solar Radiation Expedition, in Cooperation with the Smithsonian Institution."

The first step was to choose the location. Perhaps it seems a vague order to pick out the best spot in the Old World of Europe, Asia, Africa, and (shall we call it old?) Australia. Several things were desirable, including a maximum number of cloudless days; high elevation to surmount the variable ground-haze; near-tropical location so that the sun would be high at noon all through the year; a generally calm atmosphere with freedom from many heavy gales or electric storms; nearness to a railway, so as to promote the transportation of the large outfit of apparatus; accessibility to a base of supply for food and assistance in time of need; and, finally, a well-governed population, so that the observers would not be in danger of assassination or of having their effects stolen.

The requirement of a fairly high desert mountain in an accessible well-governed subtropical territory of itself limited our search very greatly. Australia was hardly suitable because the accessible desert parts have no high peaks. On consulting Bartholemew's Atlas of Meteorology, and eliminating Australia, we seemed to be guided for cloudless conditions to the great desert belt extending across Africa and Western Asia, from Morocco to Baluchistan, or else to the southwest coast of Africa. Thus, considering all requirements, we decided to limit our search to Algeria, Egypt, Baluchistan, and South West Africa.

Preferring to examine these locations in their most cloudy season, the writer, with Mrs. Abbot, sailed from New York and arrived at Algiers late in November, 1925.

Leaving Mrs. Abbot at the beautiful Hotel St. George, gorgeous in its semitropical gardens, the writer, with an interpreter, started on Thanksgiving evening for Ain Sefra, in southwestern Algeria, about 600 miles by rail from Algiers. The country and the people seemed familiar enough to me from remembrance of our expeditions of 1911 and 1912, when we lived among the peasant Arabs for many months. (See Plates 13 to 17.) Railroad travel is very simple and comfortable in Algeria, and we found the trainmen on the line southward from Oran to Ain Sefra particularly courteous and obliging.

We had, however, to wait all day in Oran, a seaport not

too prepossessing, where one notices the Moroccan type of Arabs far more prominently than in Algiers. It was surprising, by comparison with bookstores in American cities as small as Oran, to be able to purchase there for a few francs detailed topographic maps of Algeria, similar to our Geological Survey sheets, as well as serious books of many types.

Arrived at Ain Sefra, we were met by Captain Navarre, who expressed his General's regret that business in the South detained him from meeting us. Ain Sefra is a small neat town with hotel and church, and a garrison with hospital. Daily meteorological records are kept there, and are posted regularly at the railway station. From an inspection of these records for an interval of several years, the impression of Captain Navarre was closely verified, namely, that during the nine months, March to November, more than twenty days per month would be nearly cloudless; but during the other three months only from ten to fifteen days a month could be expected.

A junior officer very kindly loaned us horses, and with a petty officer of Spahis we started early the next morning to ascend the mountain south of Ain Sefra. A well-graded, but very stony trail leads up the Djebel Mekter (for so is the mountain named). To reach it, one crosses first about a mile of trackless drifting sand-dunes. For the writer, who is no horseman, it was somewhat alarming to go up and up to the very edge of a great sand bluff, and see that the only way onward led straight down its precipitous face. But the Arab ahead made nothing of it, and the interpreter, who had been a cavalry soldier, and who rode next, said: "Lean far back, and the horse will go safely." So he did, for after sitting down, he slid down the precipices very cleverly.

Though nearly cloudless when we started, we arrived at the top of the mountain, about 7,000 feet above sea-level, in a dense fog. We inspected the old thick-walled stone heliographic station, now partly in ruins. It would be easy to repair it to serve both as observatory and dwelling. The French officers were very cordial to the undertaking, and the Government of France offered every facility to aid us. Yet the degree of cloudlessness is not apparently superior to that of the southwestern United States, which, though high, is far inferior to that of northern Chile. We hoped for better sky conditions, and after arranging with a local contractor to undertake to put the station in order, in case we should, after all, finally prefer it, we returned immediately to Algiers.

During my absence the rain had been nearly continuous, so that Mrs. Abbot's stay in Algiers was none too cheerful. However, we were entertained very cordially by old and new friends, before taking ship back to Marseilles. On the way, the Mediterranean tossed our small steamer rather roughly. The company was small, and all were served at the Captain's table. On my preferring water to some other beverages, the Captain remarked that water did well enough in its place to wash one's hands withal, but was quite unfit to drink.

In Marseilles, we received much kindness from U. S. Consul Frost and family, and embarked, after a day's stay there, on the fine new P. & O. steamer *Rawalpindi* for Port Said. Disembarked at Port Said, and while awaiting the train to Cairo, we saw an Egyptian wedding procession. First came a led camel carrying a man beating a drum, and after them followed a brass band with a rabble behind. Then came the bride's carriage, tightly closed, black and shining, with a man walking behind continually dusting it off with a gay feather duster. The horse had pantalets on his legs, and the wheels were tied with roses. A quarter of a mile of open carriages followed, each with loosely veiled ladies, their faces not so much hidden that we failed to see them, especially the pretty ones. We were told that the bridegroom furnishes a repast for the whole company.

Inquiries of scientific men at Cairo confirmed my im-

PLATE 40

The observatory of the emperor-mathematician, Jai Singh II, at Jaipur, India. The enormous instruments long obsolete, give the places of the sun and other heavenly bodies at all times of the year. (Courtesy of the National Geographic Society)

PLATE 41

In the streets of Agra

pression that there were no mountain peaks of considerable height in Egypt reasonably accessible for a permanent station. Doctor Ball, indeed, told of a mountain on the edge of the Sudan, where, as he believed, it never rains. But he remarked that he had reached it by a 200 mile journey by caterpillar tractor, carrying water for all purposes all that distance. It was said that Mount Sinai east of the Red Sea, where the ancient monastery is located, might possibly be a suitable site, yet no very favorable case was made for it.

Since returning to America, a gentleman who has visited there has given me a more favorable account of Mount Sinai, and states that it is easily reached by motor from Port Said. Possibly it was rejected too hastily.

In a visit to Luxor and Thebes, it was notable how rapidly the haze of the Nile valley gave place to a fair blue sky, as we ascended the Valley of the Kings' Tombs. How romantic it would have been had Nature provided a high, isolated peak near Luxor, where our observers might have studied that sun which was a god of ancient Egypt, and whence they might have retired from time to time to the lovely scenes of Luxor, or the gigantic monuments of the past at Karnak, as a relaxation from too close observation.

It is useless to attempt to tell any new impressions regarding the land of Egypt, whose antiquities have astonished travelers since before the Christian era. The contrast between the care taken by those ancients to provide for a life to come, and the careless attitude towards that mystery which is expressed by the lives of most of our contemporaries, haunted my mind for a long time.

Passing through the Suez Canal, the Red Sea, the Gulf of Aden and the Arabian Sea, we came at length to Bombay, where we landed on Christmas day, and found ourselves in a land which seemed very strange. Contrasts are very sharp in Bombay; between the grandeur of the buildings and residences along the water front around to

THE SUN AND THE WELFARE OF MAN

Malabar Hill, and the squalor of Byculla; between the wealth and high culture of Parsi merchants, and the ill-fed poverty of half-clad men and women, carrying heavy burdens upon their heads, that pass and repass through the narrow streets of the back city. Women are the hod-carriers to most building operations. Swarms of people who live in the congested tenements of Byculla, and work in the cotton mills, sleep by preference in crowded rows upon the sidewalks during the stifling heat of summer. At first one is oppressed exceedingly by such contrasts to American conditions, but after some time in India the impression wears off, as one reflects that after all it may not be good clothes and luxury that spell happiness.

A few days in Jaipur seemed the strangest of all our Indian experiences. Wide streets were continually being swept with wooden hand-brooms, apparently not so much to remove as to raise a dust; while newly dyed webs of cloth, shops for the sale of every commodity, and tourists in their carriages, all received their full tale of it. Gallant, long-tailed, big gray monkeys sat upon the housetops, watching the street like philosophers, or galloped along sheet-iron cornices, racing with some passing American automobile. Often carrying little monkeys at their breasts, they lightly jumped the cross-alleys, loping along, one behind another, with a grand roar of vibrating sheet-metal accompanying their progress. Camels with loads of goods stalked majestically, and now and then some of the royal elephants, with drivers on their heads, clumped along with monstrous feet, taking their exercise.

In the ancient Palace of Amber, near Jaipur, we watched the worship of a great female idol. Formerly human sacrifices propitiated her daily, but now we saw merely the fresh blood of goats upon the pavement. Prostrating himself in rhythmic cadence to the sound of cymbal and drum, the priest of the ceremony carried on the worship. Only two or three were in attendance, all engaged in the exercises. There was no audience.

[178]

OBSERVATORY AMONG HOTTENTOTS

Nearby we saw the splendid council chambers of the palace and the mirrored throne-room with its curving walls and ceiling. It was set with thousands upon thousands of circular and triangular convex mirrors, so that whichever way one looked, thousands of little images of himself looked back upon him. Later, at Agra, we saw the same device in the queen's bath, with its rose-water fountain, where doubtless the lovely Mumtaz Mahal of Shah Jahan was accustomed to cool herself. In Agra, too, of course, we visited again and again that gem of perfection, the Taj Mahal, their final resting place.

Both in Jaipur and Delhi are enclosures, acres in extent, containing the mammoth astronomical instruments of the learned ruler Jai Singh II. Though of no present astronomical use, these enormous sun-dials and instruments for observing the positions of the heavenly bodies are quite as extraordinary in their gigantic bulk as the fossil remains of the dinosaurs in our museums.

In Delhi, which is not pronounced in India as it is in the United States, but rhymes with jelly, Mr. Field, in charge of observatories and meteorology for the Indian Empire, gave us information and letters of introduction invaluable to our search for an observatory site in Baluchistan. Also the secretary for the department administering these branches of public service, Sir Bhupindra Nath Mitra, entertained us at dinner with a company of interesting guests. In conversation, I spoke of seeing a juggler at Agra place a ring upon the middle of a bamboo cane, while both ends of the cane were firmly held in my two hands. But it was the juggler's cane and ring. "Ah!" replied Sir Bhupindra, "A juggler did the same with my own ring, while I held the two ends of my own cane!"

Later, in Quetta, Mrs. Trench told me that when she was a girl, the daughter of an officer of the Indian army, a juggler came to her father's quarters, attended by a feeble little boy. Hypnotizing the child, the juggler set him upon four canes, two under his knees, two under his elbows, so that the boy was supported as high as a table above the floor. Then the juggler removed the canes, one after another, till at length the supports appeared to be all removed, and the child seemed to be in suspension in the mere air. The officers passed their canes under and over him. In the evening the trick was repeated before the whole mess. The surgeon, struck by the emaciated and half-alive condition of the boy, made an examination, and found so sad a state, that, to prevent further cruelty, the child was placed in a mission. Mrs. Trench, however, has no idea how the illusion was produced.

It is a long dusty journey from Delhi to Quetta, through a desert which in summer is one of the hottest regions of the earth. Fortunately, we traversed it in January. Railway travel in India differs very much from long journeys in the United States. Travelers provide their own service in India, including bedding, towels, soap, drinking water, and whatever they may require in addition, outside of the meals furnished in the dining car. As the railway provides no porter, it is customary to be attended by one's own servant, who travels in the adjacent compartment.

Whatever may be the efficiency and comfort of the management of long residents, who speak some of the native languages, the casual visitor is pretty well at the mercy of his servant, who lords it over his master as well as everybody else.

He is far too grand a personage to carry any luggage, which, including as it does, mattresses, pillows, heavy bedding for the chilly nights, cases of drinking water, fruit and other extras, makes a mountain of hand packages to be removed at every junction. The servant grandly engages a bearer and loads him up with perhaps two suitcases and the enormous roll of bedding upon his head, and a couple of packages in his hands, while the servant stalks beside, carrying nothing, but condescends to unload the bearer

PLATE 42

On the plains of Baluchistan

PLATE 43

Performers in native African dance, Johannesburg, South Africa

at the end. Also your servant engages a sweeper with his split wooden broom to stir up the dust in your compartment at every long stop. However, your grand attendant does make up the beds at night, rolls them together in the morning, and wakes you before sunrise by opening the windows of the compartment to pass in an early breakfast call "chota hasri." He also gratifies your pride by calling you his kind master and benefactor, and by asking your advice and pity for his family troubles.

Your servant desires to engineer all tipping on trains and hotels, to buy for you all extras, to have all your sheets and towels laundered every day, and in general to carry on all enterprises that can deflect rupees into his own pocket. A grand opportunity for this depends on the form of sleeping cars. These, as in England, have transverse compartments, which are either coupés for two travelers at night and four by day, or larger ones designed for four travelers at night and six by day. A married couple naturally desires a coupé, but not infrequently they are all taken unless engaged long in advance, and sometimes arrangements miscarry, even when long before provided. In the event that larger compartments only are available, there are three possible courses:

1. To buy two extra tickets, which for a long journey is costly.

2. To separate the family into the compartments reserved for male and female travelers exclusively. This is inconvenient, and oftentimes not very pleasant.

3. To tip the station-master to post a large compartment as full, though in reality it contains but one couple. Here is where the great opportunity of the servant comes in play. The proper tip being unknown to the traveler, the servant secures from him double or triple, and keeps the balance himself.

This third course, or even the occupation of a coupé, is not always perfectly private. For if there is a stop in the small hours at a large place, as likely as not some travelers will go along the station platform, and let down the shaky windows and shutters opposite your bed, which you have been totally unable to fasten securely, and they will peer in under the glare of the arc lights, to see for themselves whether the outside notice of occupancy tells the truth. As the invader can not shut the window, and perhaps would not trouble to do so if he could, you must tumble out of your warm sleepy nest into the cold and garish dustiness, and try for the nth time to fix every one of those Venetian blinds so they can not be let down from outside, especially by your servant.

At Quetta, the British capital of Baluchistan, we were received with a cordial helpfulness which can not be over-acknowledged, by Col. and Mrs. Chenowix Trench at the Political Agency, and by the other members of the official family of Quetta, in so far as they had opportunity, including especially his Excellency, the Agent to the Governor General, and Colonel Barker, Royal Engineers, and Mrs. Barker. Quetta, itself, with its native quarter, its official family, and a large body of white and native troops, lies in a meagerly watered valley of some 6,000 feet elevation, surrounded by mountain chains rising in some peaks to 10,000 feet or more. The British lease some of their holdings in Baluchistan, including Quetta, from the Khan of Kalat. Their interest there is to prevent incursions upon India by the warlike tribes of the hills, and by more powerful foes beyond.

Formerly the cities of Central India were regarded by the hardy fighters of the north much as the Scottish lowlands and the northern counties of England were regarded a few centuries ago by the Highlanders. These were indeed their principal asset and estate. Horde after horde swept down on the devoted cities of Delhi and the plains, sacking or holding the country as they pleased. Few, indeed, of these conquering foreign dynasties attained to anything like the renown of the six Grand Moguls who ruled from 1525 to 1707; but one after another of them prevailed, until, growing soft in luxury, they in their turn yielded to the fierce onslaughts of new invaders.

The British in Baluchistan depend quite as much on their political agents as on their military to keep the peace. These men, selected for great ability, experience, and tact, mingle the offices of despot, judge, peacemaker, conservation engineer, and friend, endeavoring by every means to make life in this barren rugged country more tolerable and safe, and so diminish the temptation to seize from other men what scarcely can be had at home. Colonel Trench showed me, among other measures taken for these ends, block-houses erected in village streets, where armed sentries discourage the forays of restless neighbors; and on the other hand irrigation works designed to augment the tillable lands for agriculture. He told me, also, curious tales illuminating the native thought, such as the following:

Visiting a village under his jurisdiction, the political agent saw a woman with her head tied up. "What," said he, "is the matter with your face?" "My husband," said the woman, "has cut my nose off." Sending for the husband, the agent asked him why he had cut off his wife's nose. "Because I heard she was with Sharbat Khan," said he. "Well, but was she?" inquired the agent. "It seems not," said the husband, "for Sharbat Khan was 30 miles away at the time." "I can not let you cut off your wife's nose for nothing," said the agent. "You must go to jail for a year." The elders of the village when they heard of this severe sentence, remonstrated. "Surely," said they, "you will not keep Halim in jail for a whole year merely for cutting off his wife's nose. She is his property, bought with a great price. If Halim likes to cut her nose off it is only his own loss. If your excellency considers it necessary, Halim might be jailed for a month, but a year—surely that is too long." The political agent, having listened to their remonstrance, replied that he would reconsider the matter and give his decision the next day. So, in the morning, he sent for the elders and said: "Now I have decided to let Halim out, but only under one of two conditions. Either he must put his wife's nose on exactly as it was before, or he must cut his own nose off exactly like his wife's." The elders were greatly amused at this Solomon-like decision, and Halim remained in jail for the balance of his year.

It was my aim to select an isolated mountain, rising well above surrounding levels, so that the station would escape dust and haze rising from the ground. From the military maps, half a dozen such sites were selected, all fairly accessible. But not all were regarded as suitable. In a country where gentlemen are apt to take pot shots at one another with rifles as the whim strikes them, and where it is the rule that a loaded rifle and at least two persons who can use it, other than the chauffeur, shall be in a traveling automobile, it was a matter of some diplomatic concern where the representatives of a foreign power should be located. After discussion, the Khojak Peak, 7,500 feet in elevation, and about 70 miles north of Quetta, was recommended.

Colonel and Mrs. Trench were so kind as to motor me up to the Khojak Pass, only 10 miles from the Afghan border. Over excellent roads, we traversed a wide, nearly flat valley, sparsely inhabited. Occasionally we passed by rows of curious mounds of earth, with central depressions, looking like huge ant-hills. These are the only visible evidences of the native system of irrigating which prevails in that part of Asia. A deep vertical shaft is sunk to a spring at the foothills of the mountain range, and a nearly horizontal tunnel leads out from the deep-level spring, till at length it reaches the surface, perhaps a mile away. The successive vertical shafts necessary for digging and repairing the tunnel are the centers of the great ant-hill-like mounds referred to. It must have been a perfectly enormous task for the natives, with their poor appliances, to dig these irrigating systems, but the advantage of having them underground, so long as the earth does not cave in, is obvious. Evaporation can not waste for them the scanty water supply, as it does, so lamentably for Egypt, in the upper reaches of the Nile.

The proposed Khojak site, a little to the left of the railway tunnel, and near the trail, still visible, where Lord Roberts' army dragged the guns to the Afghan War, is excellent and easily accessible. However, it was regarded as unsafe for the observers to live at the Peak. They must dwell at Shelabagh, a garrison post, three miles east. Two native soldiers would be necessary to guard the station, and a third to ride to and fro daily with the observers. As is customary in India, several servants would have to be employed to do what one might do except for the caste requirements.

A heavy snow fell immediately after this first visit, and when Colonel Barker and the writer drove up a week later to locate the exact spot and to estimate the difficulties, we found it quite impossible to ascend beyond Shelabagh, as the road was impassably filled with several feet of soft snow. Yet the sky on that day had a beautiful clearness which seemed to the writer unequaled by any he had seen in a long experience in North and South America, including even Mount Whitney and Mount Montezuma.

We still wished to examine South West Africa, but left plans and specifications with Colonel Barker, such that a cabled message, with funds, would start construction at the Khojak Peak on the Afghan border of Baluchistan.

Returning to Bombay, we took ship via the Seychelles Islands and Mombassa to Durban, Union of South Africa. From that place, attractive in every feature, unless it be the climate, which in the late summer season, when we landed, was very oppressive, we went up to Johannesburg, passing through a country of very great beauty.

It seems almost incredible that little more than a generation ago that great city, with its beautiful parks and abundant shade trees was a treeless pastureland. We received extraordinary attention and assistance there from Doctor Innes, the Union Astronomer, and Mrs. Innes, Consul and Mrs. Donald, and Vice Consul Hall; also from Doctor Alden, Director of the Yale Observatory, and Mrs. Alden, from Doctor Reuning, and from Sir William and Lady Dalrymple. Just at that time, too, a great company of wealthy Americans was touring South Africa, and special entertainments were provided for them, in which we participated. Even a native war-dance was staged at the City Gold Mine, in which two bands of blacks, garbed in most striking combinations of furs, feathers, and horns, vied with each other in their vigorous evolutions. The orchestra was of itself a wonder. In the front row were many performers on instruments of the marimba type, but in the back about twenty pairs of long wooden staves mounted on twenty gallon cans made a booming that could be heard for miles.

While at Johannesburg we paid a visit to Pretoria, the capital of the Union of South Africa, and met officials who made for us the necessary approach to the Government of South West Africa. We admired the fine capitol building, with its commanding location, and were shown all about the spacious and magnificent council rooms. We also visited the Premier Diamond Mine, and caught a glimpse of the day's run of a double handful of diamonds as it was being sorted.

With necessary introductions and information, we continued our journey to Windhoek, capital of South West Africa. Naturally I was on the lookout all the way, after leaving the junction at De Aar, to see the desert unfold itself.

A gentleman on the train, to whom I had mentioned the quest, suggested, as most suitable, Mount Brukkaros, an isolated peak about 25 miles west of the railway. It loomed before and behind us for nearly half a day, so flat is the plateau, and so exceptionally pure the air of that country. As we were nearly opposite to the mountain, a herd of several hundred springbok, a kind of small antelope of the size of a goat, leaped away from the railway. Flocks of guinea fowl, and a few wild ostriches were also seen. Yet the vegetation is very sparse, and water holes far apart. Indeed the rainfall in that region averages but 3½ inches a year. It occurs mainly in February and March.

Arriving at Windhoek, I presented my letter to Colonel Venning, Chief of Posts and Telegraphs, who introduced me to various officials, and put me in the way to get the best information as to weather conditions all over South West Africa. In America it had seemed probable that the best site would be a mountain near the town of Aus, in the south-central part of the province. Doctor Reuning at Johannesburg, and the officials at Windhoek, however, all dissuaded me from locating near Aus on account of the fog which not infrequently covers that region for many days. It lies, in short, too near the ocean, though the rainfall there is very slight. Doctor Reuning had recommended mountains in the north-central section. But after a study of the meteorological data, we became fully persuaded that no place in South West Africa was more promising than Mount Brukkaros.

The Honorable H. P. Smit, Secretary for the Government of South West Africa, was attending the sessions of Parliament in Cape Town. However, on Colonel Venning's introduction, the official in charge at Windhoek authorized Mr. A. Dryden, Inspector of Public Works, of Keetmanshoop, 60 miles south of Mount Brukkaros, to accompany me to the mountain, and examine conditions upon the spot. Accordingly we returned by the next train to Keetmanshoop.

South West Africa is a sparsely settled and little developed country. On the Atlantic seaboard, there are fogs, but practically no rain ever falls near the coast. Rainfall increases from west to east and from south to north. Over a large part of the country there is no industry but grazing. The native population of Hottentots and Hereros, that occupies the country south of Windhoek, hardly numbers altogether more than 30,000. These people, living in their grass huts, are of a docile disposition, quite the opposite of the dangerous tribes of Baluchistan. No possible danger to the observers from human hands is to be feared in South West Africa. Notwithstanding the meager rainfall, there grows sufficient grass, in tufts between the rocks that cover the ground, so that herds and flocks of domestic cattle, sheep, and goats, and several species of wild animals of the antelope family, as well as wild ostriches and guinea fowl, subsist.

There are almost no developed mineral resources in that part of South West Africa, although prospecting for oil has begun. Oil, indeed, is greatly needed. Gasoline costs nearly a dollar a gallon. American automobiles with right-hand drive are used in preference to European makes, almost exclusively. If the American makers could see the severity of usage that their cars stand up against, in that country almost devoid of roads, they would surely be proud of their output. As there are no bridges, the cars have to fight their way up and down steep banks, through sand up to the hubs in the dry beds of streams, and over rocks of all sizes up to that of a soap-box. For freight hauling, teams of twelve to sixteen oxen are employed.

Keetmanshoop is one of the half dozen most important towns of South West Africa. It has a mixed population; white about 1,500, colored about 6,000. Being a railway division point, and supply center to the ranchmen for a hundred miles around, it has good hotels and stores, a hospital, school, and churches. Despite the broiling sun, its elevation of 3,300 feet and the great dryness of the air render the climate sufficiently invigorating so that tennis is a popular game there. Very curious cactus-like trees grow in the park, and here and there a tree of good size will be found outside the town. For the most part, however, sand and gravel, plentifully strewn with stones,

PLATE 44

In Durban, South Africa.   Mrs. Abbot and her rickshaw man.   (Courtesy of the National Geographic Society)

PLATE 45

A Hottentot village, South West Africa

make up the nearly level surface of the surrounding plateau which stretches as far as the eye can see.

Remaining for twelve days within moderate distance of this region, every forenoon but one was sufficiently cloudless to give fair prospects for our exacting solar observations, and this was in early March, at the height of the rainy season. A few drops of rain fell during some of the afternoons. What seemed particularly pleasing was the complete absence of cirrus clouds, and the calmness of the atmosphere. Probably it was too good to be truly representative, yet Mr. Dryden told me that the weather conditions of the whole year were apt to be as good or better for my purpose.

We made an expedition to the summit of Mount Brukkaros. Leaving Keetmanshoop about 3 o'clock one afternoon, a sixty-mile drive landed our party at Berseba, the Hottentot village seven miles from Brukkaros, about dark. The party consisted, besides Mr. Dryden and the writer, of two other white men, and three colored "boys." The combined push of the whole party was hardly enough to propel the automobile through the sand at the bottom of the Great Fish River bed.

The Captain of the Hottentots detailed a man to guide us up the mountain. After eating our evening meal, we lay out under the blazing stars on a knoll in the Hottentot village. It was hard to sleep at all under such a gem-studded sky. Sixteen of the twenty-one brightest stars of the whole heavens, besides several planets, were visible at one time. So clear was the atmosphere that the stars went right down to the horizon shining brightly, and were blotted out suddenly, as if in lunar occultation, by the low hills twenty miles away. We rose while it was still dark, finished breakfast by five, and were away towards the mountain before six o'clock.

Arriving at a gulley several feet deep, we supposed it would be necessary to walk the rest of the way, but the driver found a place where the banks were lower, drove up there over a bed of stones as large as one's head, and with two lurches, down and up, we got across the gulley and kept on right up to the base of Mount Brukkaros. Tramping up the dry bed of a stream, in a sort of corridor flanked on either side by precipitous ranges, we at length reached a precipice some 60 feet high, around which we climbed by a wide detour. At the foot of this precipice were two good-sized pools, which, as the Hottentot said, were never dry.

Having climbed high around the obstacle, we descended into a nearly level meadow of considerable extent where we had hoped to find barracks left by German heliographers many years ago. These, however, had fallen into ruin. On every side rose the mountain, like the rim of a bowl, to about 1,000 feet above the meadow. Our business was now to find near the rim a solid ledge of rock suitable for a tunnel for the observatory, and with some opportunity near it for constructing the dwelling. As the railway lay towards the east, and as it was thought likely that heliographic signals would, for a time at least, be the only means of communication, our first ascent was to the eastern rim.

The mountain has almost no soil, but only rock, seamed and split, and with its sides strewn with jagged fragments. With Mr. Fry, a Canadian miner who was Mr. Dryden's foreman, the writer scrambled and climbed about, all over the southeastern rim, from nine o'clock until nearly one o'clock, without finding any place where the rock seemed firm enough to warrant excavating the tunnel. Looking through the glass, there seemed to be a suitable ledge on the western rim. Though all the other members of the party were too fagged to continue, and though it seemed impossible any longer to set one foot before the other, it was necessary to settle the location that afternoon. We had no food upon the mountain, and scant time to make arrangements and reach Cape Town in season for our steamer's sailing.

OBSERVATORY AMONG HOTTENTOTS

Hence, taking the Hottentot to be witness of the location, the writer began the ascent of the western rim, lying down to rest under the shadow of every great rock and scrawny dwarf tree. About half-way up, we found a shallow natural cave, which seemed as if it could be easily enlarged to make a dwelling for the observers, warm in winter, cool in summer, like the tombs of Egypt which archeologists praise as dwellings under that blazing sun. The idea had to be abandoned later, as the rock proved unsafe to excavate, but it seemed comforting at the time to have made even a little apparent progress after so many hours of failure.

From the cave we went painfully upward, and at length, when so fatigued that to take another step seemed impossible, we arrived at the ledge which had been seen with the glass. It looked less firm at close range, but there was another of better texture still higher. Hence, under direction, the Hottentot made a cairn of stones to mark the place, and we began our descent towards the water pools, where the other members of the party awaited us.

We took the shortest cut right over the southern rim, not knowing what trail, if any, we should find. And now the Hottentot led the way, very solicitous for the safety of his "Baas." He knew no word of English, but would sign to me to sit down while he searched for ways to get round or down the precipitous places. It was really very dangerous in our exhausted condition, but gradually we made our way, often on hands and knees, and soon after four o'clock reached the pools.

Stopping only to take a couple of photographs, and then to drink, and drink, and drink of the water, between polliwogs, I threw myself down on the sandy bed, and lay for half an hour before attempting to begin the three-mile walk to the auto. Mr. Dryden, very solicitous, sent on a black boy to get a bottle of brandy from his provisions, and made me take a drink of the neat liquor before we quite reached the auto. The poor Hottentot had quite worn out the soles of his boots, and limped along with bloody feet, very slowly towards the last.

Finally we reached the auto, and had a good hot meal, which was very needful after fourteen hours of hard scrambling in the hot sun, without food or sufficient water since our early breakfast. We felt so much refreshed that we drove to Keetmanshoop, arriving nearly ten o'clock at night, but pleased to think that "the best site for a solar radiation observatory in the Old World" had been selected.

Leaving with Mr. Dryden a sketch and specifications of the construction required, we set off for Cape Town. There the writer got in touch with Honorable H. P. Smit, Secretary for South West Africa, and found a very helpful attitude on the part of the Government. As the upshot of the affair, they permitted Mr. Dryden to construct at cost, for the Expedition, the necessary road and trail, to build a garage at the foot of the trail and a dwelling near the observatory tunnel, to hew out the tunnel itself from the solid rock, and to build two 3,000-gallon reservoirs to catch water in the gulch near the observatory. The first attempt at a tunnel was made in the ledge a little higher than the one I reached so painfully. But after entering some distance, the rock proved unsafe, and a second and satisfactory trial was made still nearer the southwest summit of the rim. A little later, the South West African Government consented to do that which at first they declined, namely to build a telephone line, some thirty miles, to the railway, so that the isolation of the mountain is to that extent removed. Nothing could be more pleasing than the steady undismayed progress of Mr. Dryden and his white and black forces in the construction work, so far from base and so inaccessible. Beginning in May, they finished in September.

In the meantime, after my return to Washington, the last preparations for the expedition were completed; and on August 11, 1926, Mr. W. H. Hoover, Field Director,

PLATE 46

Cottage of the solar observers on Mount Brukkaros, South West Africa, on the Hottentot reservation, with their one shade tree—an aloe

PLATE 47

Water-carriers at the radiation station, Mount Brukkaros, South West Africa. All water for work and household is carried in this way from a distant water-hole, except when rare rains fill resevoirs

and Mr. F. A. Greeley, Assistant, both men of long experience, accompanied by Betty Jean Hoover, Mr. Hoover's infant daughter, and her aunt, Miss Johnson, and taking with them over 10,000 pounds of equipment in sixty cases, sailed from New York, via Southampton for Cape Town. Landing at Cape Town on September 13, they reached Keetmanshoop by September 25, with all their outfit. This was sent on by two twelve-ox wagons in a six-day crawl to Mount Brukkaros.

By October 15, the outfit was mainly at the Observatory, having been packed up the steep trail by four donkeys belonging to the expedition. Only two instruments had received injury. The mercury surrounding the thermometer bulbs in two of the three silver-disk pyrheliometers had escaped the restraining wax, and had alloyed the silver disks. These were repaired by Mr. Hoover, and by December, 1926, daily observations of the solar radiation were begun on Mount Brukkaros.

CHAPTER IX

HARNESSING THE SUN

THE United States uses at present about half a billion
tons of coal, half a billion barrels of oil, and fifty billion
horsepower hours of water power yearly for light, heat,
and power, equal if it could be wholly transformed, to a
total of seven trillion horsepower hours. All this is but
trifling compared to the enormous energy of solar radiation falling each year on the surface of this country. Altogether, if it were possible to convert this solar energy
completely, it would represent in power about seven thousand trillion horsepower hours in its rays. Even the stars
furnish the equivalent of about one billion horsepower
hours, not much compared to the sun, but an appreciable
quantity compared to our water power.

It is not surprising, in view of this astonishing comparison, that inventors have busied themselves in the
effort to discover a practical means to employ the enormous power and heat resources contained in sun rays.
Fortunately, nature does a great deal for us in this line.
If we lacked the generally diffused heating of our whole
country by the sun rays, anything which we might do
with coal and oil to replace it would be like the small
dust of the balance. Yet if all the sunlight necessary for
plant growth and for generally diffused heating is reserved,
there remains available for power purposes, local heating,
and lighting, many thousand times as much solar power
as we are using from all other sources combined.

Nothing quite satisfactory has been accomplished thus
far with it, but the story of the attempts to employ sun

rays for power is full of interest. The following are quotations from a paper by A. S. E. Ackermann, B.Sc., reprinted in the *Smithsonian Report* for 1915 by permission from the *Journal of the Royal Society of Arts*, London, April 30, 1915:

"Although the theoretical power value of the heat reaching the surface of the earth is no less than 5,000 horsepower per acre, it must not be thought that anything like this amount can be converted into mechanical power any more than can all the heat of coal be converted into its theoretical equivalent of mechanical power. For example, the heat value of good coal is about 14,500 British thermal units (B. t. u.) per pound, equal to 12,760 horsepower hours per ton, but in fact the best result, even under test conditions, ever obtained from a ton of coal by means of a boiler and steam engine is only about 1,470 brake horsepower hours, or 11.5 per cent of the heat value, while in the case of a gas engine the corresponding figure is 25.5 per cent, and of a Diesel oil engine 31 per cent. The chief loss is in converting the steam into mechanical energy, and most of the loss is inevitable for thermodynamic reasons. With this fact in mind, you will not be so surprised to learn that the best overall thermal efficiency obtained from the Shuman-Boys solar plant in Egypt was only 4.32 per cent, the chief reasons for this being so much less than 11.5 per cent being that the steam pressure was so low, and that the best efficiency of the sun-heat absorber was only 40.1 per cent, compared with 75 per cent for the best coal-fired boiler. But it has taken boilermakers many years to obtain this efficiency, so that 40.1 per cent is not a bad result when the number of sun boilers that have been made is taken into account.

* * * * * *

"To de Saussure the credit is due for inventing the 'hot box' (*i.e.*, an insulated air-tight wooden box, black inside, and covered with two layers of plain glass with an air space between them), which has since been such a favorite with other workers. (See Figure 19.) It was he, too, who found that a cover of two sheets of glass gave the best results.

* * * * * *

"The work of August Mouchot in connection with the utilization of solar energy was certainly of great importance. It is recorded in his book entitled 'La Chaleur solaire et les Applications industrielles,' second edition, 1879; but, as with other workers in this field, he gives extremely meager information as to results of experiments.

"Mouchot started his solar work in 1860 and took out his first patent No. 48,622 on March 4, 1861.

* * * * * *

"In August, 1866, Emperor Napoleon III of France saw Mouchot's first solar engine at work in Paris, and in 1872 Mouchot (with the monetary assistance of the French Government) constructed another sun boiler. This was described by M. L. Simonin in the *Revue des deux Mondes* of May 1, 1876, as follows:

"The traveler who visits the library of Tours sees in the courtyard in front a strange-looking apparatus. Imagine an immense truncated cone, a mammoth lamp shade, with its concavity directed skyward. This apparatus is of copper, coated on the inside with very thin silver leaf. On the small base of the truncated cone rests a copper cylinder, blackened on the outside, its vertical axis being identical with that of the cone. This cylinder, surrounded as it were by a great collar, terminates above in a hemispherical cap, so that it looks like an enormous thimble, and is covered with a bell glass of the same shape.

"This curious apparatus is nothing else but a solar receiver—or, in other words, a boiler—in which water is made to boil by the heat rays of the sun. This steam generator is designed to raise water to the boiling point and beyond by means of the solar rays, which are thrown upon the cylinder by the silvered inner surface of the conical reflector. The boiler receives water up to two-thirds of its capacity through a feed pipe. A glass tube and a steam gauge communicating with the inside of the generator, and attached to the outside of the reflector, indicate both the level of the water and the pressure of the

PLATE 48

A—Mouchot's multiple-tube sun-heat absorber of 1878. (After Ackermann, from an old print)

B—Ericsson's sun-power plant of 1883. (After Ackermann, from an old print)

PLATE 49

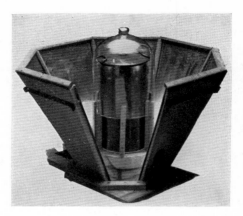

A—Adams's solar cooker. (After Ackermann, from an old print)

B—Pifre's sun-power plant of 1878 driving a printing press. (After
Ackermann, from an old print)

steam. Finally, there is a safety valve to let off the steam when the pressure is greater than desired. Thus, the engine offers all desirable safety and may be provided with all the accessories of a steam boiler.

"The reflector, which is the main portion of the generator, has a diameter of 2.60 meters at its large and 1 meter at its small base, and is 80 centimeters in height, giving 4 square meters of reflecting surface or of insulation. The interior walls are lined with burnished silver, because that metal is the best reflector of the heat rays; still, brass with a light coating of silver would also serve the purpose. The inclination of the walls of the apparatus to its axis measures 45°. Even the ancients were aware that this is the best form for this kind of metallic mirror with linear focus, inasmuch as the incident rays parallel to the axis are reflected perpendicularly to the same and thus give a focus of maximum intensity.

"The boiler is of copper, which of all the common metals is the best conductor of heat; it is blackened on the outside, because black possesses the property of absorbing all the heat rays, just as white reflects them; and it is inclosed in a glass envelope, glass being the most diathermanous of all bodies; that is to say, the most permeable by the rays of luminous heat. Glass further possesses the property of resisting the exit of these same rays after they have been transformed into dark rays on the blackened surface of the boiler.

"The boiler proper of the Tours solar engine consists of two concentric bells of copper, the larger one, which alone is visible, having the same height as the mirror, i.e., 80 centimeters, and the smaller or inner one 50 centimeters. Their respective diameters are 28 and 22 centimeters. The thickness of the metal is only 3 millimeters. The feed water lies between the two envelopes, forming an annular envelope 3 centimeters in thickness. Thus the volume of liquid is 20 liters, and the steam chamber has a capacity of 10 liters. The inner envelope is empty. Into it pass the steam pipe and the feed pipe of the boiler. To the steam pipe are attached the gauge and the safety valve. The bell glass covering the boiler is 85 centimeters high, 40 centimeters in diameter, and 5 millimeters in thickness. There is everywhere a space of 5 centimeters between its walls and those of the boiler, and this space is filled with a layer of very hot air.

"Mechanism was provided whereby the reflector was adjusted by hand to follow the movement of the sun.

"On May 8, 1875, a fine day, 20 liters of water, at 20° C., introduced into the boiler at 8.30 a. m., produced steam in 40 minutes at 2 atmospheres (30 pounds) of pressure to the square inch, i.e., a temperature of 121° C., or 21° C. above boiling water. The steam was then raised rapidly to a pressure of 5 atmospheres (75 pounds to the square inch), and if this limit was not exceeded it was because the sides of the boiler were only 3 millimeters thick, and the total effort supported by these sides was then 40,000 kilograms. It would have been dangerous to have proceeded further, as the whole apparatus might have been blown to pieces.

"Toward the middle of the same day, with 15 liters of water in the boiler, the steam at 100° C.—that is to say, at a pressure of 1 atmosphere—rose in less than a quarter of an hour to a pressure of 5 atmospheres, equal to a temperature of 153° C. Finally, on July 22, toward 1 p. m., an exceptionally hot day, the apparatus vaporized 5 liters of water per hour, which is equal to a consumption of 140 liters of steam per minute, and one-half horsepower. For these experiments the inventor used an engine which made 80 strokes per minute under a continued pressure of 1 atmosphere. Later on it was changed for a rotative engine—that is to say, an engine with a revolving cylinder—which worked admirably, putting in motion a pump to raise water, until the pump, which was too weak, was broken.

"In 1878 Mouchot used a boiler made of many tubes placed side by side and having a capacity of 100 liters (70 for water and 30 for steam). (See Plate 48A.)

"Mouchot seems to have been the only inventor of a solar plant, with the exception of Shuman, who has had his apparatus tested by independent engineers. The following refers to Mouchot's plant. In *Comptes rendus*, Vol. 94, 1882, pages 943–945, M. A. Crova reports that:

"The minister of public works appointed two commissions, one at Constantine and the other at Montpellier, to make experiments with two identical mirrors of 5.22 square meters in section normal to the sun's rays and to evaluate their practical utility.

"The commission of Montpellier was composed of MM. Duponchel, Engineer-in-chief of Bridges and Roads as president; Col. Fulcrand, R. E.; Guibal, and myself.

"The experiments (at Montpellier) lasted from January 1 to December 31, 1881, and were made from hour to hour every day during which the sun was bright and the observations possible.

"The solar rays concentrated at the focal line of the mirror were received on a black boiler placed at the axis and which was inclosed by a glass shade.

"The number of major calories utilized, divided by those incident, received in one hour upon 1 square meter of surface normal to the rays, gives the efficiency of the apparatus.

HARNESSING THE SUN

"Here are the principal results[1] obtained during 176 days which gave 930 observations during which 2,725 liters of water were distilled:

	Cal.	Max. Cal.	Date
"Direct heat received	616.1	945.0	April 25
"Heat utilized	258.8	547.5	June 15
"Efficiency calculated	0.491	0.854	June 14

"Next came that versatile engineer and successful inventor, John Ericsson, a Swede by birth and an American by adoption. He made an immense number of experiments, extending over 20 years, with costly apparatus, to determine the solar constant, and later on made apparatus for the practical utilization of solar radiation. All these experiments were made at his own expense, and he tells us they cost him £20,000; and having done all this work, the conclusion he arrived at was:

"The fact is, however, that although the heat is obtained for nothing, so extensive, costly, and complex is the concentration apparatus that solar steam is many times more costly than steam produced by burning coal. (Letter dated September 21, 1878, to R. B. Forbes.)

[1] Our author quotes these results of Crova as expressed in the French language, stating that they appeared so incomprehensible to him that he preferred his readers to draw their own conclusions. I have turned to the original source. Certainly the results are not clear, but they seem to me susceptible of the following probable explanation.

Having made pyrheliometric observations during the tests, Crova gives in kilogram-calories the mean solar radiation per square meter per hour during the whole year, and the maximum solar radiation per square meter ever received in one hour. If we change these to gram-calories per square centimeter per minute, they become 1.01 and 1.57, respectively. These values seem reasonable enough. The second line of the table is probably computed from the amount of steam generated. Similarly expressed, this indicates the absorption of 0.431 gram-calorie per square centimeter per minute in the average of the year, and 0.913 calorie during the most favorable hour of the tests.

The final line does not come directly by dividing the corresponding values in the columns just above, as one might at first sight expect. We may readily suppose that for each hour the efficiency was computed by itself, and averaging these hourly efficiencies yielded the higher value as given, 0.491, instead of 0.420 which would come directly from the table. It is very likely that the low efficiency, which must always occur at starting of daily tests, and occasional interference of clouds would have led to this discrepancy.

As for the column of maxima, it is obvious enough that one would not expect to get the maximum efficiency value on June 14 by dividing the heat absorbed on June 15 by the heat received on April 25. Very likely the maximum heat *absorbed* on June 14 was nearly equal to that of June 15, but the heat *received* on June 14 was far inferior to that *received* on April 25, thus yielding the surprisingly high efficiency stated. As Crova points out in the original paper, very hot weather is favorable to high efficiency, because it diminished the loss by cooling of the boiler. The average boiler efficiency of 49 per cent is excellent.

"He tried hot-air engines as well as steam engines, for utilizing solar energy, and claimed that the steam engine which he constructed in New York for this purpose in 1870 was the first one driven by the direct agency of solar radiation. The diameter of its cylinder was 4½ inches. He afterwards modified his solar hot-air engine so that it might be used as a small pumping engine, using gas as its heat supply.

"Ericsson gives full details of all his apparatus for determining the solar constant in the record of his life's work, entitled 'Contributions to the Centennial Exhibition,' New York, 1876; but unfortunately he did not describe in detail therein the solar boilers, explaining that 'experienced professional men will appreciate the motive, viz., that of preventing enterprising persons from procuring patents for modifications.' He does, however, give us the following amount of information:

"On grounds already fully explained, minute plans of my new system of rendering sun power available for mechanical purposes will not be presented in this work. The occasion, however, demands that I should present an outline of the concentration apparatus before referred to. It consists of a series of polished parabolic troughs, in combination with a system of metallic tubes charged with water under pressure, exposed to the influence of converging solar rays, the augmented molecular action produced by the concentration being transferred to a central receiver, from which the accumulated energy is communicated to a single motor.

"Thus the mechanical power developed by concentrated solar heat is imparted to the solar steam engine without the intervention of a multitude of boilers, glass bells, gauges, feeders, etc. Moreover, the concentration apparatus, unlike the instrument of Mouchot, requires no parallactic motion, nor does its management call for any knowledge of the sun's declination from day to day. Its position is regulated by simply turning a handle until a certain index coincides with a certain bright line produced by the reflection of the sun's rays.

"His boilers seem to have been exceedingly efficient, for he claims that 'the mechanism which I have adopted for concentrating the sun's radiant heat abstracts, on an average, during nine hours a day, for all latitudes between the equator and 45°, fully 3.5 units of heat per minute for each square foot of area presented perpendicularly to the sun's rays.' Three and five-tenths B. t. u. per square-foot-minute = 0.95 calories per square-centimeter-minute. The mean transmission of solar radiation by the atmosphere over a zenith distance from 45° E. to 45° W. is 67.5 per cent when the sky is clear. Thus $0.675 \times 1.93 = 1.31$ calories per square-centimeter-minute are available at the earth's surface.[2] Hence the efficiency of Ericsson's boiler was $\frac{0.95}{1.31} \times 100 = 72.5$ per cent, which is remarkably high.

"Ericsson wrote in *Nature* of January 3, 1884, an illustrated article describing another of his sun motors which he erected in New York in 1883, in spite of his opinion as to the cost of solar steam (previously quoted) expressed in 1878 (Figure 48B). His description was as follows:

"The leading feature of the sun motor is that of concentrating the radiant heat by means of a rectangular trough having a curved bottom lined on the inside with polished plates so arranged that they reflect the sun's rays toward a cylindrical heater placed longitudinally above the trough. This heater, it is scarcely necessary to state, contains the acting medium, steam or air, employed to transfer the solar energy to the motor, the transfer being effected by means of cylinders provided with pistons and valves resembling those of motive engines of the ordinary type. Practical engineers, as well as scientists, have demonstrated that solar energy can not be rendered available for producing motive power, in consequence of the feebleness of solar radiation. The great cost of large reflectors and the difficulty of producing accurate curvature on a large scale, besides the great amount of labor called for in preventing the polished surface from becoming tarnished, are objections which have been supposed to render direct solar energy practically useless for producing mechanical power.

"The device under consideration overcomes the stated objections by very simple means, as will be seen by the following description: The bottom of the rectangular trough consists of straight wooden staves, supported by iron ribs of parabolic curvature secured to the

[2] It is not unusual to receive 1.45 calories per square centimeter per minute at Washington with fairly high sun. This would reduce the figure of efficiency to 65.5 per cent, which seems more probable.

sides of the trough. On these staves the reflecting plates, consisting of flat window glass silvered on the underside, are fastened. It will be readily understood that the method thus adopted for concentrating the radiant heat does not call for a structure of great accuracy, provided the wooden staves are secured to the iron ribs in such a position that the silvered plates attached to the same reflect the solar rays toward the heater.

"Referring to the illustration, it will be seen that the trough, 11 feet long and 16 feet broad, including a parallel opening in the bottom, 12 inches wide, is sustained by a light truss attached to each end, the heater being supported by vertical plates secured to the truss. The heater is $6\frac{1}{4}$ inches in diameter, 11 feet long, exposing $130 \times 9.8 = 1,274$ superficial inches to the action of the reflected solar rays. The reflecting plates, each 3 inches wide and 26 inches long, intercept a sunbeam of $130 \times 180 = 23,400$ square inches section. The trough is supported by a central pivot, round which it revolves. The change of inclination is effected by means of a horizontal axle, concealed by the trough, the entire mass being so accurately balanced that a pull of 5 pounds applied at the extremity enables a person to change the inclination or cause the whole to revolve. A single revolution of the motive engine develops more power than needed to turn the trough, and regulates its inclination so as to face the sun during a day's operation.

"The motor shown by the illustration is a steam engine, the working cylinder being 6 inches in diameter, with 8-inch stroke. The piston rod, passing through the bottom of the cylinder, operates a force pump of 5 inches diameter. By means of an ordinary crosshead secured to the piston rod below the steam cylinder, and by ordinary connecting rods motion is imparted to a crank shaft and flywheel, applied at the top of the engine frame, the object of this arrangement being that of showing the capability of the engine to work either pumps or mills. It should be noticed that the flexible steam pipe employed to convey the steam to the engine, as well as to the steam chamber attached to the upper end of the heater, have been excluded in the illustration. The average speed of the engine during the trials last summer was 120 turns per minute, the absolute pressure on the working piston being 35 pounds per square inch. The steam was worked expansively in the ratio of 1 to 3, with a nearly perfect vacuum kept up in the condenser inclosed in the pedestal which supports the engine frame.

"In view of the foregoing, experts need not be told that the sun motor can be carried out on a sufficient scale to benefit very materially the sun-burnt regions of our planet.

* * * * * *

"W. Adams, deputy registrar, High Court, Bombay, seems to be the sole Englishman who has worked on the practical side of the problem of the utilization of solar energy. His work was done in India, and is recorded in his interesting book, 'Solar Heat' (Bombay, 1878). He started on the work in 1876, and his experiments led him to conclude, as did Buffon, that silvered glass mirrors were superior to polished metal ones. This is no doubt true for ordinary use, though for laboratory experiments the polished metal ones give better results, as there is then no absorption by the glass (Plate 49A).

* * * * * *

"Adams also made a solar cooker, the reflector of which was formed of eight sheets of plane glass arranged so as to form a hollow truncated octagonal pyramid 2 feet 4 inches in diameter at the larger end. The food was placed in a cylindrical copper vessel, at the axis, covered with an octagonal glass shade. With this he and others cooked many meals, both stews and roasts.

* * * * * *

"In *Comptes rendus*, Volume 91, 1880, pages 388–389, M. Abel Pifre claims an efficiency of 80 per cent for his apparatus when he says he obtained a rate of absorption of 1.21 calories per square-centimeter-minute. If such a rate were obtained we now know it would mean an efficiency of 89.7 per cent,[3] which is improbable. Pifre used a parabolic reflector (instead of a truncated cone), and reduced the surface of the boiler, thus increasing the concentration. The capacity of his boiler was 11 gallons, and he collected 100 square feet of solar radiation so the diameter of his reflector was about 11 feet 4 inches. He used a rotary pump, and raised 99 liters of water 3 meters in 14 minutes, which is equivalent to 0.065 horsepower. He ran a printing press with his sun-power plant, and

[3] Perhaps the solar radiation at the time measured may have been as high as 1.56 calories per square centimeter per minute. If so the figure of efficiency would be 77 per cent, which indeed is improbably high.

claimed that if he had collected 216 square feet of radiation he could have produced 1 horsepower which is quite likely (Plate 49B). * * * * * *

"In Volume 73 of the *Proceedings, Inst. C. E.,* 1883, page 284, is described a plant designed by J. Harding, M. Inst. C. E., for distilling water by solar radiation.

"This plant was erected at Salinas, Chile, 4,300 feet above sea-level, and had 51,200 square feet of glass arranged in sections 4 feet wide, and in the form of a very flat ∧, forming the roof of a shallow water trough. The sun evaporated the water, and the resulting vapor condensed on the glass, for the temperature in the box was far higher than that of the atmosphere and hence of the glass. The pure water trickled down the sloping glass and dripped from its lower edge into a small channel on the top of each side of the box. These channels delivered into larger ones, and thus the distilled water was collected. The plant yielded 5,000 gallons of pure water per day in summer, *i.e.,* 1 pound of water per square foot of glass. Allowing for interest on capital, cost of repairs, etc., the cost of the pure water is said to have been less than one-half penny per gallon. The chief item of expense was the breakage of glass by whirlwinds. Distillation started at 10 a m. and continued to 10 p. m. The maximum temperature of the water in the troughs was 150° F. The total cost of the plant, including pumps, windmills, and tanks, was $50,000, or 1s. 6d. per square foot of glass.

* * * * * *

"A. G. Eneas, in the United States, used the popular truncated, cone-shaped reflector, collecting about 700 square feet of solar radiation. The weight of the reflector was 8,300 pounds.

"The boiler was formed of two concentric steel tubes, the two together being incased in two glass tubes with an air space between them and another air space between the inner glass one and the outer steel tube. The water

PLATE 50

Eneas's sun-power plant at Pasadena, 1901. (After Ackermann, from an old print)

PLATE 51

The Shuman-Boys solar engine at Meadi, Egypt, 1913. (After Ackermann. From "The Earth and the Stars," courtesy of the Van Nostrand Co.)

circulated up between the inner and outer steel tubes and down the inner tube. The boiler was placed at the axis of the cone. Its length was 13 feet 6 inches, its water capacity 834 pounds (13.4 cubic feet), and steam space 8 cubic feet. Hence the diameter of the outer tube appears to have been 1 foot 2 inches and the concentration of radiation 13.4; *i.e.,* 13.4 square feet of sunshine were concentrated on each square foot of the external surface of the boiler.

"C. G. Abbot ('The Sun,' p. 369) states that Eneas gave him the following particulars:

"*February 14, 1901.*—Pasadena, Cal., 11.30 a.m.—0.30 p.m.; 642 square feet sunshine. Temperature of air, 61° F. Steam pressure, 145–151 pounds per square inch. Steam condensed, 123 pounds.

"*October 3, 1903.*—Mesa, Ariz., 'about midday'; 700 square feet sunshine. Temperature of air, 74° F. Average steam pressure, 141 pounds per square inch. Steam condensed, 133 pounds.

"*October 9, 1904.*—Willcox, Ariz., 11 a.m.—12 a.m.; 700 square feet sunshine. Steam pressure, 148–156 pounds per square inch. Steam condensed, 144.5 pounds.

"The temperature of the feed water is not given, but, assuming it to be the same as the temperature of the air, we can deduce the rate of absorption per square foot of radiation and the thermal efficiency of the absorber. This being done, we obtain the following table:

Place and date	Period	Weight of steam produced in pounds	Mean pressure of steam in pounds per square inch of absorber	Rate of absorption per square foot of radiation collected, B. t. u. per hour	Thermal efficiency of the absorber
					Per cent[4]
Pasadena, Feb. 14, 1901	11.30 a.m. to 0.30 p.m.	123	163	223	74.6
Mesa, Oct. 3, 1903	"About midday"	133	156	219	73.3
Willcox, Oct. 9, 1904	11 a.m. to 12 m.	144.5	167	238	79.6

"[4]For a maximum transmssion of radiation through the atmosphere of 70 per cent.[5]"

[5] The writer believes Mr. Ackermann should have used atmospheric transmission 80 per cent. This would have diminished the thermal efficiency percentages in the ratio ⅞.

"Eneas refers to his 'nine different types of large reflectors,' and found that he obtained better results when he concentrated the reflected rays 'on two parts of the boiler instead of its entire length, as in the Pasadena machine.' The unexposed portions of the boiler then appear to have been lagged.

"Eneas said, 'I find 3.71 B. t. u. per square foot per minute as the greatest amount of heat obtainable during the trial runs.' This gives a maximum efficiency of 74.5 per cent, which agrees with the result given for his Pasadena plant in the foregoing table.[6]

* * * * * *

"The sun-power plant known as the Pasadena[7] one was described and illustrated in the August, 1901, issue of *Cassier's Magazine* by Prof. R. H. Thurston, LL.D.,D.E., and on page 103 of the *Railway and Engineering Review* of February 23, 1901. It is stated to have been designed by, and erected at the expense of, 'a party of Boston inventors whose names have not been made public.' It consisted of a truncated cone reflector, 33 feet 6 inches in diameter at the larger end and 15 feet diameter at the smaller, with a boiler 13 feet 6 inches long, having a capacity of 100 gallons (U. S. A.) plus 8 cubic feet of steam space (Plate 50).

"The article in the *Railway and Engineering Review* states: 'According to newspaper accounts, the all-day average work performed by the engine is 1,400 gallons (U. S. A.) of water lifted 12 feet per minute, which is at the rate of 4 horsepower.' It is more nearly 4¼ horsepower; thus, this plant required 150 square feet of radiation per horsepower, and the concentration appears to have been 13.4.

"The Pasadena plant is said to have cost £1,000, and Willsie, writing of it in 1909, says it was 'the largest

[6] See note on page 203.

[7] There appear to have been several plants erected at Pasadena by different experimenters. Probably Eneas designed the plant above described.

and strongest of the mirror type of solar motor ever
built.'

"H. E. Willsie and John Boyle, Jr., started their work
in America in 1902. The method they adopted was to
let the solar radiation pass through glass and heat water,
which in turn was used to vaporize some volatile fluid
such as ammonium hydrate, ether, or sulphur dioxide,
the vapor being used to drive an engine.

"Willsie thinks he was the first to propose this two-
fluid method for the utilization of solar energy, and, so
far as the author knows, his claim is correct. Their first
sun-heat absorber was built at Olney, Ill., and consisted of:

"A shallow wooden tank tightly covered with a double layer of
window glass. The sides and bottom were insulated by inclosed air
spaces filled with hay. The tank was lined with tar paper, well pitched,
to hold water to the depth of 3 inches. Although the weather was
cold and raw, even for October, with occasional clouds, the thermometer in the water showed temperatures higher than were needed to
operate a sulphur dioxide engine.

"The next solar heater was built at Hardyville, Ariz. Sand was used
for insulation. Three tests for the amount of heat gave these average
results in December:

Test No.	Heat units absorbed per square foot per hour
1	120
2	122
3	148

"An estimate showed that 50 per cent of the heat reaching the glass
was absorbed into the water.

"In 1903 some further heater tests were made, patent applications
filed, and to carry on experiments on a more extensive scale the
Willsie Sun Power Co. was incorporated.

"In the spring of 1904 a complete sun-power plant was built at
St. Louis. In this installation a 6-horsepower engine was operated
by ammonia. The heater consisted of a shallow wooden basin coated
with asphalt and divided by strips into troughs. It was covered by
two layers of window glass and insulated at the sides and bottom by
double air spaces. Each trough of the heater formed a compartment.
The troughs were inclined so that a thin layer of water flowed from
one trough to the next. In this heater was collected and absorbed
into the water from the sun's rays 211,500 heat units per hour at

noon, or 377 heat units per hour per square foot of glass exposed to the sun. As, according to accepted solar observations, about 440[8] heat units per hour reached a square foot of glass, this heater was showing the surprising efficiency of 85 per cent, and collecting nearly twice as much solar heat per square foot per hour as did the apparatus of Ericsson. Of the lost heat I estimated that 40 heat units were reflected and absorbed by the glass and that 23 heat units were radiated. On cloudy days the water could be heated by burning fuel. A description of this plant appeared in a St. Louis paper and in a New York paper, but, so far as I know, it has not been mentioned in any technical publication.

"It was then decided to build a sun-power plant on the desert, and some land about a mile from The Needles, Cal., was purchased for a site.

"This Needles Plant used sulphur dioxide, and its results decided them to build a larger plant, which Willsie speaks of as their third sun-power plant, and describes as follows:

"A 20-horsepower slide-valve engine was connected to an open-air water-drip condenser and to a fire-tube boiler 22 inches by 19 feet having fifty-two 1-inch tubes. The solar-heated liquid flowed through the tubes giving up its heat to the sulphur dioxide within the boiler. Boiler pressures of over 200 pounds were easily obtained. The engine operated a centrifugal pump, lifting water from a well 43 feet deep (*sic*), and also a compressor, in addition to two circulating pumps.

"Their fourth plant was a rebuilding of the third, and they tried the expedient of covering the heat-absorbing water with a layer of oil, but the results were not so good as when a heat-absorbing liquid (water, or oil, or a solution of chloride of calcium) was rapidly circulated in a thin layer. The sun-heat absorber for this plant was in two sections, one covered with one layer of glass and one with two layers, and both on a slope, the liquid running from the first to the second, and its temperature in the two sections being 150° F. and 180° F., respectively. The liquid at 180° F. was distributed over a 'heat exchanger' consisting of horizontal pipes about 3 inches in

[8] No; only 299. Note: $0.70 \times 1.93 = 1.352$ calories per square-centimeter-minute $= 299$ B. t. u. per square-foot-hour. (Here, again, the writer would propose the higher value of 80 per cent in place of 70. Yet Willsie and Boyle's solar-radiation measures may have been erroneous. There were few sound types of pyrheliometers at that period.)

diameter, arranged in a vertical plane, something like an
air condenser. The pipes contained sulphur dioxide, and
the heat-absorbing liquid lost about 100° F. in its descent.
The cooled liquid was returned to the two sections of the
absorber to be reheated. The heat exchanger was inclosed in a glass-covered shed. Willsie says:

"The engine used in this experiment was a vertical automatic cut-
off, which at times, with a boiler pressure of 215 pounds, probably
developed 15 horsepower. The two-heater sections exposed an area
of about 1,000 square feet to the sun, but as the heat was taken from
storage and not directly from the heater, it is not fair to assume the
above proportion of heater surface to horsepower developed.

"The condenser consisted of 6 stacks of horizontal pipes, 12 pipes
to the stack. The cooling water, pumped from a well 43 feet deep,
had a temperature of 75° F. Only enough water was allowed to drip
over the pipes to keep them wet, and so great was the evaporation
in the dry desert breeze that the cooling water left the lower pipes
at 64°. By using the cooling water over and over, the condenser gave
very satisfactory results. A shade of arrow weed, a straight willow-
like shrub abundant along the Colorado River, kept the sunshine
from the condenser pipes and permitted a good air circulation.

"Willsie estimated the cost of his sun-power plant,
complete with engine, at £33 12s. per horsepower.

"With regard to Willsie's results, it is to be noted that
377 B. t. u. per hour means an efficiency of $\dfrac{377 \times 100}{60 \times 0.70 \times 7.12}$
= 126 per cent, for we now know that a maximum of
only about 299 B. t. u. per square foot per hour penetrate
the atmosphere. The author agrees with the 50 per cent
efficiency given a little earlier by Willsie.

"Frank Shuman, of America, started on the problem
in 1906, and in 1907 he had a plant running which developed about 3½ horsepower; 1,200 square feet of sunshine
fell onto a fixed, horizontal water box with a glass top.
In the water there were rows of parallel horizontal black
pipes containing ether, and exposing 900 square feet of
surface to the solar radiation. The water also became
heated and conveyed heat to the under sides of the pipes.

The ether boiled, and its 'steam' drove a small vertical, simple, single-cylinder engine. The exhaust ether vapor passed into an air surface condenser, and the liquid ether from this was pumped back into the tubes of the 'boiler' already described.

"This plant, Shuman says, ran well even when snow was lying on the ground. This at first seems very remarkable, but though in the winter the number of solar rays falling on a given horizontal area is smaller than in summer, the permeability of the atmosphere is about 20 per cent greater in winter than in summer, which counteracts the other effect; but of course the loss of heat by conduction from the boiler is greater in winter than in summer.

"In 1910 Shuman constructed an experimental unit of an absorber measuring 6 by 9 feet. This unit combined the lamellar boiler of Tellier and the 'hot box' of de Saussure, for it consisted of a shallow black box with double glass top, with 1 inch of air space between the two layers of glass, another air space of an inch between the lower glass and the boiler, which was 6 feet long (up the slant), 2 feet 6 inches wide, and 1/4 inch thick over all. The box was so sloped that at noon the rays of the sun were perpendicular to the glass. The box was not moved to follow the sun, but it was adjusted about every three weeks, so that the condition just named was complied with. The remarkable thing about the absorber was that there was no concentration of any kind of the sunshine by mirrors, lenses, or other means, and yet the author on one occasion recorded a temperature of 250° F. in the box. The best run of an hour's duration produced steam at atmospheric pressure at the rate of 7½ pounds per 100 square feet of sunshine falling on the box. The author's tests of a Shuman 100-horsepower low-pressure engine at Erith showed the steam consumption to be 22 pounds at atmospheric pressure per brake-horsepower-hour. Hence, with an absorber of the type just described, it would be necessary to collect solar radiation to the extent of 300 square feet per brake horsepower, which is a much larger area than any named by other workers. The maximum thermal efficiency of this absorber was 24.1 per cent.

"In 1911, with the aid of some English capitalists, Shuman constructed his third absorber at Tacony (a suburb of Philadelphia), which was almost identical with the one just described, except that it had two plane mirrors, one at the upper edge of the 'hot box' and one at the lower, so arranged that 6 square feet of sunshine were concentrated onto 3 square feet of 'hot box'; i.e., the concentration was 2 to 1. Its position was adjusted about every three weeks. This time the total quantity of solar radiation collected was many times as large as the largest collected by any previous worker, for the total area was 10,296 square feet. In the best run of one hour this plant produced 816 pounds of steam at atmospheric pressure. This is at the rate of 9 pounds per 100 square feet of sunshine, and therefore equivalent to an allowance of 245 square feet of sunshine per brake horsepower. The maximum thermal efficiency of this absorber was 29.5 per cent.

"Toward the end of 1911 the Sun Power Co. (Eastern Hemisphere), Ltd., requested their consulting engineers (Messrs. A. S. E. Ackermann and C. T. Walrond) to select and invite some distinguished physicist to join them in a consultative capacity. Hence Prof. C. V. Boys, F.R.S., became associated with the work, and he suggested a vital change in the design of the absorber, viz., that the boilers should be placed on edge in a channel-shaped reflector of parabolic cross section, so that solar radiation was received on both their surfaces, instead of one being worse than idle, as it was when the boilers were placed side on to the sun. The design immediately received the hearty approval of the consulting engineers and Shuman, and at the time we all thought the arrangement was novel, but the author has since found and recorded herein that Ericsson used a very similar reflector and boiler.

"An absorber of this design was constructed and erected at Meadi on the Nile, 7 miles south of Cairo, in 1912, but the boiler was constructed of thin zinc and failed before the official tests could be made. This boiler was replaced by a cast-iron one in 1913, and the author (accompanied by his old pupil, G. W. Hilditch, A. M. Inst. C. E., as his chief assistant, now Lieut. Hilditch of the Divisional Engineers, Royal Naval Division) spent two most interesting months with the plant in July and August, 1913. He went out in time to tune up the Shuman engine (a 100-horsepower one) taken out from Tacony, and make all the necessary preparations for the trials, of which there were over 35.

"In addition to the alteration of the shape of the reflectors, another very important change was made. Their axes were placed north and south, and they were automatically heeled over from an eastern aspect in the morning to a western one in the evening, so as to follow the sun. Thus the same number of solar rays were caught all day long, and the small decrease in steam production in the morning and evening was almost entirely due to the greater thickness of atmosphere through which the rays had to pass. The total area of sunshine collected was 13,269 square feet (Plate 51).

"The boilers were placed at the focus of the reflectors and were covered with a single layer of glass inclosing an air space around the boilers. Each channel-shaped reflector and its boiler was 205 feet long, and there were five such sections placed side by side. The concentration was 4½ to 1. The maximum quantity of steam produced was 12 pounds per 100 square feet of sunshine, equivalent to 183 square feet per brake horsepower, and the maximum thermal efficiency was 40.1 per cent. The best hour's run gave 1,442 pounds of steam at atmospheric pressure; hence, allowing the 22 pounds of steam per brake-horsepower-hour, the maximum output for an hour was 55.5 brake horsepower—a result about 10 times as large as anything previously attained, and equal to 63 brake horsepower per acre of land occupied by the plant. A pleasing result was that the output did not fall off much in the morning and evening. Thus on August 22, 1913, the average power for the five hour's run was no less than 59.4 brake horsepower per acre, while the maximum and minimum power on that day were 63 and 52.4 brake horsepower per acre, respectively.

"In spite of this history of comparative failures, the author is of opinion that the problem of the utilization of solar energy is well worthy of the attention of engineers, for even now it is very nearly a solved problem where there is plenty of sunshine and coal costs £3 10s. a ton. It is fortunate that where coal is dear sunshine is often plentiful, and it is to be remembered that coal will gradually get dearer while the cost of manufacture of sun-power plants should decrease. Sun-power plants are admirably suitable for pumping in connection with irrigation, for where there is most sunshine there is need for most irrigation, and the slight variation in the quantity of water pumped throughout the day does not matter. Also, when temporarily there is no sunshine (due to clouds), probably little or no irrigation is required."

We see in these accounts by Ackermann, three principal types of devices for collecting solar heat for power purposes. There is the conical mirror of Mouchot, Pifre, Eneas and others; the cylindrical reflector of Ericsson, Shuman-Boys, and others; and the hot box of de Saussure, as applied by Willsie and Boyle, and by Shuman. These three types are all very interesting on account of the balance of advantages between high efficiency and low cost which they present.

It is well known that any heat engine which receives its driving fluid at one temperature, and gives it up at a lower one, cannot possibly attain a greater efficiency in its conversion of heat into mechanical work than is expressed by the formula:

$$E = \frac{T_1 - T_2}{T_1}$$

In this formula, E represents efficiency, and T_1 and T_2 are the initial and final temperatures. Both are expressed on the absolute scale, where zero is $-273°$ C., or $-459°$ F. The highest temperature which solar rays can produce at the earth's surface may be assumed to be 3,000° Abs. C. If a heat engine could be worked between this temperature and that of the air, roughly 300° Abs. C., the limiting possible efficiency would be

$$\frac{3000 - 300}{3000} = 90 \text{ per cent.}$$

Practically, the properties of metals must restrict us to much lower initial temperatures and to a maximum possible efficiency not higher than 70 per cent.

If, however, our solar heat collector should deliver the engine fluid at but 400° Abs. C., which is but little above boiling (373° Abs. C.) and the engine should work to 300°, as before, the maximum possible efficiency is but

$$\frac{400 - 300}{400} = 25 \text{ per cent.}$$

The examples just given are not at all concerned with the efficiency of collecting the solar heat. That might be anything from 80 per cent to zero, in either case. Whatever the proportion collected of what the sun furnishes, the efficiency of using it, after collection, could in no case exceed the values given, if the maximum temperatures attained stood as assumed. In reality heat engines used with steam boilers seldom reach 50 per cent of theoretical possible efficiency.

With these points in mind, it will be appreciated that on account of their high concentration of the solar rays, and the resulting high temperatures, the conical reflectors, especially if parabolic, like that of Pifre, give maximum theoretical possibilities of engine efficiency. On the other hand, the hot-box principle of de Saussure, as used by Willsie and Boyle, must necessarily give very low engine efficiency. The cylindrical-mirror type stands between them in this respect. On the other hand, the cheapness of installation and operation of heat collectors of the three types runs in the opposite order. What could be simpler than a glass-covered, black-bottomed pond, like Willsie and Boyle's, or what more cumbrous than an immense conical mirror, driven with the march of the sun, like that of Eneas? Cylindrical mirrors, horizontally mounted, as is possible at the equator, unite some of the high temperature possibilities of the conical collector, with some approach to the cheapness of the black-bottomed pond.

The problem of collecting solar heat for power purposes is indeed a very pretty one. It involves knowledge of optics, of mechanism, of the properties of radiation, and of heat engineering. Financial success probably awaits the solver, for with our present outlook it seems likely that within another generation or two power demands will lead to the sun as the most available source of supply.

To conclude this chapter, let us turn our attention to the solar cooker which has been operated with considerable success in connection with the Smithsonian expeditions to Mount Wilson, California. We have noted the device which Adams used so successfully in India about fifty years ago. As his instrument had no reservoir for storing the heat collected, it could operate only when the sun was shining. In my own experiments, begun at Mount Wilson, California, in the year 1916, I desired to store the heat in a suitable reservoir at such a temperature as would permit all the usual cooking operations, such as stewing, preserving, boiling and baking of meats, and even including the baking of bread, to be carried on for some time after the cutting off of sunlight.

THE SUN AND THE WELFARE OF MAN

As the most convenient way to combine a solar heat-collector with a suitable high-temperature reservoir, it seemed best to concentrate the solar rays upon a metal tube communicating to a reservoir at some distance above the collector. The scheme is exactly that of a common bath-water heater, merely substituting concentrated sun rays for a fire as the source of heat. In this way, the hot fluid, expanding, rises by the differential action of gravity into the top of the reservoir, while the cooler fluid at the bottom of it flows downward to the heat source in replacement. A continuous circulation of hot fluid would thus maintain the temperature of the reservoir. Water, the cheapest liquid, could not be used in the cooker unless under such pressure as would introduce a costly and dangerous element. Temperatures approaching 200° C. were desired, where if water were used steam pressures of nearly fifteen atmospheres would prevail. Instead of water, therefore, engine-cylinder oil was preferred. This fluid can be heated to temperatures somewhat above 200° C., without boiling, flashing, or strongly evaporating.

The hot-box principle of de Saussure had to be abandoned. The temperatures desired were too high for its scope. As most suitable from the point of view of cheapness and simplicity, I chose the cylindrical reflector of parabolic cross-section for the purpose of collecting and focusing the solar rays. It may not be known to all readers that a cylindrical reflector does not require, like a conical one, to have motions about two axes in order to follow the sun. If the cylindrical mirror is mounted upon an axis parallel to the earth's axis, a rotation from east towards west at the same rate as the earth's daily rotation from west towards east, is all that is required. To be sure, the full aperture of the mirror is attained only at the dates of the equinoxes. Yet if the mirror is made rather long from north to south, compared to its width from east to west, this loss is trifling, even in June and December.

PLATE 52

Abbot's solar cooker. Rays caught by the great mirror heat oil in the focus tube. The oil, circulating, bathes the cooking ovens in the reservoir above. The ovens stay heated night as well as day, and bake bread, meat, etc.

The mirror was made 12½ feet long, 7½ feet wide, and mounted with its long dimension parallel to an axis pointing towards the North Star. For rigidity and cheapness, the mirror was framed on five sections of structural steel. Each of these comprised a pair of parabolically curved L-bars, a, b, Figure 36, the straight bars, c, c, and a sheet of thin steel, d, bent to the parabolic curvature, and riveted

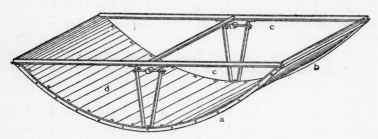

FIG. 36. Section of the steel mirror-frame of Abbot's solar cooker. Width, 7½ feet, length 12½ feet. Five sections like this, placed end to end, make the whole mirror

to the curved pieces a, b. The five sections, being exactly alike, were interchangeable, and, when bolted together, made up a structure which lacked only two end plates, to compose the complete mirror frame. This method of building the mirror frame in sections of the exact width of standard sheets of steel is a very economical one, and, owing to its form, a very rigid one.

But how should it become a brightly reflecting mirror? My first thought was to cover the steel with strips of tinfoil. This was tried in the year 1916. A long roll of brightest tinfoil, one foot wide, was readily procured. With the aid of shellac, the steel was smoothly coated with it. The result was very unsatisfactory. As the mirror warmed, the shellac evaporated, puffed up the tinfoil, and spoiled the shape of the reflecting surface. We pricked many of the blisters, and rolled the surface down, but though used in 1916, the shape of the mirror surface was not satisfactory. Moreover, the tinfoil tarnished, and lost its high reflecting power.

This defect was cured when the experiments were resumed in 1920 by substituting sheets of glossy rolled aluminum. These aluminum sheets were thick enough to preserve their shape when screwed to the steel. They added very little to the weight of the mirror, and were found to reflect about 75 per cent of the total solar radiation. Mirror-glasses laid on in narrow strips would have reflected nearly 10 per cent more than aluminum, but being heavy, costly, and fragile, and more difficult to clean, would have been far less satisfactory. Experience shows that aluminum sheets retain their highly reflecting surface for several years if kept dry.

Having thus made a light, rigid, parabolic, cylindrical mirror, the next care was to mount it free to turn about an axis parallel to the earth's. For this purpose, holes of 4 inches diameter were cut in the steel sheets at the two ends. Their centers lay in the line of focus of the parabolic curve. Hollow cast-iron trunnions were bolted on, concentric to these holes. A skeleton steel frame was erected on piers to support the mirror. Upon it were bolted two pairs of 4-inch brass rollers. They served as bearings for the mirror trunnions, similar to the roller bearings which support a grindstone shaft. A fifth supporting roller was mounted at the lower end to carry the end-thrust of the mirror as it lay, in its roller bearings, parallel to the axis of the earth. A roof-shaped steel frame above the mirror supported long thin weights of lead. These weights, interfering very little with the entering sun rays, exactly counterbalanced the whole mirror about its axis, so that it rotated thereon very readily.

It was necessary to provide a driving mechanism to cause the mirror to follow the apparent daily march of the sun from east to west. Much expense might have been lavished on this part, for the combination of an astronomical driving clock and a worm-and-wheel mech-

anism, as usually employed by astronomers to drive telescopes of a similar size, often costs hundreds of dollars.
A very inexpensive device was used for the mirror of the
cooker. A cast-iron wheel, formerly used on a foot-lathe,
was fitted to the lower trunnion. It had three grooves
originally intended for different lathe-speeds. From one
groove a piece of piano wire was attached to a lead weight,

FIG. 37. Diagram of the driving gear of the Abbot solar cooker. The
weight turns the mirror westward at a rate governed by an ordinary
alarm clock

acting to turn the mirror westward. A second wire was
wound in another groove in the opposite sense, so as to hold
back this westward rotation.

This second wire led to a drum, within a cheap clockwork, or motor-movement, such as used to serve to turn
ladies' hats and other models in show-windows, before
the days of electric motors. This clockwork ended in
what is called a fly-vane, which indeed retarded its motion,
but allowed the mirror to turn a little faster than it
should to follow the sun. A light arm, like a clock-hand,
was fixed to the central shaft of the motor-movement.
This hand engaged with a stop at every revolution. The

[219]

stop was disengaged, at the end of each five minutes, by a lever operated by a twelve-pin wheel fixed to the minute-hand shaft of a cheap alarm clock.

So the little alarm clock was master of the situation. It gave the signal which at each five minutes allowed the machinery to run. The machinery ran a little too fast, and after a short run was held back for about a minute, awaiting the next pleasure of the little master-clock. The whole driving outfit cost about fifteen dollars in money, and about three days' work. It has operated perfectly satisfactorily, for about eight hours a day, through several summers.

The reservoir, $20 \times 24 \times 36$ inches, was made of steel, with welded corners. Two ovens, each $9 \times 11 \times 16\frac{1}{2}$ inches, were let in at the back. The reservoir stands on a platform about six feet above the top end of the mirror. To conduct the heated oil, there is a copper pipe, $1\frac{1}{4}$ inches in diameter, bent so as to pass from the reservoir down under the mirror, returning in the focus of the sun rays through the hollow trunnions. The hot oil is delivered at a level above the upper oven. The returning oil-circuit has two inlets, one between the ovens, the other at the bottom of the reservoir. Either of them may be used. This alternative device, automatically regulated by a floating valve, is intended to restrict the heating in the early morn-

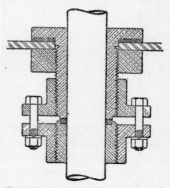

Fig. 38. Oil-tight insertion of the heater tube of the solar cooker into the hot reservoir

ing to the upper oven, and then, when this is hot, to distribute the heat throughout the whole reservoir.

In order to be able to make oil-tight joints when setting up the cooker in the field, and still to have the pipes

PLATE 53

A group of diatoms, microscopic sea plants whose remains
make up great cliffs in California from which bricks are cut
for insulating furnaces

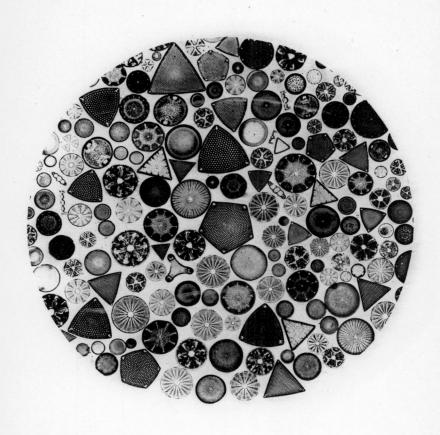

small enough to pass through certain glass tubes, soon to be described, peculiar connectors as shown in Figure 38 are employed. The parts are brazed permanently to the copper tubes, and tested under pressure for leakage. The remainder of the fitting is easily done in the field. To make connection with the reservoir itself, another connecting device, also shown in Figure 38, is used. These arrangements proved perfectly satisfactory.

The reservoir and pipes are protected from loss of heat by brickwork composed of diatomaceous earth. Such bricks are called by the trade name of "silocel." Diatoms, it is well known, are microscopic plants, and are among the most beautiful objects in creation. Growing in immense colonies, their fossil remains in some localities make up large deposits of a soft rock-like consistency. From beds of these deposits are cut the bricks much used in furnace walls, because extremely non-conducting of heat. Only substances like cotton and silk-fluff are less conducting, and their insulating advantage over the bricks is very slight. As these bricks are perfectly fireproof, they are highly suitable for use around an oil reservoir, heated nearly to the limit of safe oil temperatures.

It remains to speak of the coverings of the mirror, and of the heater-tube within it. In order to avoid cooling by air currents, and to prevent the mirror surface from being fouled by dust and other things, the whole top of the mirror frame is covered by sheets of window glass. To prevent the loss of heat by air-convection from the very hot blackened heater-tube, this metal tube is surrounded by a glass tube, leaving an air-space of about 3/4 inch all around it. But the glass tube grows very hot, and itself tends to cool, so that great losses of heat would still occur there. This is hindered by a second concentric tube of glass, larger than the first, and separated from it by the highest practicable vacuum. In this way, the heated inner tube is, like the inner part of a thermos bottle, prevented from cooling by a vacuum jacket. Of course it is not practicable to coat the inner glass with silver, like a thermos bottle. Complete silvering of it would shut out the sun rays. However, the upper one-third of its surface is silvered, which helps decidedly to prevent the escape of heat, and hinders very little the sun rays from entering.

The whole cooker, with all of its coverings, is shown in Plate 52. Temperatures of 175° C. are readily attained. This is quite hot enough to bake bread. In its present situation, on Mount Wilson, the mirror is partly shaded in the early morning, and altogether shaded after about 2 o'clock in the afternoon, by trees. Hence, only about 7 hours a day of sunlight are available. Nevertheless the temperature of the ovens remains always above boiling, so that many kinds of food may be cooked at night, if desired.

Fruit is preserved with great ease. The prepared fruit is put into glass jars, covered over with syrup, and left over night in the lower oven. In the morning, the jar covers are fastened down while still hot. That is all! Indeed, the cooker is highly convenient. Foods may be prepared in a cool kitchen, having no fire. A beautiful mountain view is seen as they are set into the ovens out-of-doors. There is no danger of burning in the well-tempered heat. Foods may be left to cook for many hours without harm. All meats and vegetables are most deliciously prepared.

In short, the solar cooker is a delightful luxury. Whether improvements and simplifications may reduce it to less than a luxury is still questionable. As an experiment in collecting solar heat, it has served a very useful purpose. Several of the devices tried out thereby seem likely to be of value for the greater problem of harnessing the sun rays for power.

CHAPTER X

SUN RAYS, PLANTS, AND ANIMALS

THE delight which we take in the lovely shapes, colors, and odors of the many species of flowering plants suggests a different emphasis on a famous argument. Hardly any work was more celebrated in its time than Dean Paley's "Natural Theology," although it is little read now. The author conceives one to be wandering upon a desolate moor remote from human habitation. He chances to strike his foot upon a round object so curious as to arouse his careful attention. It is, in short, a watch, provided with the little wheels, the springs, the hands, the hour marks, and all the intricate parts that we know so well. Although there is no man in sight, nor indeed any habitation for many miles, there can be but one conclusion. The plain evidence of complex contrivance for a sagacious purpose demands the previous existence of a highly intelligent contriver. The watch could not just have happened to come into being.

We need not follow the logical unfolding of the theme, in which the able Dean argues from the evidences of design in the human body to the existence of an intelligent creator. Paley's argument was indeed illustrated mainly from the animal kingdom, but, as we shall see, plants exhibit adaptations almost equally curious.

Our present thought, however, is slightly different. Such contrivances as the human eye and ear, and others which Paley refers to, are plainly suitable means to attain certain objects of utility. If they be evidences of design,

[223]

the character of the designer that seems to be suggested is the careful parent providing necessary things for the use of his children. But a rose or a violet seems to turn our thought differently. It might well be the expression of a beauty-loving, benevolent, pleasure-providing creator, designing not merely necessities, but delicately refined joys and pleasures for the promotion of graces of character in his noblest creatures.

The sun's place in plant life is more extraordinary by far than it is in the animal economy. Growing vegetation is a laboratory where sun rays unite carbonic acid gas of the air with watery fluid brought up through the roots of the plant, building up from these two simple materials some of the most complex substances known to organic chemistry. Although consisting mainly of water, traces of the other chemical elements are dissolved in the fluid which the roots imbibe, sufficient to complete those complex compounds so indispensable to life.

It has been estimated that a square mile of dense hardwood forest may use over 500 tons of carbonic acid gas, and over a million tons of water in a season, for such chemical activities. In dry countries such prodigality with water would be, of course, impossible. This figure represents a depth of nearly 1½ feet of liquid water over the whole area, which is from 1/3 to 1/6 of the total yearly rainfall of very moist climates, and exceeds by fivefold the yearly rainfall of some of the great deserts.

Only a small part of the imbibed water is retained by vegetation. The leaves have a multitude of little mouths, called *stomata*, which, when under the influence of light, suck in carbonic acid gas, and exude oxygen and water-vapor. In darkness plants exude carbonic acid gas slowly. This seems to be an attribute of all living cells, plant as well as animal. It no doubt goes on in the light with plants also, but is obscured by the opposite reaction just mentioned. The combined area of all the stomata hardly amounts to one per cent of the area of the leaves, so that

PLATE 54

Wheeled light-frame of the Boyce Thompson Institute for Plant Research, at Yonkers, N. Y., for experiments on plant growth under different colors and for prolonging the radiation beyond the length of daylight

PLATE 55

A—The effect of different colors of light on the growth of plants. H1 and H2 have favorable lighting. In H3, H4, and H5, respectively, the ultra-violet, the violet, the blue, and half of the green rays were successively cut off. Experiments of the Boyce Thompson Institute for Plant Research

B—Experiments with lettuce under different daily durations of artificial light. They were all small plants bearing two or three leaves when placed in the light frames 38 days before. Experiments of the Boyce Thompson Institute for Plant Research

it is hard to see how so much material can pass through such tiny orifices. It has, indeed, been shown that if one-half the leaf area were kept wet with fresh, strong caustic potash solution, it could not absorb carbonic acid gas faster than the stomata.

Brown and Escombe resolved the puzzle. They showed by laboratory experiments that when carbonic gas acid is admitted through a small orifice into a medium which absorbs it as fast as admitted, the amount transmitted is proportional, not to the *area*, but to the *diameter* of the orifice. For example, the same area of opening, if split up into four parts, will admit twice as much carbonic acid gas as when forming only one orifice, since the diameter of the large orifice is twice the diameter of each of the four small ones. This paradox, of course, depends on a more rapid rate of flow of the gases through the smaller apertures.

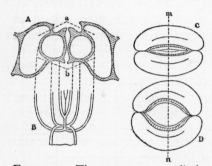

Fig. 39. The stomata, or little mouths, of plant-leaves by which they feed on the carbonic acid of the air. After Schwendener. (From "The Sun" by C. G. Abbot, D. Appleton Co., New York)

Nature avails herself of this strange secret by crowding stomata something like a million to the square inch. She thus adapts her leaves to suck in their sustenance and give out the waste products almost as rapidly as if the whole leaf were one aperture, while really about 99 per cent of its surface is closed to protect the delicate cells within.

Even this is not the whole story. The stomata, like mouths of animals, may be either wide open, shut, or partly open, and they go through all of these variations. It is not known exactly how they are regulated. We, at least, do not suppose that the plants use volition as men do in opening their mouths. Yet it is conceivable that, if sunlight was exceedingly bright on a hot summer day, the evaporation of water could be so great that the chemical products left behind would exceed the requirements of the plant, and kill it by over-feeding. Against such a possibility perhaps the stomata might need to be partially closed. On the other hand, if the air was very free from clouds and moisture, and a strong cool breeze blowing, the plant might become chilled by excessive evaporation unless the stomata were partly closed. There are, at all events, automatic devices within the leaf mechanism which attend to this needful regulation of the stomata. Besides these regulating devices, the leaves themselves, under the influence of changing sunlight, turn face or edge toward the sun according to the plant's requirements.

If the penetration of gases through the stomata in such profusion was a great puzzle, the ascent of the sap is, perhaps, even more extraordinary. For imagine a forest of gigantic eucalyptus trees, which sometimes reach heights of 500 feet, and conceive of the energy demanded to lift in a single summer hundreds of thousands of tons of water on each square mile from the ground to the leafy tops. A common vacuum pump, it is well known, cannot lift water above 33 feet, so that we dismiss at once the thought that the air pressure is working for the trees. What form of energy and application of force are these which the tree commands to do this lifting?

The energy is the heat of sun rays, and the forces at work are the capillary attraction and surface tension of water. By means of the capillary tube-like network of cells, which runs from the roots up through the trunk of the tree, there is formed a connection between the stomata of the leaves and the water of the ground. These enormously numerous capillary passages are filled with fluid, partly liquid, partly gaseous. At their orifices, which are the stomata of the leaves and twigs, the sun's heat produces a continuous evaporation of pure water, leaving behind in the tree the traces of chemicals which the soil furnishes with the water, and which yield plant food.

We seldom think of the forces of capillarity and surface tension which come into play, though they are the same that raise kerosene oil in a lamp wick and that make drops of oil spread over a wet pavement. These forces are limited in their action to distances far less than the thickness of a single sheet of tissue paper, but are extremely powerful in circumstances where they are at their maximum strength. For instance, a single drop of water introduced between two clean flat glasses slightly inclined to each other, will run rapidly to the narrowest spaces, and will draw the two plates together so strongly as even to bruise or crush the glass. Similarly, two blocks of ice placed loosely together, and so that the water which melts from them can drain away, will be drawn together by the remaining water so closely that the two ice blocks become united into one by cohering together. This process is called regelation. On the contrary, the fluid, mercury, which does not wet glass, will, on account of surface tension escape from between two glasses, even if by doing so it must create a vacuum behind.

The rise of water and other liquids in very fine tubes is a consequence of surface tension, which in this connection is often called capillary force. The height to which a column of liquid will rise in a tube which it wets is inversely proportional to the diameter of the tube. The extreme fineness of the porous structure of the trunks, twigs, and leaves of trees, therefore, is adapted to convey the liquids imbibed by the roots to very great heights. The evaporation of water from the stomata of the leaves and twigs makes place for the continuous renewal of liquid by capillary action from below. This upward current is conveyed by the interior part of the tree stem. As it has been observed to reach great heights in dead trees, we must adopt some such physical explanation as has been given, and not invent a mysterious "life force" for the purpose, as older botanists were prone to do.

The soft, live, outer part of the plant, just within the bark, has another function. It is to carry downwards to the extremities of the roots the chemical products built up in the leaves and green parts under the action of sunlight.

Thus in a live plant, as in a live animal, there is a fluid circulation. The manner of it, to be sure, is exceedingly different. Instead of the force-pump which we called the heart, there is substituted in the plant the force of capillary action, lifting the watery fluid to the tops of majestic trees. It brings, dissolved, the chemical plant foods from the ground, and so feeds the trees. The return current, much less in volume, is probably maintained by still another modification of surface tension which we call osmotic pressure. This is a force, which often greatly exceeds atmospheric pressure. It always exists between watery solutions of chemical substances in different concentrations, tending to drive the more concentrated solution into the one less concentrated. Thus, the force of osmotic pressure tends to produce a uniform mixture. In a tree, it takes the more concentrated products of solar chemistry from the laboratory of the leaves, and conveys them downward through the living layers under the bark to the roots, to nourish these, and to be laid up, beyond the influence of wintry frosts, for the renewal of the leaves in the spring.

The reader should not conclude from what has been said that the life processes of a tree are wholly understood. On the contrary, the best-informed plant physiologists admit that they are confronted by a maze of mysteries which becomes more bewildering with additional research. They are becoming convinced that the simple protoplasmic living cells in plants and animals have much in common. A plant, like an animal, is to be looked upon as a colony of cells. Just as in a society of bees, or of ants, some individuals are told off and become modified in structure to perform certain duties necessary to the life of the society as a whole, so in plants and in animals the protoplasmic cells are, as physiologists say, differentiated, some for one function, some for another. By what physical agencies this is done is the mystery of life. Thus, we have in the plant, the root with a variety of cells, some for imbibing ground water, others for storing food during wintry cold, still others forming a protecting covering. Again in the stem are some adapted for mechanical resistance to pressures like those of winds, others promoting the passage of food stuffs, and still others protecting the interior from exposure. In the leaves there are the variety of special cells, adapted for the several different functions involved in nature's solar chemistry. Finally, in the flowers and ripening fruits are other varieties of cells set apart for the many functions associated with reproduction.

All of these modifications of the primordial cell work together in admirable harmony to promote life and growth of the cell colony which we call a plant. One may be apt to think of it as very inferior to the cell colony which we call the animal. For does it not lack a nervous system for communication, and also the capacity for motion? But the latest researches seem to show that the plant is not so deficient in these respects as might be supposed. What, for instance, causes a bending of the stem towards the light, and the development of rudimentary buds into growing shoots when the terminal bud is lost, if there be no communication of useful impulses through the body of a plant? What leads to the great storage of food in the root system, to prepare for the dormant period of winter, and for the uprush of the sap in spring, to cause the leaves and buds to burst forth? These are but a few of the great mysteries which, the closer they are studied, the higher they tend to raise our admiration. Finally, the plant kingdom has the great superiority over the animal that, like the farmer among men, it furnishes by its unique employment of solar radiation, not only the means to feed its own living cells, but those of the animal world besides.

Already, therefore, we have discovered in the plant two indispensable activities of the sun. The first is the mysterious combining influence of certain solar rays, which, acting in green leaves, builds up the most complex life chemicals from such simple materials as carbonic acid gas of the air and weakly impregnated water from the ground. This is an action as yet inimitable in the laboratory. We have yet to learn its intricacy and causation. The second indispensable action of solar energy is to evaporate from the leaves and twigs enormous quantities of water. Thus are left behind, in suitable concentration for the use of the chemistry of plants, the various needful chemicals brought up in extremely diluted form in the water imbibed by the roots.

But this is not all. In producing this immense evaporation, the sun counteracts its own influence to unduly heat and scorch the delicate leaves. Turning liquid water to vapor requires a very large supply of heat. So the sun heat absorbed by the leaves is safely dissipated. Indeed, as in the human body, there is a rough uniformity of temperature preserved in plant leaves, and largely by the regulatory action of evaporation. Some plants, indeed, have automatic mechanisms which turn their parts towards the sun, or edgewise to its rays, according to requirement. These plant motions are well known, as we see them in the sunflower and the nasturtium, and are, indeed, very common in the plant realm.

Fourthly, the sun maintains a suitable temperature. Plant growth requires a state of temperature whose range is practically limited between 0° and 50° C. (32° and 122° F.). It is this state of affairs which the sun maintains constantly in the tropics, and through a part of the year in temperate and polar zones. As we have discussed this office of sun rays in other chapters, we need not dwell upon the manner of it here, though we shall note some curious effects which temperature regulation may produce in plants.

Such are the four great services of sun rays to plants, but in their response to these influences the plants exhibit a most interesting variety. Astonishing changes in growth and texture may be brought about merely by altering the temperature of environment, the duration of sunlight, and the intensity and spectral quality of sun rays. Changes in the water ration, the chemistry of the soil, and the concentration of carbonic acid gas in the air, also produce profound effects, but as these are but indirectly affected by the sun, we shall not discuss them, but turn our attention to the direct influences first mentioned.

Col. Boyce Thompson has munificently established in Yonkers, New York, a laboratory splendidly equipped for the investigation of such effects, as well as for the study of plant diseases. In basement rooms there are provided cooling pipes and automatic regulators adapted to keep plants for as long as desired at definite temperatures and under powerful batteries of electric lamps as a substitute for sun rays. The potted plants are mounted on little perambulators so that when the desired time of exposure in one temperature has elapsed, they may be removed to different temperature surroundings. Instances of the curious results are shown in the accompanying illustrations.

In another part of the laboratory is a glass-roofed hothouse. But the glass is not all the same. One part is tinged with violet, another with blue green, another with yellow orange, another with red, and one is of clear glass. Thus the rays of sun and sky are modified by the absorption of the glass so that different regions of the spectrum are most effective for the several little gardens. It is very curious to see the changes of color in a lady's dress as she passes from garden to garden under the control of these different colored lights. These conditions change remarkably the character of the plant growth as shown by the accompanying illustrations.

There is also a great movable roof which can be rolled over the hothouses. This is provided with clusters of powerful electric lamps sufficient to be a substitute for sunlight. With this apparatus, experiments in the effect of continuous and part-time illumination are performed. This field has had much attention by Doctor Garner and associates of the U. S. Department of Agriculture. Some of his results are shown in the illustrations.

Everyone knows how a potato in a dark cellar in spring-time sends out its white sprouts, which stretch away sometimes a yard or more towards some feeble crack of light. Here we see two things of importance. First, that the healthy green development necessary to sound growth cannot take place without adequate light, and, second, that insufficient light leads to monstrous elongation of plant stems.

In the solar chemistry of the leaves, their green coloring matter, called chlorophyl, seems to be indispensable. Yet it does not itself join permanently in the reactions, but rather seems to be what is called a catalyst, which in chemistry means some substance that is necessary to cause reactions to happen, but is not itself a part either of the original materials or of the end products. What must happen in plant chemistry is to join with each molecule of carbonic acid gas a certain number of molecules of water, remove from the mixture one molecule of oxygen, and leave the compound a single stable molecule of the type called a sugar. There are many sugars and near sugars. Of these our ordinary cane-sugar molecule includes 12 atoms of carbon with 11 atoms of oxygen and 22 atoms of hydrogen. Much simpler sugarlike substances exist, but all, as we remarked above, have the general formula $C_n O_m H_{2m}$, where C, O, H stand for atoms of carbon, oxygen, and hydrogen, and n and m stand for numbers which may run up nearly to a score.

The sugars are closely allied to the starches, whose molecules have the same general relations of numbers of

PLATE 56

B—The evening primrose, a "long-day" plant, exposed to 10-hour day is unable to develop flower stems, but when exposed to full-length day of Washington summer, is almost ready to bloom. Experiments of Garner, U. S. Department of Agriculture

A—The Klondike cosmos, a "short-day" plant. The tall specimen, exposed to full Washington summer days, refused to blossom, while the other, exposed but eight hours daily, flowered at a few inches in height. Experiments of Garner, U. S. Department of Agriculture.

PLATE 57

Little patients of the J. N. Adam Memorial Hospital, Perrysburg, N. Y., who are being cured by the rays from the sun. Photograph from Dr. Horace LoGrasso

the three chemical constituents, but contain several or many times as many atoms as the sugars. Starches are stored up by the plants in great profusion in their roots, tubers, and fruits. They break up readily into sugars. Starches, sugars, and, in addition, cellulose, in whose molecules are also found the same general proportions of the three constituents, carbon, oxygen, and hydrogen, as in starch and sugar, compose the main part of plant substance. Some of the other chemical elements, to be sure, are necessary to healthy plants, though in very small proportions. The chemical formulas of some of these compounds are excessively complicated, and raise our admiration for plant chemistry.

As plants must have light in order to grow, they strongly compete for it by stretching towards the sky. Where light is inadequate the stems lengthen. This is called by botanists etiolation. Its effect is very marked in the comparative shapes of two pines, one growing alone on a clearing, the other in a thick wood. Another well-known effect of scarcity of light is to thin and broaden the leaves. This is taken advantage of by some tobacco growers, who by erecting semi-transparent tents over their crops produce a higher grade of tobacco.

It is at first sight quite surprising, but after all quite in harmony with the fact of etiolation, that plants grow tall faster in the night than in the day. Their maximum rate of growth is just after sunset, when it is apt to be over twice as rapid as in midday.

There is also a curious expansion and contraction of plant stems in growing. The contraction seems to be caused by the rapid evaporation of water from the leaves during the daylight hours, and a resulting upward tension of the liquid in the conducting channels of the stem, which relieves the horizontal pressures to some extent.

When we inquire which of the spectrum rays and in what intensity are required for plant growth and for seed formation, we find that a great gap in exact knowledge exists here. Most of the experiments hitherto made relate to plants of little or no commercial value, and lack exactness both as to the intensity and the quality of the rays used. It would be, indeed, difficult and costly to employ the spectroscope to select rays for such experiments, because the use of a slit and numerous optical pieces so greatly reduces the intensity of the rays of every color. Most experimenters, therefore, have made shift to employ colored glasses to give certain rough separations of color.

These experiments indicate that the blue, violet, and ultra-violet rays are the most important for plant growth. Deep-red rays, also, are very active to promote photosynthesis, but the green rays lying between these spectral regions seem to behave as darkness to the plant. It is greatly to be hoped that more exact measurements of wave-length and intensity may soon be associated with studies of the growth and fruiting of the valuable food crops and the favorite flowers. It will be necessary to use very large and costly apparatus in such an investigation, because not more than 1 per cent of the intensity of sun rays may be expected to remain after the rays have been collected and accurately selected by the optical spectroscopic train. It may be that specific functions like flower bearing, seed developing, leaf growing, and stem expansion may be found to require different and very special qualities and intensities of rays for optimum conditions. The experiment is fascinating, for perhaps new and remarkable varieties of the most useful plants may be developed by controlling their radiation supply.

With the higher plants, it must be sunshine or death. With man and the higher animals, it must be sunshine or sickness. To be sure, there is nothing in the life of man or animals like the photosynthesis of the food of all plants and all animals which goes on in green leaves. That is unique with plants. But child humanity in dusky cities, shut in by smoke and dust from receiving the ultra-violet rays of the sun and sky, is afflicted by rickets and other ills which yield to the healing influence of exposure of the body to full sun rays in the manner that nature intended.

The outstanding exponent of this solar therapy is Doctor Rollier of Switzerland, who has maintained a sanitarium for sun treatments since 1903. Of later years, he has been imitated in other countries. One would hardly think of sun rays as dangerous, but the patients of Doctor Rollier commence their treatments on the first day with only 20 minutes' exposure, and of the feet alone. From this gentle beginning there is a gradual progress to the stage of complete exposure of the person for hours. Naturally there accompanies this course a gradual darkening of the skin. The patients become brown and hardy-looking. Skin sores disappear.

Two principal diseases successfully treated by solar therapy are rickets and surgical tuberculosis. Rickets, as everyone knows, is a sort of lack of stamina, apt to invade the whole body of children. A weak digestion, a poor appetite, emaciation, profuse night sweating, weakness of the limbs, tenderness of the bones, enlargements of the wrists and ends of the ribs, bow legs, curvature of the spine, misshapen head, contracted chest—all these deformities and miseries may come in the early years of the poor little patient.

The layman is apt to think of tuberculosis as a disease of the lungs, but essentially the same malady attacks many other parts of the body. Glands of the neck, skin, bones, joints, mucous membrane, intestines, and liver are commonly infected by the tubercle bacillus. In cases of superficial tuberculosis, recognizing how the germs may pass from one part to another in the blood stream, the surgeon is frequently called in to excise the infected part before the disease does its fatal mischief in a less accessible organ of the body. This is termed surgical tuberculosis.

It appears to be definitely proved that ultra-violet rays

[235]

of less than 3,200 Ångströms in wave-length are the active agents in the cure of rickets by ray-therapy. As the ozone of the higher air cuts off solar radiation at about 2,900 Ångströms, it leaves but a narrow band of solar rays available. Not only in rickets but in certain superficial skin diseases, physicians have used with advantage the quartz mercury-vapor arc light, which is rich in ultra-violet rays of these and shorter wave-lengths. Recent experiments in poultry raising at the Maine Agricultural Experiment Station are exceedingly instructive in this line, though it would be rash to carry over the results unquestioned to human pathology.

In the summer of 1924, about 250 one-week old chicks were separated into six groups for different treatments. Those of group 1 ran about in the open sunlight as they pleased, but came indoors to eat. The remaining five groups lived in a glass-roofed greenhouse. Groups 2 and 3, however, in addition to the light which reached them from sun and sky, were exposed for twenty minutes each day to the rays of a quartz mercury-vapor lamp, rich in the ultra-violet. The remaining three groups had only the sun's light as it came through their glass-roofed house.

All the groups had the usual regular food, composed of chick grain, dry mash, sour milk, and rock grit, and had access to fresh water and sand bath. Groups 3 and 4 were given, in addition to the regular diet, chopped alfalfa and grass, and group 6 had, in addition to the regular diet, a small ration of cod-liver oil.

What was the result? Groups 1, 2, 3, which had either full sunlight or glass-transmitted sunlight plus ultra-violet rays, all thrived. Groups 4 and 5 began to act less vigorously than these others by the end of the fourth week. They ate with less appetite and scratched less. Chickens of group 6, which had the cod-liver oil, although they did not relish this medicine, yet thrived better than groups 4 and 5, but not as well as groups 1, 2, 3. These differences became more and more marked. The chickens of groups 4 and 5 developed weak legs. They remained smaller in size. Their plumage looked rough. By the end of the ninth week, the fowls of groups 1, 2, 3, all having developed normally, were about double the weight of the spindling chicks of groups 4 and 5. The chicks of the first three groups had their bones well-set and full-sized, while

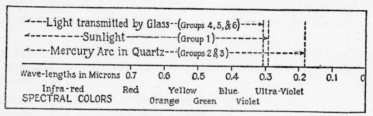

FIG. 40. The sun rays that cure rickets in chickens and in children lie in the narrow spectral region centering at 0.3 microns

the bones of groups 4 and 5 were small, curved, and weak. Chickens of group 6 were intermediate in their development. Fifteen deaths occurred in groups 4 and 5, and only one in groups 1, 2, 3.

Why this difference? Evidently it was solely due to some deficiency in radiation. Figure 40 shows graphically what the difference was. A narrow band of rays in the extreme ultra-violet—far beyond the extreme limit visible to the eye, and exactly in the region, by the way, where the ozone of the upper air begins to work absorption on solar rays—this little group of feeble sun rays was cut off by the glass cover of the greenhouse. These indispensable rays were supplied in sufficient measure by the daily 20 minute exposure to the mercury-vapor arc. The want of them was partly made up to group 6 by the medicine of cod-liver oil. Groups 4 and 5, lacking both the saving medicine and the rays, languished.

It is astonishing to remember that this very group of rays, thus proved so indispensable to the development of growing creatures, just misses being cut off from sun

[237]

rays by the trace of ozone which exists in our upper atmosphere. So near, apparently, as this is the world to lacking a condition favorable to life, that if the ozone band, which cuts off the spectrum of the sun and stars completely at 2,900 Ångströms or wave-length, had extended to 3,200 Ångströms in full force, the mischief would have been done. And yet the solar spectrum has little energy there, but runs on through the visible and infra-red regions in great strength to 20,000 Ångströms.

Another astonishing thing has lately been discovered. Doctor Steenbock and Doctor Daniels, experimenting with rats in the years 1922 and after, were testing the value of butter fat and cod-liver oil for the prevention or cure of rickets. Their experiments also involved the use of ultra-violet light. Some of the animals having been radiated upon and others not, they were confined in cages in common. The doctors were surprised to find that both sets of rats grew alike, except in one instance where some non-irradiated animals began to grow only when, after five weeks, irradiated rats were for the first time put into their cage.

It seemed as if the irradiated rats were able to supply to the non-irradiated ones something that hitherto they had lacked. On trying various experiments, it was found that irradiating the air, or touching non-irradiated rats with their irradiated brethren did not give the magic curative influence. The effect was indirect, not a consequence of direct action on the outside of the body. Finally the secret appeared. Some bodily excretions of the irradiated animals were eaten by the others and produced the extraordinary result.

Various articles of diet were then tried in irradiated and non-irradiated condition. It was proved that many, but not all, grains, fats, and oils, when treated with ultra-violet rays, receive and hold curative properties adapted to conquer the disease of rickets. Cod-liver oil, then, is by no means alone as a carrier of the curative agent. Some modification takes place in many other kinds of foods, if irradiated, which makes them effective to cure rickets by indirect ray-therapy, fully as effectively as by the direct application of the rays to the skin of the patient himself. The irradiated oil may indeed be boiled with strong alkali and reduced to a soap and still retain its curative property unimpaired.

It appears that while there are several rare chemical substances in cod-liver oil which possess this curative virtue when irradiated, the most active of them is one named cholesterol. While this substance does not occur in plant foods, there are certain somewhat similar chemicals in the grains, which are named phytosterols, and some of these have similar value against rickets. Not only in rickets, but in some allied disorders, this new discovery may prove of high medical value.

As regards light-therapy and rickets, the conclusions so far arrived at are these:

(1) Exposure of an animal to light of wave-length less than about 3,200 Ångströms will cure rickets and also prevent its occurrence on a diet that normally will produce rickets.

(2) Cod-liver oil will act just like ultra-violet light in curing and preventing rickets.

(3) Some other substances have a slight curative value in rickets but most other oils—such as cottonseed oil—have no antirachitic value.

(4) These oils without antirachitic value can most of them be made antirachitic by exposing them to ultra-violet light.

(5) A large number of solid food materials also become antirachitic on exposure to ultra-violet light.

(6) Cholesterol—a practically universal constituent of animal cells—becomes activated by ultra-violet light. So also does phytosterol which is a constituent of plant cells, so that presumably food materials are made antirachitic by activating the cholesterol and phytosterol in them.

[239]

(7) Since the human tissues contain cholesterol, the skin on absorbing ultra-violet light has its cholesterol activated, and this activated cholesterol, being absorbed into the blood, acts just like cod-liver oil absorbed from the intestines in promoting bone formation.

The striking results obtained in the treatment of surgical tuberculosis by Dr. Rollier at his Swiss solar sanitarium are indicated by the following table:

RESULTS OF LIGHT TREATMENT IN SURGICAL TUBERCULOSIS (ROLLIER)

	Cured	Improved
	Per cent	Per cent
Skin tuberculosis	81.25	18.75
Bone and joint	75.98	7.80
Glandular	89.80	5.20
Peritonitis	80.30	8.20
Genito-urinary	77.80	22.20
Kidney	52.94	33.00

Total mortality 0.9 per cent.

X-ray photographs, after the light treatment, give striking evidence of the effect upon bone formation. According to Rollier, finger bones that have entirely disappeared may be so completely recalcified as to be indistinguishable, in radiographs, from normal tissue, and adults seem to be as easily affected as children. This means that, for early cases at least, the disease can be checked, and motion preserved in the affected joint, the gradual establishment of motion going hand in hand with the healing process.

Rollier insists on the fact that the benefit is always proportional to the degree of pigmentation. Without knowing accurately which wave-lengths are responsible for pigmentation and which are most beneficial in the treatment of tuberculosis, it is not possible to be very sure in this matter, and here as in plant physiology an alliance between the doctor of medicine and physicists, expert in

PLATE 58

Cold and sun have no terrors for these little patients but are their health-giving friends.   Photograph from
Dr. Horace LoGrasso

PLATE 59

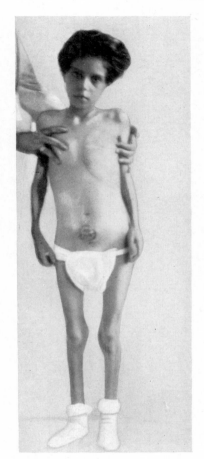 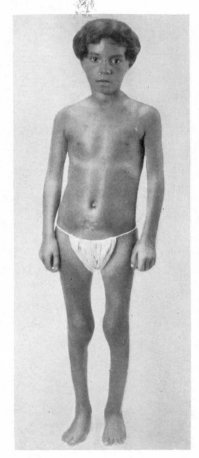

A small patient of the J. N. Adam Memorial Hospital, Perrysburg, N. Y. (Left) on admission, and (right) after two years of radiation treatment. Photograph from Dr. Horace LoGrasso

isolating rays and exactly measuring radiation intensities, would be of great advantage.

The subject of this chapter is only recently coming to the fore. Doubtless the future holds in store for us here, as in other lines, highly wonderful and inspiring revelations of the importance of sun rays in the welfare of man.

CHAPTER XI

DOES THE SUN MAKE OTHER WORLDS HABITABLE?

THERE is no subject more alluring than weighing the possibilities of other habitable worlds than ours. If, by some superwireless telegraphy, we could enter into fluent communication with beings as intelligent as ourselves, who had been brought up under other skies, in other scenes, with different vegetation and animals about them, and had developed social customs, religions, and laws independent of ours, what a revelation would be unfolded!

Such worlds there may be, forming planetary systems attached to some of the billions of stars. The enormous distances between us and the stars probably forever will prevent our knowing positively whether such stellar planets exist. Our observations in this field, therefore, must be restricted to the solar system. This comprises ten large globes, namely: Sun, Mercury, Venus, Earth, Moon, Mars, Jupiter, Saturn, Uranus, and Neptune. Life upon the sun is out of the question altogether. With temperatures far exceeding the electric arc, not even molecules can exist there, much less intelligent organisms.

If there were inhabitants on the moon, we could discern their cities with the telescope. It is impossible that there should be any, for there is neither appreciable air nor water on the moon. When the sun or a star sets, its rays are curved by our atmosphere, so that we see a slow and lingering departure. If the moon had an atmosphere, the same sort of lingering and ray curving, would attend her passage over our line of sight from every star she occults. Nothing of this sort happens. When the edge of the moon overtakes them, the stars disappear as instantly as a flash of lightning comes. If water existed on the moon, it would produce there an atmosphere of steam. This would give similar effects to those we have described. On these grounds, therefore, we know that the moon is uninhabitable, but we shall take note of still other fatal objections later.

Before considering the other planets, let us survey the conditions which make life possible on the earth, in order that we may see how far these conditions prevail upon the other bodies of the solar system. Living organisms can hardly be formed of any substances other than the compounds of carbon. We are acquainted with all the possible chemical elements excepting three or four, and we know the properties of the few yet undiscovered ones. We know all the compounds which all these elements form with each other, excepting only those with carbon and its compounds.

It is customary to speak of chemistry in two divisions called organic and inorganic. The latter includes the chemistry of all the elements excepting carbon; the former is devoted to carbon compounds only. Yet the present extent of the chemistry of carbon far exceeds that of all other elements together. Not only so, but while we are fairly conversant with the chemistry of all other elements, the chemistry of carbon opens up vistas upon vistas which generations of future chemists can never completely explore. In short, there is no chemical element except carbon fitted by the complexity of its possible combinations to be the foundation element of living organisms.

In the second place, water is the indispensable associate of carbon in the organization of life. A living being must have flexibility and intercommunication of parts. A rigid solid body cannot be alive. Flexibility is impossible without liquid constituents. Water has the unique property of being, at ordinary temperatures, the only substance which is a natural liquid, or, in other words, not depending for its production on life or the processes of life. Water, moreover, is the most universal solvent known to chemistry. The properties of its solutions are also unique electrically and chemically. In the human body, nearly 70 per cent, by weight, is composed of water. Even our teeth contain about 20 per cent of it. Under temperature conditions where water would be either solid or gaseous, we may well believe that living organisms would be out of the question.

Highly organized life, therefore, apparently requires temperatures exceeding 32° F., and below 212° F., the boiling point. The upper limit of temperature can be further restricted, because complex carbon compounds break up in the presence of each other and of water at temperatures less than boiling. The complexities of living forms thus seem to require surroundings above 32° and below, perhaps, 150° F., that is, between 0° and 65° C.

Why do the earth's surface temperatures generally lie within these limits? The answer involves the rays of the sun; the rays of the earth; the atmosphere with its clouds; the oceans with their great receptivity for radiation and their immense capacity for heat; and, finally, it involves the rapid rotation of the earth. As we have seen, the sun's rays would furnish nearly 2.0 calories of heat every minute on each square centimeter of an imaginary hollow spherical surface which we may think of as lying at the earth's mean solar distance. How hot would this supply of heat maintain a body situated in the void of space?

It depends on the kind of surface which the body presents. Suppose it were a sheet of plate glass. Except for about 8 per cent reflected, the solar rays would mainly pass through the glass, losing but 1 or 2 per cent absorbed in the glass and tending to warm it. Being of fairly good

PLATE 60

A portion of the surface of the moon.   Photo by Mount Wilson Observatory

PLATE 61

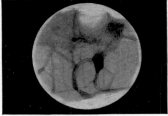
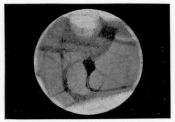

Mars, June 17, 1922, from drawings 1 hour apart by E. C. Slipher, Lowell Observatory. (From "The Earth and the Stars," courtesy of the Van Nostrand Co.)

Jupiter, October 19, 1915, and December 19, 1917. Photo by E. C. Slipher, Lowell Observatory. (From "The Earth and the Stars," courtesy of the Van Nostrand Co.)

Saturn, February 11, 1916 and, May 24, 1922. Photo by E. C. Slipher, Lowell Observatory. (From "The Earth and the Stars," courtesy of the Van Nostrand Co.)

radiating power for rays of great wave-length, the glass plate would part with its absorbed heat by radiation at a very low temperature. With such rough information as is available, it may be estimated that such a sheet of glass, placed in void space at right angles to sun rays at the earth's mean solar distance, would not rise above $-150°$ C. which means below the liquefying point of air.

Quite different would be the effect on other substances. Take for the next example a small silver ball painted with lampblack. Such a body would absorb about 98 per cent of all solar rays striking it. Being a fine conductor of heat, it would be of nearly uniform temperature over its whole surface, even though the sun rays fell on one hemisphere only. It would also radiate long-wave rays of its own pretty freely, and the temperature reached would be that at which the energy of its long-wave radiation, sent out in every direction, equalled the energy contained in the sun's nearly parallel beam, intercepted by the silver ball. If situated in free space at the earth's mean solar distance, our black silver ball would maintain a temperature of about $+10°$ C.

Next consider the moon, whose surface is similar to one of the earth's deserts, but which has neither air nor water, and which rotates only once a month. Consider first the surface squarely under the direct solar rays. For a week the sun has shone thereon with gradually growing power. The surface may be supposed to have reached its maximum temperature. About 90 per cent of the sun's rays are being absorbed. The radiating power of the moon's surface for long-wave rays is high, but not nearly as high as that of the blackened silver, just considered. It is, perhaps, not over 60 per cent of what we term perfect radiating capacity. We should expect on the center of the moon's sunlit hemisphere a surface temperature of about $+160°$ C., or quite hot enough to bake bread easily. Water would hiss there as if on a hot stove.

But how about the opposite point which has been dark for a whole week? Only the stars and the earth would warm it by rays from without, and these sources combined would not be a ten-thousandth part as considerable as the sun rays. Practically all that would keep up a feeble supply of heat at the surface would be the flow of heat from within the moon itself. Generously allowing that this would be as rapid as the present rate of flow of heat from within the earth, it would not keep the dark surface of the moon above $-100°$ C. This would be below the liquefying points either of carbonic acid gas or of the dentist's "laughing-gas" at atmospheric pressure, and far below the freezing point of mercury.

Observations support this theory. Many observers, including Lord Rosse, Dr. S. P. Langley, Doctor Coblentz, and others, have found that within the brief period of only a few hours occupied by a total lunar eclipse, the temporarily darkened moon falls to so low a temperature that no long-wave rays can be discerned to come from it. This means that even in that brief time the lunar temperature falls apparently from $+160°$ to $-30°$ C., and possibly much farther. The moon, indeed, would have to rotate very fast, surely once every hour, to be of a habitable temperature. For if it rotated no more rapidly than the earth does, there would be a range of temperatures between night and day far too great to be withstood by living beings.

Why is it that the earth does not feel these extremes? Because the atmosphere, like a blanket, protects us from losing our heat to the cold of space, and because the oceans are great conservers of heat. Steam-fitters are accustomed to protect their pipes from cooling by coverings of asbestos, or other nonconductors. The atmosphere serves in the same capacity for our earth. The earth as a planet can cool only by radiating, that is by sending out waves to space. The effect of the atmosphere is to cut off rays arising from the warmest part of the earth, its solid surface, and to allow only those to pass freely which arise from the much cooler upper air, which emits them far less plentifully. This, owing to its humidity, the atmosphere would do even if it were quite cloudless. But, as we know, the atmosphere is about 50 per cent cloudy. Rays of great wave-length, such as a body of the earth's temperature sends out, are fully absorbed if they encounter an unbroken layer of clouds. Hence, half of the earth's surface rays are entirely prevented by clouds from escaping.

But clouds are not the only heat-saving devices. The atmosphere contains much water-vapor. This, too, is a powerful absorber of long-wave rays. Not over 30 per cent of the rays from the earth's surface can penetrate to space through a cloudless atmosphere of average humidity. Altogether, therefore, clouds and water-vapor cut off at least 85 per cent of the radiation arising from the earth's surface.

At higher and higher levels, the air becomes clearer and clearer to long-wave rays. But the temperature of the air becomes lower and lower at higher levels. Hence, it comes about that, viewed as a planet in space, the earth radiates, not as a body at the temperature prevailing at its surface, but as one of some 30° C. lower temperature. This makes a saving of heat to the earth amounting to about 40 per cent.

Our surface temperatures average about 30° C. higher than they would be if, receiving the same solar heating, the earth's surface was stripped of water-vapor and clouds. This blanketing acts to keep us warm during our nights, when the sun's heat is withdrawn. If, however, the earth rotated much more slowly, so that the day was, for instance, nearly thirty times as long as ours, just as the moon's day actually is, even our efficient atmospheric blanket could not prevent the nights from growing very much colder and the days considerably hotter than they are now.

THE SUN AND THE WELFARE OF MAN

In all parts of the earth which lie near the oceans and great lakes, there is an additional equalizing influence. Water is very transparent to sun rays, so that it becomes warm quite deeply. Thus it absorbs large quantities of solar heat. This heat cannot escape by radiation arising at great depths because water is opaque to long-wave rays. The heat escapes only by warming the air at the surface by contact and by surface radiation. Hence, the oceans and lakes change temperature but very little during the twenty-four hours, and powerfully control the temperature of the air moved over them by the winds. For example, taking two stations at nearly the same latitude: Port au Prince, Haiti, under strong oceanic control, has only 8.5° C. change of temperature between night and day, and only 3.5° yearly range, while Timbuctu, in the Desert of Sahara, has 16.2° C. average change daily, and 13.6° yearly range. The moon's surface, with no water and no atmospheric blanket at all, falls nearly 200° C. in a single hour of darkness.

These examples indicate the value of the oceans and the atmosphere for preserving that equable temperature of night and day, so necessary to the life of the plants which are the food on which the lives of animals and men depend. We may now ask whether any of the other planets of our solar system are likely to have favorable temperature ranges and other conditions suited to life.

Mercury. This planet is the nearest one to the sun. Being but 2/5 as far from the sun as our earth, the solar rays there have over six times the intensity that they have when they reach our planet. The reflecting power of Mercury is only 7 per cent, compared to 44 per cent for the earth, so that almost twice as large a fraction of solar rays remains available to warm Mercury as the surface of our earth. Altogether, therefore, Mercury's surface is heated with about twelve times the intensity of the sun rays that come to the earth's surface, and may be hot enough to melt tin or even lead. It is not necessary to go farther. Any one can see that life there is not probable. Yet it is believed that Mercury presents always the same side toward the sun, just as the moon does toward the earth. If anything further were needed to prove the planet uninhabitable, this is it. Certainly Mercury must be regarded as a lifeless world.

The four outer planets, Neptune, Uranus, Saturn, and Jupiter. If Mercury, the nearest of the sun's family of planets, is uninhabitable because too closely under the mighty dominion of the sun's heat and gravitation, the four great planets, which lie beyond the orbit of Mars, represent quite the opposite conditions. The sun rays at Neptune's distance contain hardly more than a thousandth part of the intensity they bring to the earth. A blackened silver ball there would maintain a temperature of about $-240°$ C., which is close to the liquefying point of hydrogen. Even Jupiter, the nearest of the four, receives sun rays of only about 1/28 the intensity of those which reach our earth. They would maintain our blackened silver ball at approximately $-150°$ C., or near the liquefying temperature of nitrogen, or of air.

These probable low temperatures are to some degree verified by Doctor Coblentz's measures with the thermopile, made at the Lowell Observatory. He could not detect the slightest indications of heat from either Jupiter or Saturn. Formerly, astronomers thought that Jupiter, at least, might still retain heat of his own, not depending on solar supplies, but this view is now disposed of by Doctor Coblentz's experiments. It seems impossible to believe that any of the four great outer planets is warm enough to sustain life.

Mars. Much more attention has been given to this planet than to any other except the earth. With a diameter of 4,230 miles, and a solar distance of 141 million miles, Mars has little more than 1/10 the mass of our earth and receives only 43 per cent as intense a supply of solar radiation. Though possessed of an atmosphere, it contains so little cloudiness that the surface markings of Mars are always visible when the planet is observed. White polar caps form and disappear as the two poles alternately present themselves towards the sun in the Martian year, which is nearly twice as long as ours. Mars, like the earth, rotates in about 24 hours.

With a visible surface, an atmosphere, melting polar caps, and a similar rotation period, Mars presents so many interesting conditions in common with the earth that it is no wonder that many have supposed that the planet may be inhabited. Indeed the late Dr. Percival Lowell was so firmly convinced of it that he created a great observatory mainly in order to prove it. A writer and lecturer of unusual grace and power of expression, Doctor Lowell's books and lectures led very many people to adopt his point of view on this subject.

Nevertheless, there seem to be very strong objections to urge against the habitability of Mars. As regards water, Doctor Campbell and Doctor Albrecht, observing with the spectroscope, in the years 1909 and 1910, first on Mount Whitney and later on Mount Hamilton, proved that sunlight in passing quite through the atmosphere of Mars to its surface and then back again by reflection on its way to the earth, encounters in that whole path, twice through the Martian atmosphere, less than one-fifth as much water-vapor as exists in our air in coldest midwinter weather above Mount Hamilton. In fact, the observers were quite unable to discover either water-vapor or oxygen in the atmosphere of Mars, though small quantities of these gases might have been present without detection. Adams and St. John, observing with the spectroscope on Mount Wilson in the year 1926, published still more definite conclusions. Namely: Mars's atmosphere contains 6 per cent as much water-vapor and 16 per cent as much oxygen as the earth's atmosphere above Mount Wilson.

Are not the polar caps of Mars positive proof of the

presence of water plentifully there? Not necessarily. Carbonic-acid gas may solidify to a white snow in the frigid Martian polar night. It seems almost equally as probable that the polar caps are of carbon dioxide as that they are of frozen water. Of whichever substance, they seem to be very thin indeed. Certainly the melting of them during each Martian summer proves that they contain very much less water than our permanent polar ice-caps.

Apart from scarcity of water and oxygen, there is another great handicap to the habitability of Mars. As we have said, sun rays there have but 43 per cent of their intensity at the earth. Yet as it is very cloudless there, and the reflecting power of Mars is but 15 per cent, as against 44 per cent for the earth, there is really $85/56 \times 43$, or 62 per cent as much solar heat there to warm the surface as with us. This is quite sufficient to give a very comfortable temperature near the Martian equator by day. But what of the night? With more than our driest desert clearness of sky, few clouds, and little humidity, the Martian surface must fall far below freezing soon after sunset every day.

Doctor Coblentz has investigated the Martian temperatures experimentally, and concludes that the equatorial temperature range from midday to midnight is from about $+40°$ to $-70°$ F. Under these temperature conditions of the planet Mars, the growth of vegetation, if possible at all, must be confined to very low forms, such as mosses and lichens, and the opportunity for higher forms of animal life must be very unfavorable.

Venus. This planet is almost like a twin to the earth in many respects. At two-thirds the earth's solar distance, within 3 per cent of equal diameter, highly reflecting, which most probably indicates a cloudy exterior, and certainly possessing an abundant atmosphere, Venus seems to a superficial view equally as suitable as our earth for an abode of life. It is only the impossibility of

seeing her surface that has discouraged speculation on the
inhabitants of Venus, while the Martian life has been so
often picturesquely imagined. As it is impossible to see
surface markings, there is no easy way to discover the
period of rotation of Venus. Observers have had recourse
to the spectroscope for this purpose. Many attempts
have been made to measure the rate of rotation spectro-
scopically, but without success. For this reason, some
have believed that Venus rotates on her axis in the same
time that she revolves around the sun, or 225 days.

If this were true, it would spoil her habitability. One
side would be always too hot, the other always too cold.
The late Dr. Alexander Graham Bell pointed out that this
state of affairs was unlikely. If it existed, the water
would distill over to the permanently dark side, and would
all congeal there. Hence, there could be no clouds on the
bright side. If so, we should almost certainly see surface
markings. As none are seen, we must believe that the
bright side is so cloudy as to obscure them.

In the year 1924, Messrs. Pettit and Nicholson, observing with the thermoelectric pile and the 100-inch
telescope on Mount Wilson, found that the dark side of
Venus is not much below freezing, and nearly equally
warm from one edge to the other. This, of course, proves
that the planet rotates rather rapidly. We may suppose
its rotation occurs in an interval of perhaps ten days.
If this were so, the spectroscope could not detect such
leisurely rotation, and yet the dark side would not get
extremely cold, if protected by a blanket of cloudy
atmosphere.

One other difficulty has been raised. Venus gives no
spectroscopic indication of either water-vapor or oxygen.
But unlike Mars, our view of Venus seems to be cut off
high above the surface. It may probably be that an im-
penetrable featureless veil of high-level clouds is all that
we see upon Venus, and that the water-vapor and oxygen
of her atmosphere lie almost wholly underneath these

PLATE 62

A—Dr. Percival Lowell, 1855-1916, founder and first director of the Lowell Observatory, Flagstaff, Ariz., for the study of the planets

B—Dr. W. W. Campbell, Director of Lick Observatory since 1901, and President of the University of California since 1923

high-level clouds, so that the spectroscope cannot reveal them.

With a reflecting power of 59 per cent, as compared to 44 per cent for our earth, and with an intensity of solar radiation 1.9 times as great, there is available $41/56 \times 1.9 = 1.4$ times as much solar heat to warm Venus as to warm the earth. Hence, her surface temperature is doubtless tropical to much higher latitudes than the earth's. Yet much of her surface is probably entirely favorable as an abode for abundant life. We can not say positively that life exists on Venus, but so far as we know there are no conditions there which would prevent its existence. If any attempt shall ever be made to communicate across the void, it seems fortunate that Venus, the nearest of all the planets, is the one above all others most likely to reward our costly signals by intelligent replies.

CHAPTER XII

THE LANDSCAPE OF THE SUN

COMPARED to Saturn, Jupiter, and the moon, there is little that is striking in a telescopic view of the sun. Just a dazzling disk with faint markings, and often a few dusky spots with darker centers, that is about all that is presented. One gets a thrill, however, if he reflects that the sun's disk is 865,000 miles in diameter, that the faint markings would cover New York or Texas, and that the dark spots might easily engulf the world itself, and leave room around the edges.

To the eye, the whole solar disk is so bright that gradations of brightness are lost. Yet there are great differences of brilliancy between the center and the edge. In the work of the Smithsonian Astrophysical Observatory on Mount Wilson, this feature was carefully investigated. We made a telescopic image of the sun about 8 inches in diameter. By stopping the clock of the telescope mounting we allowed this solar image to drift in an east and west direction in consequence of the earth's daily rotation. A short slit at the middle of the image admitted a sample of the sun rays to the spectroscope, which formed their spectrum upon the sensitive bolometer. Any chosen ray of the spectrum could thus be selected for examination. As the sun's image drifted over the slit, we were able in this way to measure the intensity of a ray of any chosen wave-length at every point along a diameter of the solar disk.

Our results are represented in Figures 5 and 6. Violet rays, as the figures show, are less than half as intense at the edge as at the center of the sun's disk. With red and infra-red rays, the contrast between center and edge is much less marked. The explanation of these differences of brightness along the sun's diameter lies in a difference of effective temperature of the sources of the rays which come to us from the center and the edge. The sun is so very hot that no solids or liquids can exist there. Being thus altogether gaseous, owing to its high temperature, we see a good way down into the gaseous mass. Our line of sight at the center goes straight-away towards the center of the sun and reaches depths much hotter than the surface. At the edge, on the other hand, our line of sight grazes along obliquely, and does not penetrate to these hotter inner layers. Violet rays suffer much more diminution than red and infra-red ones with decreasing temperatures of their sources. Thus, the greater contrast of brightness between the sun's edge and center in violet rays is readily explained.

There are some persons who do not believe that the sun is hot. The Smithsonian Institution occasionally receives letters from some of them. Several facts unite to prove the high solar temperature. First of all, the earth receives immense quantities of heat from the solar rays. This is as reasonable a proof of a hot sun as to feel at many yards' distance the hot rays from a bonfire is a proof of the high temperature of the conflagration. Proofs far more exact than this exist. They depend on observing the sun's spectrum.

We have seen in earlier chapters how the bolometer measures the intensity of the solar rays in all parts of the spectrum, and how its measurements are expressed in the form of a curve called a bolograph. Such a curve may be corrected for instrumental and atmospheric absorption, and reduced to a scale of equal increments of wavelength. Beside the same figure may be drawn curves of a similar kind, observed in the laboratory, and giving the energy distribution in the spectrum of bodies of known temperatures, from moderate ones up to the hottest that we can command. (See Figure 52.) It is easy to see that in form and place of maximum energy they more and more approach the solar energy-spectrum curve. Two German physicists, Wien and Planck, succeeded in expressing the form of all such curves by a complicated mathematical formula which gives with great accuracy the distribution proper to what is called a perfect radiator. Using this formula, we see that at 6,000° C. of absolute temperature, a perfect radiator would give a distribution very close to that of the sun. Still more convincing, if there was a perfectly radiating 6,000° sphere, 865,000 miles in diameter, and 93,000,000 miles away, we can compute from this laboratory-made law that such a sphere would furnish almost exactly as much heat in its rays to the earth as the earth has been observed to receive from the sun.

But even this is not the plainest proof we have of the sun's high temperature. The relative intensities of the lines that metals emit in the different parts of their spectra depend on their temperatures. It is only at a very exalted temperature that the lines so familiar in the solar spectrum are found. It is even possible, by exploding a wire at a temperature of 6,000°, to produce a spectrum nearly a counterpart of the sun's, in so far as the one metal which composes the wire is concerned. Of course, the sun contains a great many metals, and gives the complex spectrum of the mixture of all of them on that account, but its individual spectral features may be imitated by use of very hot wires of different substances.

In short, the sun's rays yield such a spectrum as could only be reproduced by the rays of a very hot body. This statement holds as regards total energy, distribution of that energy in the spectrum, and the special features which we call the Fraunhofer lines. But some one may suggest the query, why is it that we grow colder as we ascend on a mountain, or in a balloon, if we are going

PLATE 63

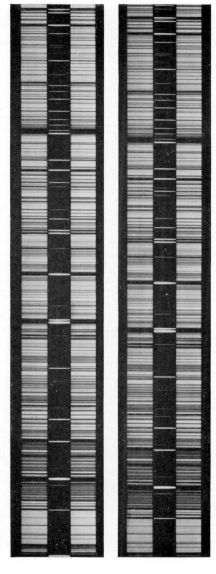

The bright metallic lines of the laboratory, as shown in the two central bands, agreeing in place and strength with the dark lines in the solar spectrum, as shown in the four outer bands, prove that iron exists in the sun.   Photo by Mount Wilson Observatory

PLATE 64

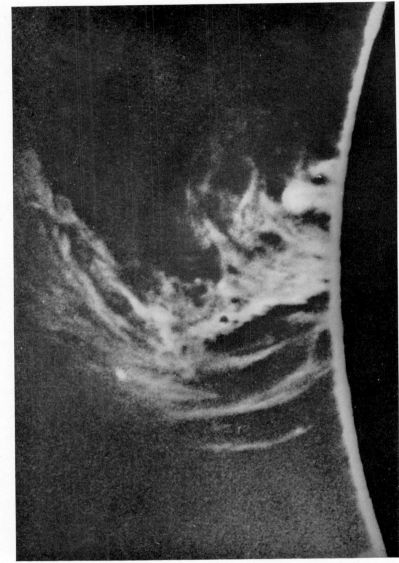

Crimson flames shooting from the sun's surface to a height of 150,000 miles. Photo by Mount Wilson Observatory

nearer to a very hot body? [1] It is because the air that blows about us at these great altitudes is very cold. The upper air is very cold because it is very transparent. Place your hand on the transparent window pane, and you find it cold. But if your black shoe happens to rest on the floor of the room in the sun rays that have passed through the window pane, you find it becoming very warm. Similarly, the transparent air is cold, and, as it cools an automobile radiator, so it cools whatever else it bathes. The Astrophysical Observatory has made exact measurements of solar heating at Washington (sea-level), Mount Wilson (5,700 feet), Mount Whitney (14,500 feet), and from a free balloon at 75,000 feet altitude. The values increased with the altitude as shown in Figure 4. So the sun rays produce more heat, not less, at high elevations. The increased solar heating at high altitudes occurs because the atmospheric losses, which sun rays suffer in coming to us, are less the higher one goes, so that the direct solar beam remains of greater vigor.

The spectroscope not only tells how hot the sun is but what materials compose it. Plate 63 shows the sun's spectrum photographed. It is filled with the dark lines. These lines mean something very particular. We often see upon a square of cement sidewalk the tracks of some dog which ran over it while the cement was soft. Though we never saw that dog we know he existed. Fossil slabs have been found bearing the imprint of the feet of animals unlike any that man has ever seen upon the earth. (See Plate 3.) Over a gulf of time that we can never cross, we recognize the existence of the creature, though we never saw him or his like. In a similar way, the spectrum of the sun shows us, in the Fraunhofer lines, the unmistakable signatures of the atoms of metals like iron, magnesium, and a great many others of the chemical elements whose spectra are perfectly familiar to us in the laboratory.

[1] What, however, is 2 or 3 miles compared to 93,000,000 miles to produce any such distance-effect?

Certain solar lines, indeed, were found in the year 1868 which did not belong to any chemical which was known at that time on the earth. This new element was called *helium* because discovered on the sun. However, nearly thirty years later it was recognized in gases evolved from certain Norwegian ores, and recently has been found in considerable amounts in gases escaping from oil wells in Oklahoma and Texas. This gas, helium, next to hydrogen the lightest which exists, being absolutely non-inflammable, is now stored up for use in military balloons instead of the dangerously explosive hydrogen.

Besides informing us how very hot the sun is and of what chemicals it is composed, the spectroscope reveals certain remarkable plumelike flaming forms that shoot out from the sun, but can not ordinarily be seen with the telescope alone, because obliterated by the blinding glare of the sky light. As these flames, called *prominences*, concentrate all their rays into a spectrum of single lines, while the sky spectrum is a long continuous band, the observer has only to apply sufficiently high spectroscopic dispersion to weaken the sky light till it is less bright than the prominences. A remarkable example of what appears then is given in Plate 64.

Still another remarkable view of the sun is presented by the special form of spectroscope called the spectroheliograph. This instrument, devised by Dr. George E. Hale, the distinguished solar observer, about the year 1890, allows us to photograph the sun in rays of a single gas, such as hydrogen or calcium. These light gases, resting above the ordinary solar surface like clouds in our atmosphere, present a billowy structure marked by lanes and rifts of great beauty, especially in the neighborhood of sun-spots. An example of this is shown in Plate 65. Doctor Hale about the year 1925 invented a further improvement to the spectroheliograph, by means of which the eye may continuously examine these several solar gases, each by itself, over a considerable area of the sun's surface, and actually follow their motions as they swirl about.

Sun-spots themselves are full of interest. Galileo discovered them with his new-made telescope in the year 1610. Many observers made notes of them in the centuries following. It was not until 1843 that Schwabe of Dessau, after 20 years of painstaking observations, announced their periodicity. This was very fully examined by Wolf of Zurich, who sought out all the old records on the subject back to the sun-spot discovery by Galileo. He expressed the prevalence of sun-spots by what are

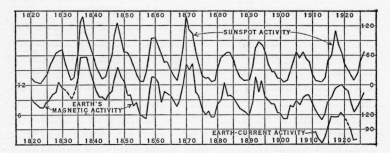

FIG. 41. Sun-spots and terrestrial magnetism varied in close agreement during the past century. (After Bauer)

now called Wolf's sun-spot numbers. These run from zero to something like 200 at times of greatest solar activity. His work was continued by his successor at Zurich, Wolfer, who still publishes quarterly a tabular digest of all the sun-spot observations of the world.

Figure 41 shows the remarkable but irregular periodicity which has been discovered. In the figure, too, are curves showing the variability of the earth's magnetic condition, obviously closely associated with sunspots. Our celebrated "northern lights," the aurora borealis, also has a well-marked variability which is closely associated with sun-spots.

THE SUN AND THE WELFARE OF MAN

The late Professor Young, of Princeton, in his book "The Sun," gives a most interesting account of a simultaneous disturbance of solar and terrestrial conditions, as follows. He was observing at Sherman, Wyoming:

"On August 3, 1872, the chromosphere [that region of solar-flame outbursts of which we have just spoken] in the neighborhood of a sun-spot, which was just coming into view around the edge of the sun, was greatly disturbed on several occasions during the forenoon. Jets of luminous matter of intense brilliance were projected, and the dark lines of the spectrum were reversed [*i.e.*, became bright] by hundreds for a few minutes at a time. There were three especially notable paroxysms at 8:45, 10:30, and 11:50 a.m., local time. At dinner the photographer of the party, who was determining the magnetic constants of our station, told me, without knowing anything about my observations, that he had been obliged to give up work, his magnet having swung clear off the scale. Two days later the spot had come around the edge of the limb [or edge of the sun]. On the morning of August 5th, I began observations at 6:40, and for about an hour witnessed some of the most remarkable phenomena I have ever seen. The hydrogen lines, with many others, were brilliantly reversed in the spectrum of the [sun-spot] nucleus, and at one point in the penumbra [the less dark exterior of a sun-spot] the C line sent out what looked like a blowpipe-jet, projecting toward the upper end of the spectrum, and indicating a motion along the line of sight of about one hundred and twenty miles per second. This motion would die out and be renewed again at intervals of a minute or two. The disturbance ceased before eight o'clock and was not renewed that forenoon. On writing to England, I received from Greenwich and Stonyhurst, through the kindness of Sir G. B. Airy and Rev. S. J. Perry, copies of the photographic magnetic records for those two days. On August 3d, which was a day of general magnetic disturbance, the three paroxysms I

PLATE 65

A great sun-spot pair and the adjacent solar surface photographed
in red hydrogen light. Photo by L. H. Humason, Mount Wilson
Observatory. (From "The Earth and the Stars," courtesy of the
Van Nostrand Co.)

PLATE 66

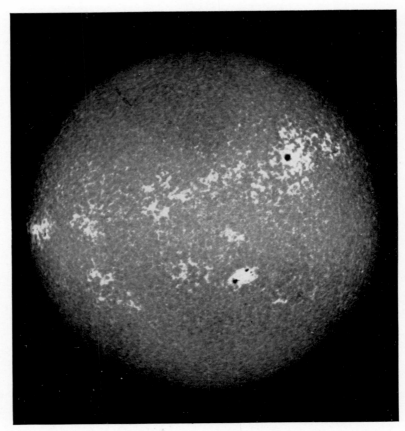

The sun's surface photographed in light of calcium. Note sun-spots
and faculæ. Photo by Mount Wilson Observatory. (From "The
Earth and the Stars," courtesy of the Van Nostrand Co.)

noticed at Sherman were accompanied by peculiar twitches of the magnets in England. Again, August 5th was a quiet day, magnetically speaking, but just during that hour when the sun-spot was active, the magnet shivered and trembled. So far as appears, too, the magnetic action of the sun was instantaneous. After making allowance for longitude, the magnetic disturbance in England appears strictly simultaneous, so far as can be judged, with the spectroscopic disturbance seen on the Rocky Mountains, and the difference can not have been more than about ten minutes. But the time at Sherman was not noted with any great precision."

Professor Young's final statement is exceedingly interesting, for it seems to show that the electromagnetic influence traveled with the same speed as light from the sun to the earth, since Professor Young saw, and English observers obtained magnetic records simultaneously. If so, it must have been transmitted, we must suppose, by waves such as those of radio-programs. This is interesting in connection with the remarks of Doctor Pupin at the American Association for the Advancement of Science, meeting in Philadelphia in December, 1926, when he said that he believed that we perceive in so-called "static" the pulses of celestial bodies, especially the sun.

So we see that the sun, far from being so quiet and uninteresting a body as a cursory telescopic view indicates, is the scene of such enormous disturbances as not only shoot out crimson flamelike prominences to heights of half a million miles, but even put out of commission the telegraph and radio, and flood the sky with weird dancing lights, on our earth, 93,000,000 miles away. Compared to these solar disturbances, even our greatest volcanic eruptions, like that of Colima, and the still greater one of Krakatoa, are really trifling phenomena.

We have remarked in an earlier chapter how closely associated in a double sense the sun-spots are with our supply of solar radiation. We also remarked that Mr.

THE SUN AND THE WELFARE OF MAN

Clayton has found means to predict for several days in advance something of the changes which are to occur in the sun's heating. He does this from telescopic observations of the sun's disk. He notes the places and conspicuousness of what are called the *faculæ*. These are extra-brilliant patches upon the glaring surface of the sun. They are apt to surround sun-spots, and to make their appearance before sun-spots appear. They often continue in the neighborhood after sun-spots have decayed.

The sun rotates upon its axis in about 26 days in its equatorial zone, but slower and slower at higher and higher latitudes towards the solar poles. This extraordinary behavior would prove, if we did not know it from consideration of its immense temperature, that there is nothing solid about the sun. Only a fluid could form a sphere which rotates at different speeds in different zones. On account of the rotation, the sun-spots and faculæ cross over the sun's visible disk in about two weeks. Near the central position the faculæ are very indistinctly seen, doubtless because we see them there against a so much hotter background than we do nearer the edge. However, they are also inconspicuous close to the edge of the disk. But this is obviously due to foreshortening near the boundary of the sun's disk, where we see them so nearly edgewise. About a quarter-way in from the edge of the solar disk the faculæ are most conspicuous. Mr. Clayton finds that when these are strongly developed at that region the solar radiation tends to be high.

Sun-spots have other extraordinary properties. Doctor Hale discovered that every spot is the seat of a powerful magnetic field. Not only is this so, but they go in pairs, either obviously or incipiently, of which one of the two is a north pole, the other a south pole. There is a great regularity about these magnetic pairs of sun-spots. During the full period, which averages 11.1 years, between one epoch of minimum sun-spot numbers and the next, all the pairs in the northern solar hemisphere will have their south poles to the west of their north poles. At the same time the opposite arrangement prevails in the sun's southern hemisphere. But still more curious, when the succeeding sun-spot period sets in, the polarities are reversed in both hemispheres. Hence, the complete sun-spot period, necessary to carry magnetic polarity as well as everything else through its whole cycle, is 22.2 years.

Sun-spots are whirls, like waterspouts and desert dust-whirlwinds. In the cores of sun-spots, the gases from within the sun whirl outwards. Arrived at the sun's surface, where lower pressures prevail, they spread out. This release of pressure, attending outward movement of the solar gases, cools them by expansion. Hence, the spots look dark against the still more brilliant, because hotter, solar background. But they are not dark. Compared to their tremendous glare, our brightest electric lights would seem coffee-colored. The gases in these solar spouts, as they whirl, leave a region of diminished pressure in their centers just as an outrush of water in a bathtub is apt to do. In such a core of a sun-spot, St. John photographed the disappearance of a wisp of hydrogen gas, sucked down into the fiery polar depths below, and Hale, with his newest apparatus, has actually seen it happening.

As for the magnetism in sun-spots, that also probably depends on rotation. The late Professor Rowland proved experimentally that electric charges in rotation produce the same sort of electromagnetic effects as currents of electricity do in the spools of wire used in the electric telegraph. Under the tremendous solar temperatures, its gases are ionized. The ions are electric charges. In a sun-spot they are in rotation. This doubtless is the cause of the magnetic character of sun-spots, though the theory of the subject is still incomplete.

But though we believe we know pretty well what a sun-spot is, no one knows why it is. The 11.1-year periodicity is so near to the revolution period (11.86 years) of the greatest of all the planets, Jupiter, that some astronomers have tried to connect these two phenomena. But even when the modifications that other planets might make in the varying attractions of Jupiter are considered, there is nothing satisfactory in this hypothesis as a basis of explanation of sun-spots. The irregularity of their periodicity, the sudden rise and slow decline of spotted-ness, their extraordinary associations with magnetic po-larity and with solar rotation, make this problem of sun-spot origin one of great fascination.

Doctor Bjerknes, the great Norwegian meteorologist and student of hydrodynamics has, indeed, proposed a theory of sun-spots which is favored by many. He suggests on hydrodynamic grounds the probable existence beneath the sun's visible surface of two vortical swirls in each solar hemisphere extending like immense endless spirals entirely around the sun, roughly parallel to its equator, and having opposite swirling rotations. These vortices rise occasion-ally to the sun's surface, and being cut off by the surface so as to present two ends, exhibit themselves as sun-spots of opposite polarities. But most of the time they reside be-low the surface and are continuous. According as one or the other of the two oppositely swirling vortices cuts the surface we see the corresponding relation of direction of the two oppositely signed magnetic fields produced. By virtue of the internal circulation of the sun the two vor-tices revolve round each other, thus changing their separation from the solar equator, one approaching, the other receding from it, with a period of 22.2 years for a complete rotation. Thus during the ordinary sun-spot cycle, 11.1 years, one of the vortices is permanently nearest the surface and approaching the solar equator. As it dives downward at the equator, the other vortex of opposite sign appears at some 30° of solar latitude at the surface, and gradually approaches the equator during the suc-ceeding 11.1 years.

CHAPTER XIII

ECLIPSES

If the moon had been 200 miles less in diameter, or 20,-000 miles farther away from us than it is, we should never have seen the greatest beauty of the sun. For there is a feature of the sun which remains invisible except when the moon intercepts the bright glare of sun rays from our atmosphere. On such occasions, which we call total solar eclipses, we see the wonderful corona, or glory of delicately curved rays, streaming outwards in all directions from the sun. The appearance of the corona changes remarkably. Plates 67 and 68 are from coronal photographs of May 28, 1900, and August 30, 1905. The form on the earlier occasion reminds one of an arrow-head, with the point east of the sun and two great barbs to the west. Not less interesting are the beautifully curved streamers extending towards north and south, much like the wonderful streamers of our northern lights.

Very different is the corona of August 30, 1905. Nearly equally developed in all directions, there is such a complex crisscross of streamers as to give an impression of greatest confusion. No semblance of the polar streamers remains. These two forms of the solar corona are the types of the remarkable changes which it undergoes in connection with the march of the sun-spot cycle. In May, 1900, the sun was barely past the time of minimum of spots. It is true that this was not quite so pronounced a minimum as that of 1913, which has not been equaled for a century, but still it was a time of very little activity. In August, 1905, on the other hand, the sun was at a period of maximum sun-spots, not by any means a great maximum like that of 1870, or even 1917, but still at the greatest activity prevailing between 1894 and 1917.

Observations before 1900 and since 1905 confirm the typical nature of these two illustrations. At other times of intermediate solar activity, the corona partakes more or less of the character of 1900, or of 1905, according as the measure of the sun's activity is toward minimum or toward maximum periods in the course of the march of the eleven-year sun-spot cycle.

Unfortunately, it is only when the moon, coming exactly between the sun and the earth, completely hides the brilliant solar disk, and cuts off the glare of our atmosphere, that we can see the solar corona at all. It would be most interesting to watch such a wonderfully changeful and beautiful celestial object as the solar corona, if we could see it day after day, and especially with its accompanying crimson prominences. These flaming objects frequently dart out as much as several hundred thousand miles in a single hour, and then, perhaps, almost completely disappear again within the hour following.

The corona, as it appears in the illustrations, seems to extend only a little more than a solar diameter in any direction. But this is by no means the longest recorded extension of it. Dr. S. P. Langley, who observed the total solar eclipse of August 29, 1878, from the summit of Pike's Peak, in Colorado, records that he could observe the equatorial extension on one side of the sun to twelve solar diameters. How tantalizing to think that so extraordinary a celestial object as the corona is always going through its evolutions close to our sun, while we are prevented from ever seeing it except in the rare moments of total solar eclipses. These phenomena, indeed, have usually to be observed by making journeys of thousands of miles and with great risk of loss of the whole view by cloudiness.

The orbits of the earth and moon are slightly elliptical. So nearly is the moon of the same angular diameter as the sun, to our view, that it altogether depends on whether the sun and the moon are near their minimum or their maximum distances from the earth, as to whether an eclipse will be total. Figure 42 indicates in an exaggerated manner how this comes about.

The sun is 865,000 miles in diameter and the moon only 2,163, so that the shadow of the moon is conical.

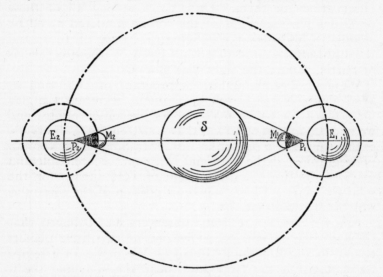

Fig. 42. How the eccentricities of the orbits of the earth and moon determine whether the sun is in total or annular eclipse

The point of it may fall as much as 20,000 miles outside the earth's surface, or as much as 18,000 miles to the inside of it according to the circumstance of position of the earth and moon in their orbits. In the former case, we have what is called an annular eclipse of the sun. In the latter it is the longest possible total eclipse, 7½ minutes. Most total eclipses are not over 3 minutes long.

A man might attend every total solar eclipse visible during his lifetime without seeing the corona over half an hour altogether. The Smithsonian Astrophysical Observatory sent expeditions to the eclipses of May 28, 1900, May 18, 1901, January 3, 1908, June 18, 1918, and May 29, 1919. Also the writer of these pages saw the eclipses of September 10, 1923, from a field in Southern California, and that of January 24, 1925, from the house of a friend near New York City, but made no special observations of them. Only twice among all of these occasions was our sight of the corona hindered at all by clouds. This was at the Sumatra eclipse of 1901, and the California eclipse of 1923. Even on these occasions of partial failure the sight was glorious.

We had a very ambitious program of observing at Wadesboro, North Carolina, in 1900. Secretary Langley himself used a 5-inch telescope for eye observations, and we had, besides him, no less than fourteen other observers, each with his own particular task. Mr. Smillie, the veteran photographer of the National Museum, secured splendid pictures on the enormous scale of 15¼ inches for the solar diameter. Plate 70 gives a portion of the corona as Mr. Smillie photographed it.

Many years before, some observers had believed that they saw on several occasions one or two little planets nearer to the sun than Mercury. We made an attempt to photograph the faint stars near the sun, and see if among them would be found these possible rarely observed members of the solar system. We actually were able to photograph many stars, some as faint as 8.4 magnitudes, more than ten times too faint to see on a dark night. There were several starlike objects among them not to be found on star maps. But neither at that eclipse, nor at subsequent ones, have these objects been confirmed by other observers. It is likely that they were no more than starlike defects of the photographic plates. The Lick Observatory made the search for new planets a special feature in several of its subsequent eclipse expeditions. Their results seem to prove definitely that the

PLATE 67

The total solar eclipse of May 28, 1900. Photo by Smillie, Smithsonian Expedition. Notice the little planet Mercury at the extreme right

PLATE 68

The total solar eclipse of August 30, 1905.   Drawing by Mrs. C. G. Abbot from photographs by U. S. Naval Observatory.   (From "The Sun," courtesy of D. Appleton Co.)

supposed planets nearer the sun than Mercury do not exist.

Our third principal line of work at the 1900 eclipse was the measurement of the heat of radiation of the corona by means of the bolometer. As it was a new experiment, we could not know just what to expect, and were little prepared for what happened. We were surprised to find that, though the bolometer responded strongly by indications of heat while the least bit of sunlight remained, as soon as totality came the galvanometer deflections at once passed to negative. This indicated that the corona, even in its hottest parts, gave less radiation than the bolometer was losing to the air and to space. This was so disconcerting to us (the galvanometer pointing to the very limit of its scale and no time to change it) that we could make but rough comparisons between the bolometer losses towards the hottest part of the corona and towards the dark, cold moon. These indicated, however, a slightly lesser loss in the direction of the corona, so that we could fairly say that we had detected heat from it.

We compared this feeble output of heat from the brightest part of the solar corona with that which we had observed with the same apparatus as coming in the rays of the full moon, usually regarded as about equally bright. We concluded that our experiments indicated the corona to shine by some process less productive of heat in proportion to its intrinsic visible brightness than moonlight.

It was perhaps a less generally understood matter in 1900 than it is to-day that the production of light varies tremendously in its efficiency and expensiveness, according to the success of the producer in excluding useless invisible rays. Langley, while at Allegheny, had, indeed, published a striking paper entitled "The Cheapest Form of Light." He had examined the light and the heat of radiation emitted by the Cuban firefly, *Pyrophorus noc-*

tilucus, using the photometer to compare its light to the standard candle, and the bolometer to compare its total heat of radiation to that of ordinary forms of light. We had repeated these experiments for him at Washington but without adding anything worth while to his results. These were to the effect that the Cuban firefly produces his light with an efficiency probably fully 1,000 times as great as that of the incandescent electric light of those days. We measured the efficiency by the proportion of total spectral energy produced which lies in the region of spectrum where the eye is highly sensitive.

Since those days tremendous advances have come in the art of electric lighting. While the *Pyrophorus noctilucus* would still probably outstrip in efficiency the best commercial practice, his lead has been cut down enormously by the inventions which find place in modern incandescent and arc lights.

We thought ourselves to have discovered in the corona a similarly high efficiency of light-production, compared to total energy of radiation. This point, and the possible discovery of the intra-Mercurial planets interested Doctor Langley very strongly. Hence, he accepted, in 1901, the invitation of the Superintendent of the U. S. Naval Observatory, and dispatched the present writer with one assistant, Mr. P. A. Draper, as guests of the Naval party to observe the very long total eclipse of May 18, 1901, in Sumatra. We carried four intra-Mercurial planet cameras, and a bolometric outfit for measuring the coronal radiation.

So it happened that, as a young man of 29, I began that long series of scientific journeys which in twenty-five years have led me to cross North America thirty-six times, the Atlantic eight times, the Pacific four times; have carried me to the South Seas and back once; to Chile, South America, and return twice; and lately to Algeria, Egypt, India, Baluchistan, and South Africa in search of the best site for a solar-radiation observatory;

besides numerous shorter journeys, all undertaken for the purpose of studying the sun. This first long expedition of 1901 was full of interest. Besides the Washington members of the party, we had the famous and lovable Professor Barnard of Yerkes Observatory. Of men young then like myself, I met for the first time Dr. S. A. Mitchell, now Director of Leander McCormick Observatory; Dr. N. A. Gilbert, now Professor at Dartmouth College; Dr. H. D. Curtis, now Director of Allegheny Observatory; Prof. W. S. Eichelberger, Director of the Nautical Almanac Office, and Prof. Frank Littell of the Naval Observatory. Mr. L. E. Jewell, the celebrated assistant of the great Professor Rowland of Baltimore, was also of the party.

It was midwinter. A great snow-storm threatened to block all transportation in the northwest. Hence, we of the Washington contingent took the New Orleans route, and I had my first sight of the gloomy mysterious-looking swamp country of the Gulf States, with the trailing Spanish moss heightening the eerie effect of the prospect. A short delightful stay in romantic old New Orleans, and the impressive crossing of the mighty Mississippi River, led us on to the almost never-ending land of Texas. Gradually we left behind swamps and mosses, then the well-watered country, until we came out into the wide cattle ranges along the Rio Grande. After taking a few steps across the Mexican boundary at El Paso, we went on through that then desolate country called the Gadsden Purchase.

After my return to Washington, I asked an old friend in the General Land Office why the United States had *purchased* such a forbidding property as that. He explained to me the circumstances of its acquisition as being the liquidation of a claim of the United States against Mexico arising out of a certain stipulation of the treaty of Guadalupe Hidalgo which closed the war with Mexico. Then he remarked that he was reminded of a certain Easterner who went west and filed his claim on Government land. After being away some years, he returned to his old home. Having a visit one day from a neighbor, the caller asked him if he still held land out west. "No," said he. "I sold half of it." "But you still have the other half then." "No, I've not got any now." "Why, how is that? You said you sold only half of what you had." "My friend," said the returned settler, "I do not wish to get a bad reputation, and do not care to tell everybody just what happened to that other half." "But," said the other, "I'll never tell." "Very well. It happened in this way. I sold half of my lot to a blind man. There was no lawyer within 200 miles, so I had to write the deed. I am ashamed to tell it, but I worked off the other half upon him too, and the poor blind man never knew the difference!"

Possibly, nevertheless, if solar engines ever succeed well, the 45,000 square miles of the desolate Gadsden Purchase may come to be a great asset, because of the very absence of clouds which makes of them now a desert.

As a boy at school in New Hampshire, I had looked out of the northern windows across a valley almost at sea-level towards a beautiful range of low mountains that rose up sharply to their culminating ridge. So they looked fully twice their height, and gave my childish mind an exalted impression of the grandeur that a great mountain chain should present. And now that we were to cross the Rockies, the backbone of the North American continent, naturally I expected something awe-inspiring. We would probably go up and up (just how the train would manage to climb I formed no idea) and when we arrived at the top it would be, I supposed, like standing on the ridge-pole of a New England church, with its A-pitched roof. We would then go down on the western side by a reverse of whatever process trains used to climb such grand natural barriers. Mingled recollections of the Biblical account of Moses on Mount Nebo looking over

PLATE 69

Secretary Langley observing the total solar eclipse at Wadesboro, N. C., May 28, 1900

PLATE 70

Polar region of the solar corona, total eclipse, May 28, 1900. Photo by Smillie, Smithsonian Expedition

into the Promised Land, and of high school valedictorians' essays on "Beyond the Alps Lies Italy," helped to make up my great anticipation of the crossing of the Rockies.

We crossed them. Scattered mesas here and there upon an endless desert plain, were all that appeared to fulfil these glorious anticipations. We reached more than twice the elevation of my childhood's ideal mountain range, and never a mountain came into view. It was not until my return in July, through the gorges of the Canadian northwest, when I saw the towering snow-clad peaks surrounding the Canadian National Park, that my faith in mountains fully returned.

Giant cacti, and all the other strange desert flora, were seen for the first time. A long delay, owing to a freight wreck near Pantano, Arizona, gave to one who had never before been away from plentiful rain and trees and grass, time to look about more closely on so different a country. There was a little cross there upon a round hill, where some poor fellow was said to be buried.

At length we arrived at Yuma, famous in comic poems as a spot where the sun is but too kind. Leaving this station in the January afternoon, a brisk breeze blew fine dust all through the car, and made a thick haze outside. We had passed many long embankments beside the tracks, which, as I was informed, were to protect them against washouts. It seemed to me a most unlikely thing that they would ever be needed in such a flat dry country. But soon we entered rain. In a little while all about us were torrents surging along those despised embankments. About dark the train stopped. Men were all along the track, tamping and testing. We crawled along a short piece and stopped for more tamping and testing, and so on again and again. The storm was so serious that we reached Los Angeles six hours late, and were there late in the night, to our great disappointment.

We awoke the next morning in the Tehachapi mountains, with further progress blocked by snow. For hours we were held up there in what at last seemed familiar and suitable—snow in winter! But finally we began to descend, and I found out how trains climb real mountains, doubling and redoubling their zigzag way, often through tunnels, and frequently so curved that the engines seemed to be almost coming to meet us. One could have walked, so it seemed, quicker.

When at last we were out of the snow and mountains, fairyland began again. For though the time was about February 1, in midwinter, we came out into the lovely San Joaquin Valley with its fruits and flowers and grazing sheep and cattle, looking as beautiful as a New England June.

So at length, having lost all our scheduled train-rights, we crept into San Francisco twenty-four hours behind time. All of that twenty-four hours' time was lost by the rain-storm near Yuma, and the snow-storm on the Tehachapi mountains. Not having seen Los Angeles as yet, I was properly surprised as I walked about, seeing the great port city, to find there a fuchsia, such as my mother raised indoors to about a foot high, and which was often covered with lovely flowers. Yet here it grew out-of-doors, blossoming in midwinter, and climbed cheerfully to the second story of the house it grew upon.

The other members of the party joined us at San Francisco, and one day all went down by invitation to the Lick Observatory, at Mount Hamilton. Here was the greatest astronomical observatory of America at that time. Here Professor Barnard and Doctor Curtis introduced us to the eminent men who have enhanced its renown in the years that have passed since. We left the observatory at a late hour, and drove by stage-coach with what seemed abandoned recklessness down the zigzag road along the precipices. But I fell asleep on the end of the coach seat, and my dear friend, Dr. S. A. Mitchell, whom I first knew on that day, held me in.

The next experience was at sea upon the U. S. Army

transport *Sheridan*. Hardly were we past the Golden Gate before occurred the tragic wreck of the steamer *Rio Janeiro*, with its great loss of life. We, of course, knew nothing of it, but in those pre-wireless, pre-cable days, our friends, left behind, felt added anxiety for us until the news of our safe arrival at Honolulu at length reached them. The ocean was boisterous, and my first impressions of ocean voyaging were formed under much the same circumstances as those reported by the Persian servant, who attended his master in a journey to England. He described the crossing of the Channel in these terms: "Leaving this country, we got on board a ship, and traversed a sea the recollection of which alone heaps ashes on the front of memory, and tears the garments of unhappiness with the rents of woe. This sea is the father of sickness, and the livers of those who sail upon it are turned upside down." [1]

Our ship carried about 1,400 soldiers and their officers on their way to Manila. One of the officers, newly married, had met his wife at a ball on New Year's eve for the first time, and we were sailing February 6. I hope they lived happily ever afterwards, after such a whirlwind courtship.

At Honolulu we were made much of, because advance news of the presence of the large eclipse party had reached those hospitable people. A committee of entertainment had been formed, and, to use the quaint phrase of our Southland, "They put the big pot in the little one for us." Among the delightful things which of course included the beach at Waikiki, the Pali, and the famous crimson feather cloak of royalty, I had my first sight of a great tree covered with bougainvillea blossoms, and of a hedge of night-blooming cereus in full bloom.

We sailed, as if on a sea of glass, from Honolulu to Manila, and there burst upon me at once the first view

[1] R. Curzon, "Visits to Monasteries in the Levant," p. 188. Murray, London, 1850.

[275]

of the Orient and the first view of Spain. How strange the sampans in the Pasig River, the people with their cool quaint costumes, the Chinese coolies trotting along with great bundles of grass fodder, the *carabaos;* and on the other hand the walled city with blue, tan, and red plastered buildings, the cathedral, and the domestic architecture of old Spain! To see a Chinaman trotting along with a great square bedstead, filling the street from curb to curb; to see another at carpentry, drawing the plane and the saw instead of pushing them; to enter a house through the carriage-place, past the horse stalls, up the stone stairs, by the sleeping chambers, to the great hall, and at last to the reception room whose floor was of mahogany made of boards thirty feet long and three feet wide—these were new sights indeed to a New Englander.

A fellow traveler, Consul Williams, had been with Dewey's fleet at the battle of Manila Bay. He was so good as to take us in a launch to see the wrecks of the Spanish vessels sunk near Cavite. After an interesting stay of about a week at Manila, we were picked up by the gunboat *General Alava,* and commenced our voyage towards Sumatra. The officers, Captain Halsey, Executive Officer Chase, and the others, were very hospitable to us, though I fear that they were prepared to believe after the voyage that scientific men are a little queer. The ship was very small for accommodating so many passengers, but in the tropical weather the Marines were put out of their quarters, and several of us younger men accommodated there. I shall never forget how nearly my neck seemed to be broken, and how my bones ached for the first and second morning after sleeping on a rattan bed, with no pillow or mattress. After that it was quite as natural to me as any bed. The astronomers proved to be such prodigious fanciers of English jam that the liberal stores of it ran out, and we fared less sumptuously on the return voyage.

PLATE 71

Smithsonian eclipse outfit on Flint Island, South Seas. The Samoan chieftain's son is figuring out the use of it

ECLIPSES

As we passed through the Strait of Sunda, we sailed within a mile of the famous island of Krakatoa, which in 1883 was the scene of one of the world's greatest volcanic eruptions. It is recorded that just before the eruption a ship captain measured the ascending column of dust and vapor and found it 17 miles high; that the noise of the great explosion was heard in Australia, over 2,000 miles away; that the wave set up by the bursting of the island was still measurable by tide gauges when it reached the English Channel, over 11,000 miles away; that the air-wave went round the world, was reflected back to its source, and so on back and forth until it had made seven complete passages, four outwards, three in return, before it ceased to affect barometers. Upon the coast of Sumatra, several ships were cast ashore a mile or more inland. The loss of life in the villages inundated was reckoned by thousands. A permanent change occurred in the Strait of Sunda, leaving a passage 1,000 feet deep where there had been an island slope 1,000 feet high.

At length we arrived at Padang, capital of Sumatra's west coast, and were cordially received by Dutch officials. The U. S. Consul, Mr. Veth, in particular, showed us much attention, but was nearly nonplussed by having to entertain a company of thirteen teetotalers! The party divided itself between three stations, Fort de Kock, Solok, and Sawah Loento. The Smithsonian party remained at Solok, about ten miles from the slightly active volcano Merapi, whose red throat and occasional outbursts of stones and smoke we saw plainly at night.

All sorts of things interested us in Sumatra. In the hotel at Padang, pajamas were the fashionable morning costume, and white suits and European evening dress prevailed in afternoon and evening. We were told that three dozen white suits were an ordinary provision for a gentleman, as he never wore one after it showed wrinkles, but laid it aside for the laundry. Every European took five or six baths every day. The railway ran up hill and down without much grading, so that cogwheel engines were substituted every few miles. The speed was such that one of our party got off and picked flowers, and readily got on board again while the train ran at full speed. Everywhere the verdure was tropical, abounding in tree ferns, bananas, and palms. Rice was extensively cultivated, and in order to flow the rice fields with water it was necessary to terrace the hills. Sumatra is a very hilly country, and the rice-terraces curving about among the hills, with water trickling from terrace to terrace, and green rice everywhere, made a lovely appearance. Then, too, there were charming waterfalls on every hand and occasionally beautiful lakes, like Lake Singkarah.

The native customs and costumes interested us greatly. The language seemed an easy one to get a smattering of. They had nicknames for some of the astronomers. Mine was "Tuan Panjang," the "tall gentleman." Their long houses were particularly interesting, with numerous curved peaks, each representing a new room added to accommodate a new family added to the clan.

At Solok, our Smithsonian party lived in a little hotel and had the use of a fort for an observing site. Mr. Veth made the ten-hour railway journey of about one hundred miles to visit us while we were getting ready. He remarked that the expedition must be regarded as perfectly extraordinary by natives and whites alike, for no Sumatran, probably, had ever seen a white man work with his hands before. We found that rain was a daily feature of the weather, and had to be prepared for quick action in covering the apparatus. On eclipse day, the prospect seemed beautifully fair until nearly time for totality. But then clouds came up and when the total phase came it was only just barely possible to see the corona at all. Thus our observations were cut off. The parties at Fort de Kock and Sawah Loento had good conditions and were very successful.

A large Dutch party occupied a station near the coast.

ECLIPSES

The accounts of the finances of the expedition, which were rendered to the Academy at Amsterdam, included an item "For celebrating a religious festival." This item puzzled the auditors, and an explanation was demanded. It proved very simple. In order to draw away the natives from the vicinity of the eclipse grounds, a religious festival was prepared at some distance and proved perfectly successful as a counter attraction. So the item was passed as a necessary preparation for the eclipse.

Our next eclipse expedition was undertaken by invitation of Dr. W. W. Campbell of Lick Observatory, to go to Flint Island about 2,000 miles south of Hawaii. The eclipse occurred on January 3, 1908. The writer was assisted by Mr. A. F. Moore, who later became director of the Smithsonian solar-radiation stations in Chile and Arizona. Our investigation at this time was limited to the measurement with the bolometer of the brightness of the corona at different distances from the sun, and testing with an absorbing screen its distribution between visible and infra-red rays. The screen was of asphaltum, a substance which cuts off visible rays, and allows infra-red ones to pass very freely.

The expedition was perfectly planned in every detail by Director and Mrs. Campbell to provide for health, comfort, and success. We journeyed from San Francisco to Tahiti, were picked up there by the U. S. gunboat *Annapolis*, and landed at Flint Island about a month before eclipse day. Flint Island is an orchard of cocoanut palms, lying all by itself 400 miles from anywhere. It was peopled by one English manager, about twenty islanders and their fifty-seven dogs, besides innumerable sea birds, crabs, and snails.

The island is only 25 feet high and about 4 miles in circumference. High waves sometimes roll quite over it, and bend down the palm trees like cornstalks. Coral formations hedge it on every side, but a narrow passage has been blasted through, so that boats can reach the beach. It takes skill to make a boat landing. We were particularly fortunate in reaching there on one of the quietest days of the year.

The last ship had called there six months before. We carried mail to the manager and the islanders. They learned of family changes which had happened months before, as well as of all the events of the great world since the preceding July.

Soon another ship brought an eclipse expedition from England and Australasia. Their camp was near ours, and as they had a clergyman with them, their meals were always served with a grace, followed by a hearty lion's roar. They joined with us at Christmas time for a feast and general good time. There was turkey, cranberry sauce, and plum pudding as befitted the season, but it seemed odd to celebrate Christmas behind mosquito-bars, in a temperature approaching 90° F.

Like Sumatra, Flint Island had rain every day, only here it rained often a dozen times a day with blue sky between. On eclipse day, the morning was thinly overcast, as if a real storm was brewing. But the thin clouds seemed to burn away as the sun mounted, and the prospect for a fair eclipse grew brighter and brighter. At about eleven o'clock, only fifteen minutes before totality, a shower came up. It poured hard. I felt that all was over, but with the aid of a petty officer of the *Annapolis* I kept the instruments covered, while Mr. Moore stood by in our palm-thatched hut to read the galvanometer if by a remote chance the sky should clear.

At 11:14 the last drops fell. Just a little notch came in the edge of the cloud, and we saw the last rim of the sun. At 11:14:45, all cleared and the corona burst forth. We went through with our program exactly as we had rehearsed it, and obtained excellent results.

Doctor Campbell's party, about 1,000 feet away, did not get quite the whole of totality clear, and the English party, still further off, lost quite a few seconds. But all

PLATE 72

The lacelike nebula in the constellation Cygnus. The nebula
and stars shown are too faint to be seen with the naked eye

were lucky in snatching success from the very jaws of failure. Had it rained two minutes later, all would have been lost.

Our results on this occasion were as follows: We measured the intensity and quality of sunlight within 25 minutes of totality, both before and after, and during totality we made measurements at five different regions of the corona, and on the dark moon. We also observed the rays of the bright moon on a night some days before the eclipse, and we observed the brightness of the sky in the daytime. The values found are given in the following tables:

INTENSITY OF RAYS (OBSERVED THROUGH GLASS)

Source	Intensity for Unit Angular Area
Sun near zenith, Flint Island....................	10,000,000
Sky 20° from sun, Flint Island...................	140
Sky far from sun, Flint Island...................	31
Sky average, Flint Island........................	62
Sky average, Mount Wilson, Cal.................	15
Moon at night, Flint Island.....................	12(?)
Moon during eclipse, Flint Island...............	0
Corona 1/10 radius from sun....................	13
Corona ¼ radius from sun.......................	4
Corona ¾ radius from sun.......................	0

PROPORTION OF RAYS WHICH ASPHALTUM TRANSMITS

Source	Determination		Mean (Weighted)
	I	II	
Sun 3/10 radius from limb.......	0.333	0.331	0.332
Corona 1/10 radius from limb....	.343	.384	.364
Corona ¼ radius from limb......	.387	.323*	.362
Moon at night...................	.....	.....	.5
Sky, zenith day.................	.....	.....	.23

* This observation is entitled to only half the weight of the others.

THE SUN AND THE WELFARE OF MAN

When we recall the extreme brightness of the sky within a single degree of the sun, as compared with that 20° away, and consider also the figures just given, it seems very unlikely that the corona will ever be observed without an eclipse.

The nature of the radiation of the inner corona has been supposed by some to be principally reflected solar radiation, by others to be principally due to the incandescence of particles heated by reason of their proximity to the sun, by others to be principally luminescence perhaps similar to the aurora, and by some as a combination of all of these kinds of radiation.

The spectrum of the corona is mainly continuous, but has some inconspicuous bright lines, and in its outer part has dark solar lines. Undoubtedly there is sunlight reflected by the matter of the corona, and no less surely the corona must be hot. As for the idea of luminescence by electrical discharge, though the streamers of the corona are a reminder of the aurora, one hesitates to recommend an explanation involving a thing so little understood, so that we will here speak only of the incandescence and reflection of the corona as sources of its brightness. The bolometric results indicate that the coronal radiation differs but little in quality from that of the sun, and is, in fact, far richer than the reflected rays of the moon in visible light, although less rich than sky light.

These results indicate that if produced by virtue of high temperature, the coronal radiation must have come from a source almost as hot as the sun, which is approximately 6,000° absolute. Such temperatures as this are too high for the existence of any known solids or liquids, unless under high pressures not found in the corona, so that if the light is due to the high temperature of the corona itself, the corona must apparently be gaseous. But if it is gaseous, its spectrum should consist chiefly of bright lines, and this is not the fact. Hence it would seem that the coronal radiation, if it is produced by temperature, has its source in the sun itself, and is merely reflected by the matter of the corona, like the light of our atmosphere. But if the coronal rays are reflected they would be bluer than sunlight, if the material there is gaseous; and as they are not, the coronal material may be supposed to be composed of solid or liquid particles to a considerable extent. But it is objected that only the outer corona shows the characteristic dark lines of the solar spectrum, and that these are absent in the region of the corona now being considered. May it not be that the temperature of the inner corona is so high that gases are present there along with the solid and liquid particles, so that the bright-line spectrum of these gases may be present and be superposed upon the reflected solar spectrum? In this case the bright rays of incandescence would fall exactly upon the dark lines of the solar spectrum and tend to obliterate them. At points in the corona more remote from the sun the gases would cool to liquid drops, or solid particles, or become excessively rare, so that the bright-line spectrum of incandescent gas would fade away, leaving the dark lines of the reflected solar spectrum predominant.

So our Flint Island eclipse ended in a most exciting race between the sun and the clouds, in which the sun won out by a matter of seconds, and permitted us to have an unobstructed view of the corona. We were able to make the most of this view, owing to the excellence of our arrangements and to our diligent practice, and secured results up to that time unique in eclipse measurements. They are still regarded by astronomers with much interest. It was not until the eclipse of 1925 that they were repeated by Doctor Pettit of Mount Wilson Observatory, who found close confirmation of them. Doctor Ludendorff of Potsdam Observatory also reached similar conclusions as to the nature of the coronal light from photographic spectrum observations at the eclipse of 1923.

The next eclipse observed by Smithsonian people was that of June 18, 1918. Mr. L. B. Aldrich and Mr. A. Kramer, assisted by a volunteer observer, Rev. Clarence Woodman, who had been with our party in 1900, observed at Lakin, Kansas. Their principal work consisted in photographing the corona, and in measuring with the pyranometer the decline of brightness of the sky from conditions of full sun to those of total eclipse, and back again. As the conditions in Kansas are more familiar than those of Sumatra and Flint Island, it will suffice to give Mr. Aldrich's results on the darkening of the sky. It is interesting to compare these with some which he obtained after sunset, so as to show how dark a total eclipse is by comparison with twilight. The results, in calories per minute, refer to the heat absorbed upon a horizontal surface 1 centimeter square.

Before Totality	Sun's Heat	Sky Heat	Remarks
1h 30m	0.845	0.203	
1 8	0.600	0.195	Eclipse begins 3h 30m p.m.
0 37	0.400	0.136	
0 20	0.200	0.047	
0 10	0.0676	0.0188	
0 4	0.0136	0.0031	
After totality			Eclipse total at 4h 44m p.m.
0h 00¼m	0.0025	0.0006	
0 20	0.099	0.072	
1 00	0.150	0.148	
After sunset			Sunset at 7h 17m
0h 39m	......	0.0019	
1 17	......	0.0000	

In the year 1919, being in Chile to inspect our solar-radiation work there, the writer, with Director Moore, journeyed to La Paz, Bolivia, to observe the total eclipse

PLATE 73

The 100-inch telescope of Mount Wilson Observatory, the largest telescope in the world. Photo by F. Ellerman

PLATE 74

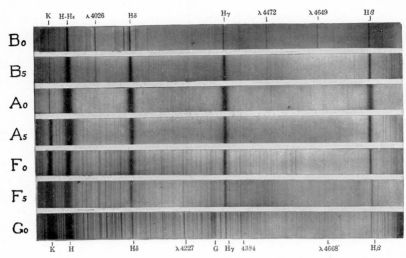

A—Spectra of typical blue, white, and yellow stars. Detroit Observatory, University of Michigan. (From "The Earth and the Stars," courtesy of the Van Nostrand Co.)

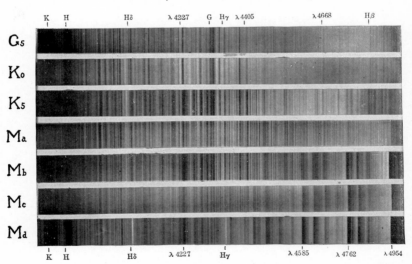

B—Spectra of typical yellow, reddish, and deep-red stars. Detroit Observatory, University of Michigan. (From "The Earth and the Stars," courtesy of the Van Nostrand Co.)

of May 29. We located ourselves upon the western rim
of the tremendous canyon which holds the city of La Paz.
Those who have not seen it may imagine, if they can, a
combination of the Grand Canyon of Arizona and the
Garden of the Gods at Colorado Springs, with the capital
city of Bolivia nestling half way down the canyon, amid
running streams and flowers, while beyond the eastern
brink rises the snow-clad range of the Andes, 20,000 feet
in elevation, with the gigantic Mount Ilimani towering
above all to 23,000 feet. Such was the inspiring view
from our station on El Alto, 13,000 feet above the sea.

We had a pair of long-focus cameras to photograph
the corona. Mr. Moore, like Mr. Aldrich in 1918, was
equipped to observe the darkening of the sky with the
pyranometer. Good weather favored us. The sun rose
partially eclipsed over a snow-clad mountain. Twenty
minutes after sunrise the eclipse became total. A gorgeous
crimson prominence, shaped like a sickle, seemed to hang
from the lower edge of the dark moon. The brilliant
corona shot out in all directions to a full solar diameter
or more.

We had very good success with our observations, although, owing to the nearness of the sun to the horizon,
the atmospheric refraction hindered exact following of the
sun, and made the moon's image a little deformed. Our
results, however, added little to the total store of eclipse
knowledge. It was the British party in Brazil that made
the epoch-making discovery on that day. Their photographs disclosed the bending of rays of stars near the
sun, in close accord with the theoretical prediction of
Einstein.

The principal contributions of the five Smithsonian
eclipse expeditions have been the beautiful photographs
secured in 1900; the pioneer bolometric observations of
the brightness of the corona in 1908, which throw some
light on the probable nature of this remarkable solar
appendage; and the measurements of the darkening of

the sky by Aldrich in 1918 and by Moore in 1919. Valuable experience was gained in forcing observations to success in distant lands despite difficult conditions. This experience has been very useful in our other work on solar radiation.

CHAPTER XIV

OUR SUN A VARIABLE STAR

THE brightest star that we see in the heavens is the sun. Next after it comes Sirius, but what a gap between! The sun sends us about ten billion times as much radiation as Sirius. However, things are not what they seem, for actually Sirius is giving off nearly thirty times as much radiation as the sun, and only seems fainter because it is over 500,000 times as far away. If we could remove the sun to be a companion star to Sirius, it would seem to be no brighter than the north star, Polaris.

It may seem surprising to call the sun one of the stars. We are accustomed to see the sun as a large round disk, glowing so intensely that no one can look towards it for more than an instant. The stars, on the contrary, seem to us but faint points of light, more like fireflies than like the effulgent sun. Yet there is no such difference in reality. It is all a matter of distance.

Astronomers are now able to measure the distances of several thousand individual stars fairly well, and by special methods they can estimate roughly the distances of millions of others. Knowing the distances, there are several methods of finding the diameters of these seeming points. Those measured thus far range from spheres of the size of the sun, about 800,000 miles in diameter, to enormously larger ones, no less than 300,000,000 miles in diameter. Thus, our sun, as the late Professor Young very happily expressed it, "is but a private in the host of heaven."

Among the stars there are many which are closely like the sun. Their light is yellowish like his. The spectroscope discloses exactly the same chemical elements in them, and proves, besides, that similar conditions of temperature and pressure prevail in the sun and in these sunlike stars. Capella, the bright northern star, is one of these. To be sure, its diameter is some ten times larger than the sun's, which leads us to think Capella is younger, as we rate star ages. Unlike humans, stars, we believe, are born big and grow smaller as they grow old! There are many other yellow stars, less conspicuous than Capella, that appear to be in every way as nearly like the sun as peas in a pod.

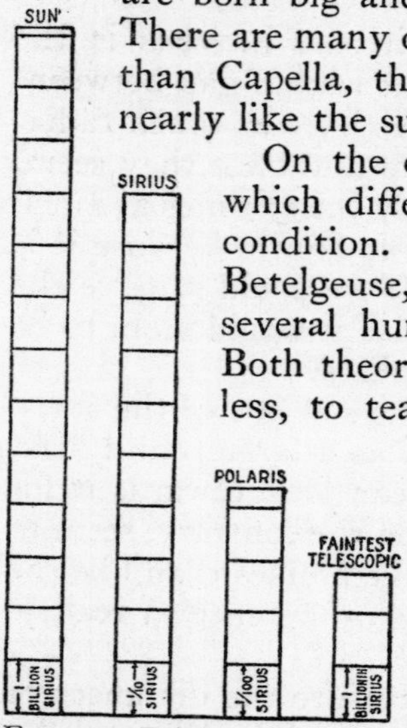

On the other hand, there are many stars which differ greatly from the sun in their condition. The bright red stars, Antares and Betelgeuse, have each been shown to be several hundred million miles in diameter. Both theory and observation join, nevertheless, to teach us that their masses are not over one hundred times greater than the sun's. With volumes some thirty million times larger and masses not above a hundredfold greater, it follows that the densities of these tremendous spheres are some three hundred thousand times less than that of the sun. We know that the sun is about 1.4 times as dense as water. Our atmosphere at sea-level is about one thousand times less dense than water. Hence, it follows that these gigantic red stars are about two hundred times less dense than the air we breathe! They consist of gases as rare as the so-called vacua pumped with the old-fashioned mechanical air pumps that used to be so common in physical lecture rooms.

FIG. 43. Brightness of sun and stars, showing that a great telescope reveals stars apparently ten billion billion times fainter than the sun, though in reality if equally near they might equal or exceed it in brightness. (From "The Earth and the Stars," courtesy of the Van Nostrand Co.)

OUR SUN A VARIABLE STAR

Not only in density but in temperature also, these giant red stars differ greatly from our sun. Comparing with familiar objects, the surfaces of red stars are only about as hot as the hottest incandescent electric lights, while the sun is over twice as hot in surface temperature. Expressed in Abs. C. degrees, we may set surface temperatures of 2,500° for the giant reds, and 6,000° for our sun. On this scale, the hottest blue stars seem to be over 20,000°. Emission of radiation increases with the fourth power of temperature, so that the supply of energy required for a red star, a solar star, and a blue star of equal sizes would be as 6 to 200 to 25,000. Among the hot blue stars is Rigel, whose transcendent effulgence constantly requires for its maintenance about ten thousand times the energy supply of our sun. Yet our sun gives out as much heat each year as the burning of four hundred thousand billions of billions of tons of anthracite coal!

What then are these stars, and how are their glowing heats maintained? They are all immense globes of gas, some very rare, like Antares, some of moderate density, like Rigel, some denser than water, like our sun. Though the most active chemicals exist side by side upon them, such for instance as oxygen and hydrogen, no stars as hot as our sun contain any chemical compounds whatever. At such exalted temperatures, hydrogen would not burn in pure oxygen. Their compound, water, if it existed in the sun, would instantly dissipate into steam, the molecules of steam would separate into oxygen and hydrogen atoms, and indeed, many of these atoms would be split partially into the ultimate constituents of matter, the positive and negative electrons.

As combinations of chemicals are quite prevented by enormous temperatures prevailing in the yellow, white, and blue stars, there can be no question of anything like the burning of coal as the source of their immense floods of energy. Combustion is not only prevented, but if compound products of combustion were there they would fly apart into their elements, and would absorb heat and cool their surroundings in order to do so. The source of solar and stellar energy is believed by many to be one of which we have no example whatever upon earth, being no less than the actual transformation of matter itself into energy.

All atoms are composed of two kinds of building materials. They are the protons, or units of positive electricity, and the electrons, or units of negative electricity. In the form of atoms these electricities are separated, and have energy possibilities. Let them unite, and they will destroy each other, and, in doing so, give up their energy of separation. This, perhaps, happens within the stars. Matter, in other words, perhaps changes to energy. Destruction of matter may be the source of star heat. Physics and geology unite to prove that our earth has been the abode of life for something like a billion years. The sun and the stars last far longer than that, before their substance ceases to destroy itself, and maintain their raging heat. Finally they will become old and cold, we believe, but only after trillions of years of star existence.

All that we find out about the sun helps us to know the stars, and all that we find out about the stars helps us to know the sun. Before the variability of the sun was much studied, there had been a great deal found out about the variability of the stars. In photographs of the heavens, taken at intervals, many of the stars seem unchanged from time to time, or, if changed, all differing in the same proportion, as might happen if the photographic exposures were unequal. But some of the stars may be found very unequal, even in some cases entirely extinguished in some of the exposures.

In cases of variable light, it is natural to make other exposures, and to measure the intensities of the light at many times. In this way one finally arrives at what is called a light curve. Such a curve for a star similar to the familiar variable, Algol (Beta Persei), is shown in

Figure 44. Here we see that a regular periodic variation occurs in 2 days 19 hours 57 minutes, with exactly the same waxing and waning of light at corresponding times in successive periods. Evidently our sun is not a variable of this kind, for its variations are quite irregular.

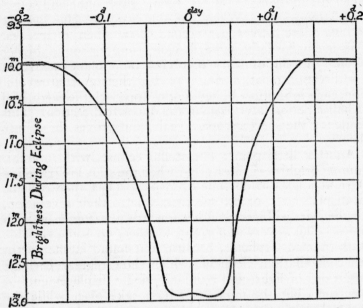

Fig. 44. A pair of eclipsing stars, of which the larger is dark, and the march of their combined brightness as they revolve. (After Shapley, courtesy of the Van Nostrand Company)

The explanation of the variation of Algol is that there are not one but two stars there. They are so close together that no telescope can show them separated. They revolve about a common center of gravity. As the plane of their orbits is nearly in our direction, one star partially hides the other or, as we say, eclipses it. This double star, Algol, then, is an eclipsing variable.

Such was the explanation proposed many years ago. It

was verified by the spectroscope, which actually proved the theory by noting displacements of the spectral lines. When a star is approaching, and similarly when a locomotive is approaching, the light of the one is more violet, and the pitch of the whistle of the other is higher, than when the motions are of recession. Both light and sound travel by waves. When the source approaches us, we receive more waves per second than when it recedes. This means for light, towards violet; and for sound, higher pitch. A pair of stars revolving in a plane nearly in our direction must, during a part of their mutual revolution, each in its turn be tending to approach the earth, and at half a period later to go in the opposite direction. This tendency the spectroscope reveals, and proves the eclipse theory.

Another little point: The stellar eclipse, with its minimum of brightness, must occur when the stars are traveling at right angles to our line of vision. Then there will be no displacement of the spectrum due to their revolution, for the stars will move neither towards nor from us at such times. This is very important, for there are some variable stars (named Cepheids, because first found in the northern constellation, Cepheus) which show regular periodic variations of light, and regular periodic displacements of spectrum, but the minima of light take place while the spectral displacements of recession are nearly at maximum. These Cepheid variables are therefore not eclipsing double stars.

Director Shapley, of Harvard College Observatory, suggested that they are pulsating stars. He conceived that they periodically expand and contract in diameter. We might call them panting stars! Shapley's hypothesis is now generally accepted. Professor Moulton, of Chicago, had investigated pulsation some years previously as a possible explanation of the variation of the sun. However, the sun's range of variability is not a tenth as great as that of most of the Cepheids, and the period of the sun-

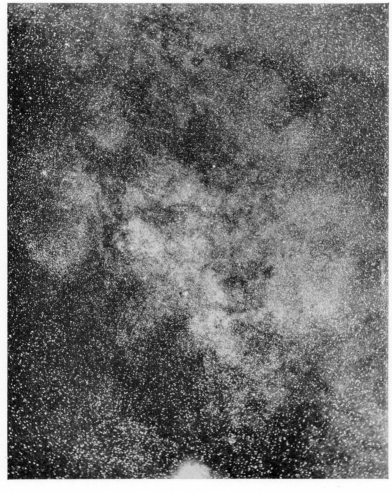

PLATE 75

A portion of the Milky Way—a star-cloud in Sagittarius. Photograph by Barnard. (From "The Earth and the Stars," courtesy of the Van Nostrand Co.)

PLATE 76

The great star-cluster in Hercules. At least 50,000 stars have been counted in it, all being suns like ours. Photo by Mount Wilson Observatory

spot cycle, approximately eleven years, is several hundredfold longer than theirs.

It is supposed to be the rush of expanding gases towards
us, and the rush of contracting gases away from us that
give the spectrum line-shifts in these stars. Variation of
brightness must evidently attend such great modifications of diameter and of density as are assumed to occur.
The Cepheids are known to be very massive and very hot

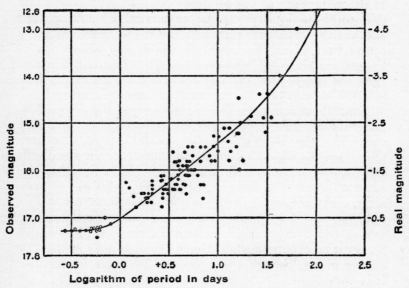

FIG. 45. Method of determining the real brightness of a Cepheid
variable star. (After Shapley.) From the real and apparent brightness, combined, the star's distance becomes known

stars. It is now believed that possibly their interior substance is actually changing into energy of radiation. This
transformation may be going on faster than radiation can
escape. Hence, as it is supposed, a rapid rise of temperature occurs, which expands the star so much that the output of radiation from the increased surface overtakes and

exceeds the supply. The supply then, indeed, diminishes owing to cooling by expansion. Then contraction sets in, as the star cools.

Be this hypothesis true or false, one thing is sure. The variation of Cepheids is of a peculiar type distinguished, like that of the sun, by a rapid rise to maximum, followed by a slow decline of brightness. The periods of change in Cepheids vary between a few hours and fifty days. Many of these stars are of known distances. In such cases their real total luminosity can be calculated by taking into account the apparent brightness and the distance. Shapley found that when the Cepheids whose real luminosity is known are arranged in order of length of period of variation, the real luminosity also changes progressively. This relation is expressed by the annexed curve (Figure 45).

From these relations, Hubble discovered the astounding fact that our galaxy of several billion stars is not the only one. The cosmos, in short, is an ocean of space, with here and there an island universe, in one of which we dwell. Besides the stars and the planets, there are found in the heavens many cloudlike objects called nebulæ. A very large class among them shows a spiral structure. The only one of these spirals which can be seen by the naked eye is the great nebula in Andromeda. A photograph shows it to occupy several times as much area in the sky as the moon, though the eye can barely see it, because it is very faint.

Hubble photographed the Andromeda nebula with the 100-inch telescope at Mount Wilson Observatory, and found the outer part resolved into a multitude of excessively faint stars. Some of them proved to be Cepheid variables. Having determined their periods, he computed their absolute luminosities according to Shapley's method. From these, in comparison with their apparent brightness, he determined the distance of the nebula.

It came out that light, traveling 186,000 miles per second, requires about 900,000 years to reach us from the

OUR SUN A VARIABLE STAR

Andromeda nebula! We may conclude that this object is really another galaxy of stars, quite as great as our own. Our galaxy is estimated to contain about 30,000,000,000 stars and requires light to travel over 100,000 years to pass across its diameter. Sir William Herschel proves to have been right in visioning "Island Universes" over a century ago! There are several hundred thousands of spiral nebulæ. Hubble finds several of the largest of them to be as distant as that in Andromeda. Others, much smaller apparently, are so, doubtless, because more distant. In view of these discoveries of his they may be scattered to such tremendous distances that the light which reveals some of them to us tonight left its source billions of years ago, ages before man, or even life itself, had arisen upon the earth!

Despite their great interest, we shall hardly regard the Cepheids as typical of the variation of the sun. Their periodicity is more regular, and the interval of it much shorter, their masses are much greater and their temperatures much more exalted than the sun's. Nevertheless, it is, perhaps, not impossible that what is taking place so vigorously in the Cepheids may be going on in a very decrepit and halting way within the sun. It may be kept in mind as one hypothesis that our sun's emission is still being maintained by transformation of mass into radiation, and that slight irregularities of balance between formation and outgo of radiation give rise to the eleven-year sunspot periodicity. The other type of solar variations, which run their course in a few days or weeks, seem, on the other hand, more probably caused by solar cloudiness.

But we have not exhausted the types of stellar variation. A famous variable is Mira, the "Wonderful," otherwise known as Omicron Ceti. It changes through from five to eight stellar magnitudes, or from 100- to 1,500-fold in brightness, in about 333 days. Like the sun, its variation is irregular in range of brightness, and the interval between maxima is not uniform. There are other stars of the Mira type, but they are all far redder than the sun. Very few of them have so long a periodic interval as the 11-year sun-spot period. Their range of brightness, too, greatly exceeds the sun's.

The possibility of finding stars of the sun's type that vary exactly as it does still remains. Hitherto there have not been sufficient observations of high enough accuracy to fully test this question. Doctor Stebbins, whose work in this line with the photoelectric cell has been so excellent, has found in several cases apparent variations of yellow and reddish stars which seemed not unlike the sun's in irregularity and smallness of range of brightness. His work has been done mainly under skies of only moderate clearness, frequently obscured by clouds, so that it has been impossible to obtain such a long-continued, first-rate series of observations as would be required to settle a point so delicate. Nevertheless, he has expressed the opinion that in some cases he has already decisive evidence of irregular variations, nearly comparable with those of the sun. Here is a field for further observations at some of the favorably located mountain observatories.

We can hardly close this chapter of comparisons between our sun and other stars without asking the questions: How did it all come about? Is there a pathway of development along which the stars march? How are they born, and do they grow old and pass away?

As yet we have no inkling as to how the stars originated at the very beginning. We know that they all contain the same chemicals as our earth, that all chemicals are composed of atoms, and that all atoms are composed of protons and electrons. Positive and negative units of electricity are therefore the foundations of all things. These units powerfully attract each other, and if they rush together the result is annihilation. To create them by separating them out of nothing is an act that transcends our understanding. Therein lay the birth of the universe.

The creation of a pair of units of electricity, a positive

PLATE 77

The great nebula in the sword of Orion. Photo by Mount Wilson Observatory. (From "The Earth and the Stars," courtesy of the Van Nostrand Co.)

PLATE 78

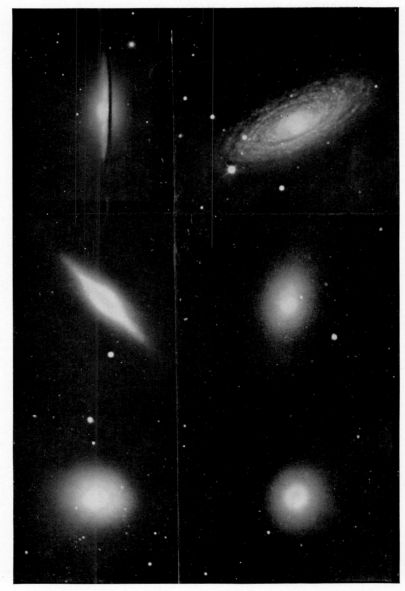

Types of nebulæ verging from the spherical, through ellipsoidal and spindle-shaped, to spiral, seen broadside and edgewise. Photographs by Mount Wilson Observatory. (From "The Earth and the Stars," courtesy of the Van Nostrand Co.)

and a negative unit, and the endowing of them with a certain configuration, is the creation of an atom of hydrogen. Atoms of hydrogen, if combined in certain relations and certain numbers, give rise to all other atoms. Neither the creation of hydrogen nor its agglomeration into other chemical elements is within the present scope of man's attainments. No man knows how these things may have been done. So the manner of creation of the universe is as yet totally unknown.

If we admit that the materials of the universe existed in the form of great nebulous masses of chemical materials, segregated in far-separated parts of space, then we may go on with some assurance to state what came of it, according to the teachings of modern astronomy.[1] In Plate 78 are shown several observed forms of nebulæ. Let us suppose that originally all matter was collected in highly tenuous spherical nebulæ like the lower right, and that these enormous nebulous balls were in feeble rotation.

In accord with well approved laws, they would accelerate in rotation, and rise in temperature. As the acceleration progressed, their equators would bulge towards the forms shown to the lower left and middle right. The process continuing, as well-known mechanical principles require, the form shown in middle left would presently result. Here becomes apparent a tendency to flatten out into a wheel.

Gravitation, however, may be overcome by sufficient rapidity of rotation, just as the forces that hold water to a grindstone are overcome by sufficient rapidity of rotation. There would be a tendency to fly away from the rim of the widening nebula. On account of the feeble, yet existing tidal forces resulting from the attractions of all the other matter in the universe, there would be two points on the rim, diametrically opposite, where the gravitational control from within would first break down. Two arms would begin to flow outward at these points.

[1] We follow here the hypotheses of Jeans and Eddington.

Here we begin to note the formation of a spiral nebula. At first short, the arms would lengthen at the expense of the central mass, for the rotation must not only go on but accelerate. There is no end until almost all of the matter has left the central mass and departed into the far-flung spiral arms. A very advanced stage of this process is seen at the top in Plate 78. But this is not all. Like the water streaming from a hose, which separates into drops, so the arms of a spiral nebula, quite in accord with well-known laws, will separate into knots.

In the separate knots the history of the original nebula is repeated. They, too, if above a certain mass, which theory specifies, will form arms, and at length disintegrate into subordinate masses. Thus finally the original great unitary nebula is divided into a multitude of masses of starlike magnitudes, of which some develop singly, like Arcturus, some doubly like Sirius, and some quadruply like Epsilon Lyræ, according to the amount of matter and circumstances of rotation of the knots of the nebulous arms out of which they were formed.

Such is supposed to be the history of a galaxy like our own. We know that the great nebula in Andromeda has progressed far enough to have formed in its outer parts a multitude of stars. Yet its interior is still nebulous. In total mass it is quite of the order of our own galaxy, but it is not advanced so far along the path of development as to have completely separated, like our system, into individual stars.

This process, however, does not give rise to systems like the sun and its planets. The masses and motions involved there are not of the proper order. In a spiral nebula, resolved into arms, the great proportion of the energy of motion is contained in the arms, and not in the central nucleus. In the solar system, on the contrary, the overwhelming preponderance of it is included within the sun, not in the planets. Another consideration must be invoked to account for planetary systems.

[298]

OUR SUN A VARIABLE STAR

It is this: Within a galaxy of billions of stars there may occur, during the trillions of years which star-history comprises, some comparatively near approaches of one star to another. When this occurs there will be tremendous tidal disturbances. Arms will be thrown out very probably from one or both of the two stars involved. But the encounter is soon over. The arms cease to flow outward. Nearly all of the matter remains in the central starry nucleus. Such, we may suppose, was the birth of the planetary system from the sun. The various planets condensed from the arms thrown out of the sun by tidal forces raised by a passing star, and they, too, may have suffered similar disturbing forces and thereby formed their satellites.

If these be the birth processes of a galaxy and a solar system, what shall we say of an individual star itself? As separated from the parent nebula, merely a raggedly proportioned, wide-reaching mass of rarest gas, the pull of its own gravitation rounds the mass into a feebly glowing sphere. Endowed with some vestiges of the rotation inhering in the nebulous arms from which it sprang, the newly formed star may separate into two or even more components if too massive to remain as one. Finally reduced to a single gaseous sphere of suitable mass, its history as a star begins.

Cooling by radiation at the surface of the immense sphere of gas, the outer parts condense under the attraction from within. This involves falling, as of a falling body above our earth. The arrest of the falling gases generates heat. According to the celebrated law of Lane, based on the well-proved laws of perfect gases, the average temperature of the sphere is thereby raised. What seems an impossible paradox nevertheless is strictly true. The act of cooling by surface radiation involves a rise of the mean temperature of the whole mass.

This extraordinary process of shrinking volume, accompanied by rising temperature, is probably, for all of the earlier stages of a star's history, the chief source of its energy of radiation. The mass is still too cool for the introduction of the interior destruction of mass, which, as we have seen, is supposed to furnish the energy supplies lavished by the hotter stars.

At the stage we are now considering, the young star may be a billion miles in diameter. Its substance may be as rare as the traces of gas contained in the bulbs of electric incandescent lamps. Its effective radiating temperature may be no higher than melting platinum. As viewed from the earth, it is a very red star. Not yet too hot to promote chemical combination, its spectrum includes the bands of such compounds as cyanogen, titanium oxide, magnesium hydride, and other molecular gaseous combinations. Although so cool, the immense area of its surface, millions of times exceeding that of the sun, builds up its feeble intensity of radiation of unit surface into a monstrous radiation of the whole, quite comparable with that of the brightest stars.

The mere continuation of the process of shrinkage, attended by rising average temperature, in harmony with Lane's law, promotes our star from deep red like Antares to light red like Arcturus, then to yellowish like Capella, pale yellow like Procyon, white like Vega, blue like Rigel, and perhaps even to the tremendous temperature of Delta Cephei. Early in this progress the temperatures become too exalted to support chemical combinations. Hence, the complexities of spectrum found in red stars disappear by the time the stage of Capella is reached. A still greater apparent simplification of spectrum presents itself as the white stage of Vega comes about. Dark lines characteristic of metals like iron grow faint, and practically disappear. But this is not caused by the destruction of these elements. It means merely that some of the electrons of their atoms become vagrant, and the remaining partial atomic structures are so constituted as to give rise to new sets of spectral lines, lying beyond the visible violet

PLATE 79

Spiral nebula seen on edge.   Photo by Mount Wilson Observatory.
(From "The Earth and the Stars," courtesy of the Van Nostrand Co.)

PLATE 80

A—Dr. W. S. Adams, Director of the Mount Wilson Observatory

B—Dr. A. S. Eddington, Plumian Professor of Astronomy, Cambridge University

end of the spectrum, and even entirely beyond the region of the ultra-violet which is transmissible by our atmosphere.

Somewhere in this progress, as we suppose, a new source of energy becomes available. It is the destruction of the mass in the interior of the star. When this source is once tapped, the life of the star becomes capable of enormous extension. Yet there is to be an end. What is destroyed is gone forever, dissipated in the prodigal outflow of radiation. Very gradually the volume of the star diminishes, not only by shrinkage but by self-destruction. At length comes a time when the sources of energy can no longer keep up the prodigal outlay. The star begins to cool. In cooling, its surface goes through, in reverse order, the change of colors and spectrum which we have noted above.

Our sun is on the descending branch. It has passed its stage of utmost glory. Probably its heat still is fed by self-destruction of the interior. A tremendously long period will pass before its radiation much diminishes. At length, however, there will be a perceptibly redder tinge. At that stage the supply of energy will be declining. Cooling will accelerate. Self-destruction will almost utterly cease. Left with only the natural heat which it contains as its sole supply, the process of cooling will go on rapidly, and finally the red sun will cease to glow. Long before that stage is reached, all life upon the planets will have been extinguished. Thus, as we suppose, the story will come to its end.

APPENDIX

THE A B C OF LIGHT AND RADIATION

In this chapter we scan the swiftest messenger that goes; one that is both visible and invisible; that, passing through our bodies discloses our ailments to the surgeon; that passing through void space brings intelligence of events that happened a million years ago, six million trillion miles away; that discourses sweet music to our ears from performers a thousand miles distant; that, coming to a world of ice and snow, changes chill winter into balmy spring; and that coming to a seed cries out in language heeded, "Awake, thou that sleepest, and arise from the dead!"

Hot sources like lamps, fires, the sun, and the stars send out visible and invisible rays in every direction. These rays are vibrations which travel by wave motion as do the rings upon still water when disturbed. If visible, we call these waves light; if invisible, then ulta-violet or infra-red rays. The moon, the planets, and all sorts of cool objects that we see in our homes send visible rays to us also, but they are reflected and originated from hot bodies like lamps or from the sun. Many people do not know that in addition to the reflected rays by which we see them, cool objects like chairs, for instance, constantly send out rays of their own in every direction. These rays, sent out by a cool body like the moon, the earth, a chair, or a book, are so long of wave-length as to be quite invisible to our eyes. Yet in their nature they are of the same sort as light. They are also essentially of the same sort as X-rays on the one hand, and radio-waves on the other. The former are merely of shorter and the latter merely of longer wave-lengths. However, X-rays, light, cool-body rays, and radio waves are all very different in character from sound waves.

X-rays, light rays, and radio rays, then, are all regular vibrations which travel 186,000 miles per second through space as wave-motions. They differ only in the wave-lengths, or intervals between their successive similar pulses. While X-rays range from 10,000,000 to 200,000,-000, and light rays from 150,000 to 200,000 waves per meter, the rays sent out by cool bodies, like this book, range only from 2,000 to 20,000 waves per meter, and radio waves range in length from 20 to 3,000 meters per single wave. (See Figure 1.)

Such is the immense gamut of light and its wave-relatives. All of them are alike in being, as we say, "transverse vibrations." In a water wave, the particles also vibrate transversely, or in other words at right angles to the direction of travel of the wave, as we can readily see. Not so sound, whose waves are "longitudinal." That is to say, each bit of the air, when it carries sound waves, undergoes alternately condensation and rarefaction. The air particles, in their vibration, move to and fro *along* the direction in which the sound is traveling, not at *right angles thereto* as the water particles do when they carry a wave upon a quiet pond.

The velocity of light and of its relatives, the X-rays and the radio waves, is about 186,000 miles per second. One way to measure it depends on observing with a telescope the times of eclipses of the planet Jupiter's four largest moons. When Jupiter in its orbit around the sun is farthest away from the earth, on the opposite side beyond the sun, these eclipses are seen about 16 minutes later by us than when Jupiter is nearest, because the light has to travel the diameter of the earth's orbit, or 186,000,000 miles farther to reach us. This method of measuring the velocity of light, though simple, is not exact enough to satisfy us.

The most accurate measurements of the velocity of light were performed lately by Dr. A. A. Michelson, who measured the time required for a ray to travel from Mount Wilson to Mount San Antonio, about 20 miles, and return. The light itself was produced by a specially bright electric arc devised by the Sperry Company, and said to be very nearly as intense, area for area, as the rays which the sun itself emits. This powerful beam of light, passing through a narrow slit, shone upon a polygonal mirror of glass of eight, twelve, or sixteen equal faces brightly silvered. One of these faces would reflect the rays onto a large concave mirror which sent the light in the form of a compact bundle of parallel rays over to the distant mountain where a second large mirror received and returned the beam to Mount Wilson. On their return, however, the rays came at length to the opposite face of the glass polygon from that on which they shone at first; and thence were reflected to form an image of the original slit on the cross-hair in the eyepiece of a telescope.

Such would be the course of the rays of light, if the polygonal reflector was stationary. But it could be rotated at a tremendous rate by means of a jet of compressed air shooting against a little windmill attached to the block of glass, which was delicately mounted on accurate bearings for rotation. In this way, at certain definite speeds, new faces of the polygon would be turned up, between the instant when the ray was reflected towards Mount San Antonio from a given silvered face, and the instant when the same ray had returned to Mount Wilson from its long journey. As the angles of the polygon were all very precisely equal, it needed only to measure the speed of the rotation required to permanently retain the returning ray on the cross-wire of the telescope, in order to fix the time required by light to make the journey.

This speed was measured in a most ingenious way by introducing a tuning fork, which carried a little mirror upon its vibrating arm, and whose time of vibration was accurately determined against a pendulum of an astronomical clock.

Without explaining the minute details and precautions required to measure with an accuracy reaching to about one part in a million, the distance through which the rays traveled, and the speed of rotation of the reflector, suffice it to say that five different sets of measurements were made, in three different years, and with three different rotating mirrors. Their several results for the velocity of light in a vacuum came out 299,796; 299,798; 299,795; 299,796; and 299,796 kilometers per second. Thus, as Doctor Michelson remarks, we now know the velocity of light so accurately, that by setting up this apparatus and measuring the time required to reflect a ray between two distant mountains, the distance between them could be determined as accurately in a month as it could be found by surveyors in a whole season, and at a cost many times less.

Sound travels in air only about 1/5 mile per second, or nearly a million times slower than light or radio-waves. Hence, it happens that speakers are heard by radio audiences hundreds of miles away a fraction of a second before the sound of their voices reaches their auditors in the back of the hall where they are speaking. Musical sound waves range from 1/100 to 10 meters in length per single wave. Sound will not travel in a vacuum. This is strikingly shown by hanging a swinging bell within a jar from which the air can be removed. As the air-pressure grows less and less, the sound of the bell grows fainter and fainter till it becomes silent, although the bell keeps on swinging and creating sound as before.

Light, on the other hand, as we know, penetrates freely the void of space through the immense distances which separate us from the sun and stars. The thoughtful person asks: What medium exists in space to carry waves of light? Are not the physicists mistaken in their belief that light is of the nature of waves? Are not the facts that it travels in vacuum, and that it casts straight-line shadows, instead of creeping around obstacles as sound does, proofs that light really consists of a rain of particles, radiating in every direction from heated bodies?

Such, indeed, was the explanation preferred by the great philosopher, Sir Isaac Newton, but nevertheless overthrown in the nineteenth century. For it was shown experimentally that light does not hold to straight lines, but creeps around obstacles to the exact degree which theory indicates. It encroaches on shadows the more, the longer its wave-length. Radio rays similar to light in their fundamental nature, but which are of very great wave-lengths, exceeding those of sound, are not cut off as light rays are, but creep around intervening buildings, and even the spherical surface of the earth. In short, the whole array of mathematical consequences which would follow from the view that light and its relatives are transverse vibratory waves, are so fully verified by careful experiments that no question remains of the reality of the propagation of light by waves, rather than by a rain of particles.

Yet the difficulty remains that light travels from the sun and stars through space where no known medium exists to transmit wave-motion. This puzzle, and this alone, has led to the conception of the "ether," filling all space continuously, and not composed like matter of discrete atomic particles. The properties of this hypothetical medium are assigned by mathematical theory, purely to suit the requirements of the propagation of light, but at the same time to permit the planets to course therein without resistance or retardation. Naturally they differ from those of such matter as we know, and some persons reject the idea of the existence of the ether altogether because they cannot understand it.

THE A B C OF LIGHT AND RADIATION

There are, however, many other things of which we have accepted the existence which are not understood. Among these are magnetism, electricity, gravitation, life, mind, the soul. All of these, like ether, are inferred to exist because of phenomena which seem to require these conceptions.

At the beginning of this century, there were almost no outstanding problems in radiation for which the concept of wave-motion in the ether did not fully suffice. But with the study of radio-activity and atomic structure, many new phenomena have been observed which, as yet, have tended to revive the older idea of a rain of particles, rather than to fall in with the conception of vibration in the luminiferous ether. These newly discovered phenomena are associated with the actions attending the creation of radiation by a hot source, and the absorption of it by a receiver, but not with the propagation of it between them.

In absorbing radiation, no substances act as complete absorbers for all wave-lengths. Even lampblack films which are 98 per cent absorbing for light, are found to be comparatively transparent for rays such as cool bodies emit. Glass, which is strongly transparent for light, is strongly absorbing for rays beyond the violet and red ends of the visible spectrum. Thus each substance has its own absorptive idiosyncrasies. The only practically complete absorber is an empty space into which radiation pours through a very small opening. Within, the rays dodge about by reflection, seldom finding the little hole of escape, until by repeated absorption they are completely exhausted. Such an apparatus is called a complete absorber, or "absolutely black body."

As for reflection of light, it follows a very simple law which is well known to everybody who plays billiards. For as a billiard-ball played without "English" rebounds from the cushion, making the same angle of exit as of entrance, so light, in its reflection at any surface also makes equal angles of incidence and of reflection. Hence, in order to see an image of some object from a mirror, it is necessary to place ourselves where equal angles may be drawn from the mirror to the object and to our eyes. If we ourselves are the objects, we wish to see, this equality of angles can be reached only when we stand squarely in front of the mirror. Standing thus we see our image apparently equally as far behind the mirror as we stand in front of it, and the image is inverted so that the right hand appears the left. These peculiarities are explained in Figure 46.

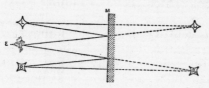

FIG. 46. How mirrors reverse images, making left appear right

The reflection of the sun or moon in water seldom gives a true round image, but usually a long column of shimmering light. This is because the surface of the water is roughened by waves, and hence is not one plane, like a flat mirror, but an ever changing combination of innumerable inclined facets, from each of which the rays are reflected with angles of incidence and reflection which are equal. If the water is but slightly rough, the surfaces at the right and left soon cease to be inclined sufficiently to reflect the sunlight in our direction, and the sparkling column of light has a narrow width. But on a rough sea there are facets of waves everywhere about us, inclined suitably to reflect the rays to us, and we see their sparkle in every direction. Water, glass, and all highly transparent substances reflect much stronger for oblique, and especially grazingly incident rays, than for those nearly perpendicular. This is uncomfortably noticeable when driving toward the sun, on a wet road, as the sun nears the horizon.

Along with the phenomenon of transparency, goes that which we call *refraction*. It is the bending of rays as they pass from one substance into another. Every one, perhaps, has seen it in the oars dipped in clear water. (See Figure 20.) Refraction is caused by the unequal velocity of light in different transparent media. In order to understand it, think of what would happen to the front of an army marching in wide array, if it should come obliquely upon a swamp, which reduced the speed to half. Every soldier as he reached the edge would slow up his progress compared to the next man, still marching freely. Thus when the whole front had reached the edge of the swamp, the direction of the front would have turned to be somewhat more nearly parallel with the edge of the swamp.

Similarly the front of a beam of light is turned, on passing from air into glass or water and other denser media. As light always travels at right angles to the wave-front, this means that the direction of travel is bent, or, as we say, *refracted*, and always in the way to become more nearly at right angles to the surface of the denser medium. The reverse is true in emerging from a denser medium to a rarer one. The retardation of light in a denser medium differs with the wave-length, being greater the shorter the wave-length. Hence a beam of white light is split up more or less into its component colors whenever it crosses a boundary between media. For the violet light will be deflected more from its original course than is the red.

When a ray of light passes through a plate with parallel walls, like a pane of glass, the separation of the colors is unnoticeable. For what is done on the one surface in passing from air into glass is exactly undone on the other surface in passing from glass into air. There is only one observable effect remaining after passing through the plate, namely, that the ray is a little displaced because it has taken a deflected course within the plate, as illustrated in Figure 47. But if the surfaces of the glass are not parallel, as in a prism, the separation of the colors and the deflection of the ray, are both manifest after emergence, as shown in Figure 48.

[309]

This property of bending of rays by media with non-parallel surfaces, is used in lenses to bring rays to a common point, or focus, as shown in Figure 143. Thus we have two kinds of telescopes, designed to form focal images of distant objects or groups of objects. They are called *refracting* if the rays are bent together by lenses, and *reflecting* if bent together by mirrors. As there is nothing in the reflection of light tending to separate colors, the images formed by a reflecting telescope are in the natural white light. But as lenses, like prisms, tend to separate the colors, refracting telescopes are marred by a color effect. This is called chromatic aberration. It can be cured in part by combining different qualities of glass in lenses.

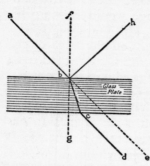

FIG. 47. The reflection and refraction of light in a plate of glass. The angles abf and hbf, of incidence and reflection, are equal. The angle of refraction, gbc, is less, because glass is denser than air. The emerging ray, cd, is parallel to the incident ray, abe

Another means of separating colors is illustrated in the soap-bubble, the oil-drop on a wet pavement, and in the diffraction grating. It is called the phenomenon of interference or diffraction of light. One sees readily that if two waves of equal height are superposed, with crest upon crest, they produce a wave of double intensity. But if superposed crest upon trough, they interfere, and destroy each other. Hence if two points close together, as in Figure 51, emit similarly each two rays of different wave-lengths, at A we shall have light, but at B darkness, for the longer waves, while at C and D we shall find light and darkness for the shorter waves. Such is the principal of the diffraction grating. This consists of a surface ruled with parallel lines very close together, often

20,000 to the inch. When such a surface reflects, each line acts as a source of light, and the result of wave-interference produces beautiful separation of colors. Very thin transparent films, like soap-bubbles and oil-spots, reflect colors, because the reflected light from the farther surface interferes with the reflected light from the nearer surface.

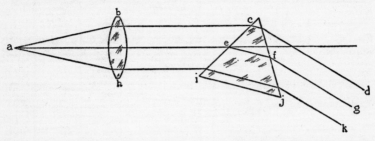

FIG. 48. How rays from a slit, a, are made parallel by a lens, b, h, deviated and dispersed by a prism, c, i, j, to form the spectrum beyond d, g, k. The figure also illustrates how parallel rays, if coming towards a lens, as cb, and ih, are brought to a focus at a

About a century ago a certain director of the British Mint, named Barton, caused some gold buttons to be made for his dress coat. On the flat surface of these buttons he had gratings ruled. Hence, when he wore his dress coat in brilliantly lighted places the buttons cast diffraction-spectrum colors about upon all the company. Ladies who wear diamonds cast refraction-spectrum colors upon the company, for diamonds are cut with nonparallel faces, so that the light which is transmitted and reflected from the interior surfaces comes out with a separation of colors, as if by a prism.

Let us return now to other considerations of radiation. As we have said, hot bodies emit radiation copiously, and it appears to consist of a continuous vibration, comprising innumerable wave-lengths, which may be distinguished by forming their spectrum with a prism of glass or other transparent substance, or with a diffraction grating. How

[311]

is it possible, we ask, that a wave motion can be so complex as to be resolvable into an infinite number of component waves such as the spectrum proves comprise a beam of light? We cannot altogether make this clear, but

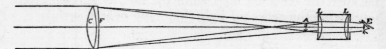

FIG. 49. Diagram of the refracting telescope whose object-glass is an achromatic lens. (From "The Earth and the Stars." Courtesy of the Van Nostrand Co.)

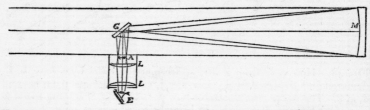

FIG. 50. Diagram of the reflecting telescope whose object-glass is a concave mirror. (From "The Earth and the Stars." Courtesy of the Van Nostrand Co.)

it may help the reader to consult Figure 23, which shows that in the apparently wholly irregular curve of solar variation there exist several well-marked regular periodicities. When rays are analyzed by a prism, the part which we call light (because our eyes are sensitive thereto) is seen to contain colors which merge continuously from violet, through indigo, blue, green, yellow, and orange, to red. With heat-measuring devices we perceive that these rays produce heat when they are absorbed. The heating effects by no means cease with the visible violet or the visible red, but continue on into dark regions which we call the ultra-violet and the infra-red spectral regions.

When the blacksmith heats his iron, it first glows red, then yellow, then white, and in arc lights we see surfaces even blue with intensity of heat. As the temperature of

PLATE 81

Dr. A. A. Michelson, of the University of Chicago, whose remarkable discoveries in optics have won for him the Nobel Prize

the source of radiation rises, the intensity of all the rays of the spectrum increases, but very unequally. This is indicated by the accompanying illustration which gives curves of relative intensity of radiation at different wave-lengths corresponding to different temperatures of a perfectly radiating source. It has been necessary to use for them different scales of intensity for different temperatures of source. This is because the copiousness of radiation increases with the fourth power of the absolute temperature of the source. Hence a body of the sun's temperature, 6,000° Abs. C., sends out no less than ten thousand times as much energy of radiation as one of equal size at 600° Abs. C., or approximately the temperature of melting lead; and this, again, sixteen times as much energy as one of equal size at the ordinary summer temperature of 300° Abs. C., or approximately 80° F.[1]

On comparing the curves of Figure 52, the reader will instantly perceive that the bulk of energies of sun rays and earth rays which are proportional to the areas under the curves 6,000° and 300°, respectively, lie in far-separated

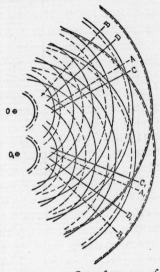

FIG. 51. Interference of light. From two sources, O and O_1, light waves of two unequal lengths, indicated by the full and the dotted circles, go out in all directions. Towards OA, O_1A_1, OC, O_1C_1, the longer and shorter waves strengthen one another, while towards, OB, O_1B_1, OD, O_1D_1, they interfere and produce darkness

[1] The reader will recall that the absolute temperature counts from absolute zero, or —273°C., and that Fahrenheit temperature is calculated from Centigrade by multiplying the latter by 9/5 and adding 32°. Thus 300° Abs. C. = 27° C., and 9/5 × 27°+32° = 80.6° F.

regions of the spectrum. Thus, while the most intense portion of the sun's spectrum is visible to us as light, no part of the earth's spectrum is visible at all. Another important fact depends on this wide wave-length separation of the principal earth rays and sun rays. They are very differently absorbed by the constituents of the atmosphere, and by such a common substance as glass.

Glass is transparent between wave-lengths 0.35 and 2.8 microns and thus, it will be seen, is particularly adapted to let through almost the whole gamut of the solar spectrum, while perfectly opaque to all earth rays. This adapts glass uniquely for use over the gardener's hot-bed, for it permits the sun rays to enter, but holds back not only the winds which might chill the tender shoots, but also hinders the escape of the radiation of the ground about them, and thus helps to maintain a forcing heat.

Atmospheric water-vapor, too, like glass, transmits nearly 90 per cent of sun rays freely, but is highly absorbing of most rays emitted by the earth. Of those remaining earth rays which water-vapor transmits freely, ozone, existing only very high up in the atmosphere, is an active absorber. Hence, as the reader will see, our atmosphere behaves towards the earth's surface much as does the glass of a hot-bed, and helps decidedly to keep the earth warm.

Ozone totally absorbs sun and star rays of less wavelength than 0.29 micron (0.00029 millimeter). If the extreme ultra-violet rays which ozone absorbs could come through the atmosphere, they would endanger human beings by their burning action on the eyes and skin. Used with care, these rays and others of the spectrum are of value in the cure of diseases. Since they cannot be employed except when the skin is bared, their curative actions are joined to the salutary influence of the air itself, and it is not certain that the latter does not assist very materially in the cures wrought by what is called "ray therapy."

Boswell, in his famous "Life of Johnson," says: "I remember that Lord Monboddo told me he awaked every morning at four, and then for his health got up and walked in his room, naked, with the window open, which he called taking an 'air-bath.' After which he went to bed

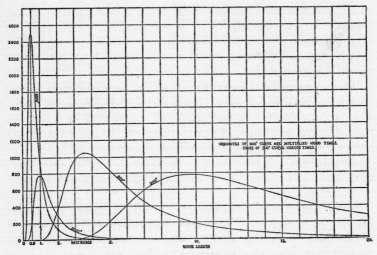

FIG. 52. How the intensity of rays is distributed in the spectrum of sources at different temperatures

again and slept two hours more." Benjamin Franklin, too, that wise old worthy, ascribed much of his good health to the air-bath, saying: "You know the cold bath has long been in vogue here as a tonic; but the shock of the cold water has always appeared to me, generally speaking, as too violent. I have found it much more agreeable to my constitution to bathe in another element, I mean, cold air." The practice of out-door sports, including especially those practiced at sea-beaches, where little clothing is worn, offers a combination of the air-bath and the ray-exposure very favorable to health. As it has greatly increased of late, it should promote a hardier human race in this and following generations.

The study of the many effects of rays of different wave-lengths upon inanimate and living tissues involves three kinds of measurements. The first is the total intensity of the rays. The second is the relative energies of rays of different wave-lengths. The third is the relative effectiveness of rays of different wave-lengths, when used in equal intensities to promote the particular phenomenon investigated. Without all three of these data the treatment is incomplete.

There are several instruments called pyrheliometers and pyranometers which have been devised by various scientists to measure the intensity of energy of a beam of radiation as a whole. They depend on, firstly, absorbing upon a blackened surface and thus converting into heat the radiation which traverses an aperture of known size, and, secondly, measuring the heat produced per minute in units of calories.

Such measurements, however, tell us nothing of the quality of the rays. They may be blue or red or invisible altogether. In order to take the next step they must be spread out into the spectrum. This requires an apparatus called the spectroscope, which, as it is not impartial in its transmission of them, must have its reflecting, transmitting, and dispersing qualities for different wave-lengths well measured. In such a well-prepared spectrum the rays indicate their relative intensities upon a highly sensitive electrical thermometer, or radiometer. These instruments are capable of detecting the heat of a ray, though of so feeble energy as to produce but a millionth of a degree of temperature change. If covered by a transparent plate, as is often the case, the instrument which measures the heat should also receive examination for its degree of impartiality towards different wave-lengths. With such an instrument, whether bolometer, radiometer, or thermopile, the rays express their relative proportions of energy in the form of an "energy curve." In such a curve, of which Figure 52 is an example, the horizontal lengths represent extent of wave-length and the vertical heights the intensity of the several wave varieties. The areas under the curve between selected verticals are everywhere proportional to the energy of corresponding wave-length ranges. The total contained area is proportional to the total energy of the beam.

So far we have taken only the steps necessary to describe the character of the beam of rays we are to study. We have measured its total energy and the intensity of its component rays. It remains to test the effects on the tissue to be examined of equal quantities of energy of different wave-lengths, when separated from the full beam by some suitable device. Such a separation for purposes of experiment may be made, for instance, by a slit placed at the focus of the spectrum which allows to pass only the narrow pencil of rays chosen, and stops the rest of the beam. The measurement of the relative effectiveness of rays of different wave-lengths may depend on the recognition and determination of a change of color, an evolution of gas, or the production of a definite quantity of a chemical substance. In the study of the human eye it depends on an estimate of apparent brightness.

Every living or inanimate receiving surface—a leaf of clover, for instance—should have, like the eye, its characteristic curve representing the chemical or physical sensitiveness of the surface to rays of different wave-lengths. These characteristic spectral curves of sensitiveness may relate to photographic darkening, to the growth of leaves, to the production of fruits, to the cure of rickets in children, or to any other of the innumerable actions of radiation. These indispensable curves are for the most part as yet practically unknown, except as regards human sight, the transparency of certain glasses, and the photographic effect on certain kinds of plates for taking pictures. In the life processes of both plants and animals, we are almost ignorant of them. Hardly anything is more desirable than a rapid increase of knowledge of these curves of radiation-sensitiveness for the many different functions of plants and animals.

Hitherto a great deal of confusion of thought has prevailed in this field, for many have supposed that some suggested chemical means of measurement of radiation indicates better than heat measurements the real intensity effective for plant growth and medical practice. But the fact is that one sort of chemical process is affected by one ill-defined group of rays of a certain range of wave-lengths, another chemical process by another ill-defined group of rays, and perhaps neither of them is affected appreciably by the group of rays of the range of wave-lengths which govern the reaction in plants or animals which the investigators wish to study. It is only when the heat-measuring processes are used in full recognition of the necessity of knowing the characteristic wave-length curves that the confusion can be removed.

And now, having traced an investigation of the variation of the sun and its influence on weather; followed the observers to distant lands in their study of the sun and his surroundings; considered how the beauties of the sky and of flowers, and the health of children and animals are conserved by rays of the sun; having tried to understand the immensity of the phenomena within and about the sun itself, and the majestic structure of the universe of which he is a humble member; we have even attempted to discern whether or not man is likely to be but one of many intelligent beings in this great cosmos, and we have particularly suggested certain researches which may add to his command over the life forces of vegetation and increase his applications of the sun in the welfare of man.

INDEX

A

B

C

D

E

INDEX

INDEX

INDEX